AeroSpace and Defence Industries
Association of Europe

SIMPLIFIED TECHNICAL ENGLISH

Specification ASD-STE100 Issue 8

ASD 지음 :: 이해종 옮김

ASD STE 100

발　행 | 2023년 10월 19일
저　자 | ASD
역　자 | 이해종
펴낸이 | 한건희
펴낸곳 | 주식회사 부크크
출판사등록 | 2014.07.15.(제2014-16호)
주　소 | 서울특별시 금천구 가산디지털1로 119 SK트윈타워 A동 305호
전　화 | 1670-8316
이메일 | info@bookk.co.kr

ISBN | 979-11-410-4800-6

www.bookk.co.kr
© ASD STE 100 2023

ASD Simplified Technical English, ASD-STE 100,
is a Copyright and a Trade Mark of ASD, Brussels, Belgium.

감사의 글

많은 분들의 도움 덕분에 "ASD STE 100"을 출판하게 되었습니다.

먼저, 번역을 허락해 주시고 응원해주신 STEMG의 Orlando Chiarello 회장님께 감사드립니다.

STE 100의 초벌번역에 많은 도움을 주신 여동철님께 감사드립니다.

최종 번역물의 검토와 윤문작업에 도움을 주신 이효정님, 박슬기님께 감사드립니다.

표지 디자인을 해주신 이예원님께 깊이 깊이 감사드립니다.

그리고, 항상 힘이 되는 사랑하는 가족에게 깊이 감사드립니다.

CONTENTS

00 General Introduction

01 Writing Rules

02 Dictionary

CHAPTER
00

General Introduction

—

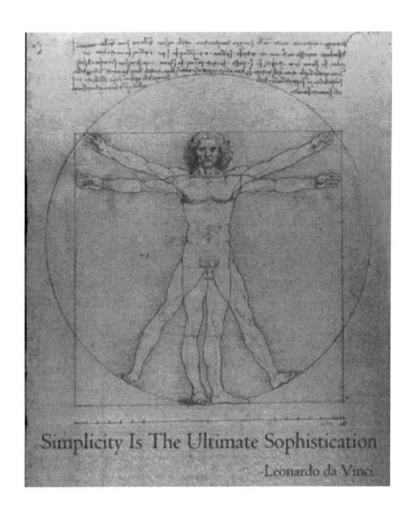

00 개 론

ASD STE(Simplified Technical English)란 무엇인가요?.

ASD STE(Simplified Technical English)는 국제적으로 사용되는 통제된 언어로, 기술 문서 작성에 사용되는 규격입니다. STE는 두 개의 장으로 이루어져 있습니다. 제 1장 '기술문서 작성 규칙'은 문법과 문장의 형식에 관한 내용을 다루고 있으며, 제 2장 '통제된 사전'은 일반적으로 사용되는 용어들을 제한된 범위로 정리하여 기술 문서를 작성하는 사람들이 사용할 수 있게 제공하고 있습니다.

STE는 언제 왜 개발되었나요?

영어는 과학, 기술 및 인문학 등 다양한 분야에서 사용하는 국제 공용 언어이며, 항공우주 및 방위 산업의 주요 언어이기도 합니다. 그러나, 이러한 분야의 다양한 기술문서를 읽는 독자들은 영어가 모국어가 아니며, 영어에 관한 지식이 제한적입니다. 복잡한 문장 구조와 다양한 의미와 동의어를 가진 영어 단어들로 인해 혼동이 일어날 수 있습니다. 항공 분야에서는 시스템이 안전하고 정확하게 작동하는지 확인하고 인명사고를 예방하기 위해 정비 및 운영 문서를 정확하게 이해하는 것은 매우 중요한 일입니다.

1970년대 후반, 유럽항공사연합회(AEA)는 유럽항공우주산업협회(AECMA)에 민간 항공 산업의 정비 관련 문서 가독성을 조사하고 정비 관련 문서 작성 시 사용하는 언어를 단순화하기 위한 해결책을 요청하였습니다.

AECMA는 미국 항공우주산업협회(AIA)에 지원을 요청했으며, AECMA와 AIA는 언어문제 해결을 위한 두 개의 프로젝트 그룹이 구성하였습니다. 이 두 그룹은 기존 통제된 언어와 여러 정비 관리 매뉴얼에 사용된 문장을 조사한 결과 정비 매뉴얼에는 간결한 언어가 필요하다는 결론에 도달했습니다.

1983년 6월 30일 암스테르담에서 AECMA Simplified English 워킹그룹이 구성되어 AECMA Simplified English 프로젝트가 시작되었습니다. 이 프로젝트의 결과로 1986년 AECMA Simplified English 가이드 초판이 발간되었으며, 2005년 ASD STE Specification인 ASD-STE 100로 발전하였습니다. 1987년 미국 항공 운송 협회(ATA)는 ATA 100 이라는 규격에 기술 문서 작성시 ASD-STE 100을 기준으로 작성하라는 요구사항을 포함했습니다. 'ASD-STE 100'이라는 이름은 STE가 ASD뿐만 아니라 ATA 100 규격에서 요구하는 사항이라는 의미로 만들어졌습니다.

현재 STE는 다양한 분야에서 성공적으로 자리 잡았습니다. 원래 목적인 항공우주 분야의 정비 관련 기술문서 이외에도 다양한 산업분야에서 STE를 사용하고 있습니다. 전문 번역 및 통역, 학계 등 다양한 분야에서 STE에 대한 관심이 급격히 늘어나고 있습니다.

STE의 목적은 무엇인가요?

STE의 목적은 기술 문서 작성자가 전 세계 독자들이 이해하기 쉬운 단순하고 명확한 방식으로 기술

문서를 작성하는 방법을 제공하는 것입니다. STE 규격은 영어 또는 기술 문서 작성 방법에 관한 학습서가 아니기 때문에 언어 문제는 다루지 않습니다. 언어 문제는 다른 참고서나 지침서를 참조하시기 바랍니다.

기술문서를 작성할 때 어떤 단어를 사용할 수 있나요?

STE는 기술 문서 작성 시 자주 사용하는 단어를 정의하여 제 2 장 '통제된 사전'에 수록하였습니다.

승인된 단어들은 간단하고 이해하기 쉬우며 일반적으로 각 단어는 하나의 의미와 하나의 품사만 가집니다. 예를 들어 "to fall"은 "중력에 의해 아래로 움직인다."는 승인된 의미를 가지며 "감소하다."는 의미로 사용하지 않습니다.

동의어가 있는 경우, STE에서는 이 중 하나의 단어만 승인하고 다른 단어는 승인된 단어로 변경하는 것을 요구합니다. 예를 들어 STE는 "begin", "commit", "initiate" 또는 "originate" 대신 "start"를 사용하도록 승인했습니다. STE가 승인한 단어의 의미와 철자는 미국 영어(Merriam-Webster 사전)에 기반합니다.

사전 외에도 STE는 회사별 또는 프로젝트별 기술 단어(STE에서 기술 명칭 및 기술 동사라고 함)의 사용을 허용합니다. STE는 이러한 기술 단어에 대한 규칙과 범주를 제공합니다.

기본적으로 기술 문서 작성자는 사전에서 승인된 단어들을 핵심 어휘로 사용해야 합니다. 관련 업체나 산업 분야에서 일반적으로 사용하고 해당 프로젝트와 제품에 적용할 수 있는 단어들도 사용 가능합니다.

STE는 약어 명명법에 대한 규칙을 제공하나요?

STE는 약어 명명법에 대한 규칙을 제공하지 않습니다. 산업별, 회사별, 프로젝트별로 사용하는 약어와 명명법을 사용할 수 있습니다. 따라서, 규칙을 만드는 것은 실용석이지 않습니다.

STE는 텍스트 서식을 규제 하나요?

STE는 텍스트 서식을 규제하지 않습니다. STE는 내용 표현 방법을 규제합니다. 서식(예: 서체, 번호 지정 및 문자)은 규제하지 않습니다. 일반적으로 이러한 요구사항은 기술 교범이나 문서, 스타일 가이드 및 기타 공식 지침의 해당 규격에 포함되어 있습니다.

STE는 측정 단위를 통제하나요?

STE는 측정 단위를 통제하지 않습니다. 기술 문서에서 측정 단위를 표시하는 방법은 여러 가지가 있습니다. 프로젝트별 또는 업체별로 어떤 측정 단위를 사용할 것인지 결정해야 합니다. 일반적으로 이러한 요구사항은 기술 교범이나 문서, 스타일 가이드 및 기타 공식 지침의 해당 규격에 포함되어 있습니다.

STE는 단독으로 사용할 수 있나요?

STE는 단독으로 사용할 수 없습니다. STE는 기술 교범이나 문서, 스타일 가이드 및 공식 지침에서 요구하는 다른 규격과 함께 사용하도록 제작되었습니다. STE 규격을 올바르게 사용하려면 높은 수준의 전문성이 필요합니다.

STE를 구어체에 사용할 수 있나요?

STE는 구어체에 사용할 수 없습니다. STE는 기술 문서용으로만 개발되었습니다. 하지만 STE의 간단한 어휘와 규칙은 회의와 발표 등에서 의사소통에 도움이 될 수 있습니다.

STE를 영어 교육에 사용할 수 있나요?

STE는 영어 교육에 사용될 수 없습니다. STE는 영어 교과서가 아닙니다. 이 규격은 기술 문서 작성자가 복잡한 정보를 쉬운 형태로 제공하는 데 도움을 줍니다. 영어를 정확하게 사용하는 것은 복잡한 작업이고 STE를 정확하게 쓰기 위해서는 높은 수준의 영어 실력이 필요합니다.

STE는 기술 번역에 도움이 되나요?

STE는 기술 번역에 도움이 됩니다. STE를 개발할 때 주요 목표 중 하나는 번역을 더 쉽게 만드는 것이었습니다. 텍스트의 어휘, 단어의 의미, 문장 구성의 종류를 통제한다면 텍스트의 변화는 최소화될 것입니다. 따라서, 번역자나 번역기가 STE로 작성된 문장을 대상 언어로 번역하는 것이 더 쉬워집니다.

STE 관련 교육을 이수하거나, 교육 관련 지원용 소프트웨어 이용이 가능한가요?

STE 사용과 관련한 마케팅, 교육 과정 등을 제공하는 다양한 조직, 업체 및 개인이 존재하며 STE 지원용 소프트웨어 제품이나 저작 툴 생산 업체들도 존재합니다.

ASD, STE 관리 그룹(STEMG)을 포함한 STE 관련 조직으로부터 공인된 지원용 소프트웨어, 저작 툴 등은 없습니다.

교육의 경우, ASD는 STE에 대한 교육을 제공하는 조직, 기업, 개인 중 공식 계약을 통하여 이들이 제공하는 교육에 대한 승인을 하였습니다.

보다 자세한 내용은 STEMG 웹사이트(www.asd-ste100.org)에서 확인할 수 있습니다.

STE 규격 개발 이력

STE 규격은 AECMA 단순영어지침서(PSC-85-16598)라는 명칭으로 1986년 초판이 발행되었습니다.

본 규격의 초판을 포함한 현재까지의 개정 현황은 다음과 같습니다.

1986년 2월 15일 초판 발간 - 작성 규칙(1장) 및 승인된 사전(2장) 수록.

1986년 9월 15일 1판 발간 - 지침서 개정.

1987년 6월 1일   2판 발간 - 기능어 및 명사(3장) 용례 추가.

1988년 6월 15일 3판 발간 - 동사(3장) 용례 추가.

1988년 12월 30일 4판 발간 - 형용사 및 부사(3장) 용례 추가.

1989년 12월 1일 5판 발간 - 4판 구성 변경. 내용 변경은 없음.

1995년 9월 15일 Issue 1 - 지침서 전면 개정. 기존 2장 삭제 및 3장를 2장로 변경.

1998년 1월 15일 Issue 1, Revision 1 - 내용 최신화 및 수정.

2001년 1월 15일 Issue 1, Revision 1 - 내용 최신화 및 수정.

2004년 1월 15일 Issue 2 - 지침서 전면 개정.

2005년 1월 15일 Issue 3 - ASD-STE100으로 New Issue 발간. 내용 변경은 없음.

2007년 1월 15일 Issue 4 - 규격서 개정.

2010년 4월 15일 Issue 5 - 규격서 개정.

2013년 1월 15일 Issue 6 - 규격서 개정.

2017년 1월 25일 Issue 7 - 작성 규칙(1장) 위주의 규격서 전면 개정.

2021년 4월 30일 Issue 8 - 승인된 사전(2장) 위주의 규격서 개정

작성 규칙 활용 방법

제 1 장 기술문서 작성 규칙은 총 53개의 규칙을 다루고 있는 9개의 절로 구성되어 있습니다.

각 절의 첫 페이지에서는 그 절에서 다루고 있는 모든 규칙들에 대한 목록을 확인할 수 있습니다. 목록 이하 부분에는 각 규칙에 관한 설명과 예문이 수록되어 있습니다.

예문은 다음과 같이 STE 규칙 준하지 않는 문장(Non-STE)과 STE에 준하는 문장(STE)을 서로 다른 글자체로 표시하였습니다.

> Non-STE: *Make sure that the valve is <u>operable</u>.*
> STE: Make sure that the valve <u>operate</u>.

STE와 연관이 없는 일반적인 예문의 경우에는 다음과 같은 글자체로 표시하였습니다.

> *An <u>opening</u> door can be dangerous.*

작성 규칙을 확인하는 경우에는 '제 2 장 승인된 사전'을 꼭 참조하시기 바랍니다.

사전을 정확하고 효율적으로 사용하는 방법은 사전의 소개 부분에 수록되어 있습니다. 수록되어 있는 설명 내용을 주의 깊게 읽어 보는 것이 매우 중요합니다. 그러한 설명을 주의 깊게 읽었을 때에만 사전을 정확하게 활용할 수 있으며, 작성 규칙에 관한 모든 설명과 예문을 보다 쉽게 이해할 수 있습니다.

Writing Rules

—

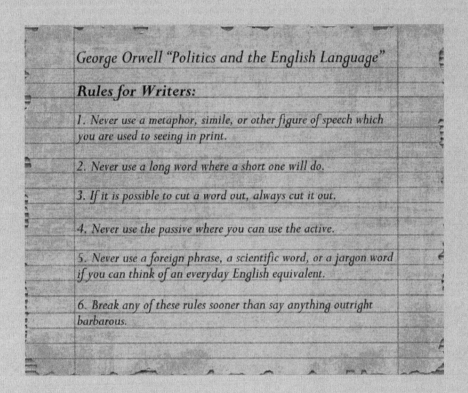

George Orwell "Politics and the English Language"

Rules for Writers:

1. Never use a metaphor, simile, or other figure of speech which you are used to seeing in print.

2. Never use a long word where a short one will do.

3. If it is possible to cut a word out, always cut it out.

4. Never use the passive where you can use the active.

5. Never use a foreign phrase, a scientific word, or a jargon word if you can think of an everyday English equivalent.

6. Break any of these rules sooner than say anything outright barbarous.

"If you simplify your English, you are freed from the worst follies of orthodoxy...
And when you make a stupid remark, its stupidity will be obvious, even to yourself."
"자신이 쓰는 영어를 간결하게 하면, 가장 우매한 통설로부터 자유로워질 수 있다. (중략)
어리석은 표현을 쓰면 그 어리석음이 스스로에게도 분명히 드러나 보인다."
조지 오웰(George Orwell)(1946) - 정치와 영어(Politics and the English Language) 중에서

1 ▌ 단어 (Words)

규칙 요약

어떤 단어들을 사용할 수 있는가?

규칙 1.1   다음과 같은 단어를 사용할 수 있다.

    - 사전(2부)에 사용 승인된 단어

    - 기술명칭(Technical Name)

    - 기술동사(Technical Verb)

품사(Part of Speech)

규칙 1.2   사전에 사용 승인된 단어를 주어진 품사로만 사용하라.

사용 승인된 의미(Approved Meaning)

규칙 1.3   승인된 의미를 가진 승인된 단어만 사용하라.

동사 및 형용사 형태(Forms of Verbs and Adjectives)

규칙 1.4   승인된 형태의 동사 및 형용사만 사용하라.

기술명칭(Technical Names)

규칙 1.5   기술명칭 범주에 포함시킬 수 있는 단어를 사용하라.

규칙 1.6   사전에서 승인되지 않은 단어는 기술명칭이거나 기술명칭의 일부일 때만 사용하라.

규칙 1.7   기술명칭인 단어를 동사로 사용하는 것을 금지한다.

규칙 1.8   승인된 품명에 일치하는 기술명칭을 사용하라.

규칙 1.9   기술명칭를 선정해야 하는 경우 짧고 이해하기 쉬운 명사를 사용하라.

규칙 1.10   속어나 은어를 기술명칭으로 사용하는 것을 금지한다.

규칙 1.11   동일한 품목에 대해 다른 기술명칭 사용을 금지한다.

기술동사(Technical Verbs)

규칙 1.12   기술동사 범주에 포함시킬 수 있는 동사를 사용하라.

규칙 1.13   기술동사를 명사로 사용하는 것을 금지한다.

철자(Spelling)

규칙 1.14   (공식적인 지침에 별도의 명시가 없는 한) 미국식 철자를 사용하라.

어떤 단어들을 사용할 수 있는가?

> 규칙 1.1   다음과 같은 단어를 사용할 수 있다.
> - 사전(2부)에 사용 승인된 단어
> - 기술명칭(Technical Name)
> - 기술동사(Technical Verb)

STE는 기술문서 작성 시 가장 자주 사용되는 단어를 제 2 장 통제된 사전에 포함하여 구성하고 있습니다. 기술명칭과 기술동사의 범주에 포함시킬 수 있는 단어들은 사전에 없어도 해당 단어들을 사용할 수 있습니다.

예 :

단어 "use"는 사전에서 사용 승인된 단어입니다.

단어 "engine"은 기술명칭입니다.

단어 "ream"은 기술동사입니다.

또한, 사전에는 대체 단어를 사용하는 방법을 보여주는 예문과 함께 미승인 단어에 대한 예문을 함께 수록하였습니다.

품사(Part of Speech)

> 규칙 1.2   사전에 사용 승인된 단어를 주어진 품사로만 사용하라.

사전에 사용 승인된 각 단어는 지정된 품사를 가지고 있습니다. 승인된 단어를 사용할 때는 지정된 품사로만 사용해야 합니다.

단어 "test"는 승인된 명사이지 승인된 동사가 아닙니다.

> STE :   Test B is an alternative to test A.

> Non-STE :   Test the system for leaks.
> STE :   Do the leak test for the system.

또는

> STE: Do a test for leaks in the system

단어 "dim"은 승인된 형용사이지 승인된 동사가 아닙니다.

> STE :   A dim light comes on.

> Non-STE :   Dim the lights.
> STE :   Set the lights to the dim position.

하나 이상의 품사로 인정되는 단어는 많지 않습니다. 예를 들어, 단어 "clean"은 승인된 동사인 동시에 승인된 형용사이기도 합니다. 동사와 형용사는 문장내에서 서로 다른 위치를 있기 때문에 문장에서 해당 단어의 위치에 따라 그 기능과 의미를 알 수 있습니다.

> STE : Clean the inner surface of the container.
>
> (여기서 "Clean"은 동사로 사용합니다.)

> STE : Make sure that the area is clean.
>
> (여기서 "Clean"은 형용사로 사용합니다.)

단어 "acceptable"은 승인되지 않은 형용사입니다. 사전에는 동일한 품사를 가진 승인된 대체 단어가 수록되어 있습니다. 이 승인된 단어를 사용하여 해당 문장에서 미승인 단어를 대체할 수 있습니다(승인된 단어와 미승인 단어 간 대체).

> Non-STE : A value of 2 mm is acceptable.
> STE : A value of 2 mm is permitted.

단어 "operable"은 승인되지 않은 형용사입니다. 사전에는 다른 품사(동사 형태의 "operate")를 가진 승인된 대체 단어가 수록되어 있습니다. 이 경우, 다른 문장 구조로 문장을 새롭게 구성해야 합니다.

> Non-STE : Make sure that the valve is operable.
> STE : Make sure that the valve can operate.

사용하려는 단어가 사전에 없는 경우, 영어 사전에서 해당 단어를 검색하여 STE 사전에 수록된 가장 유사한 동의어를 찾습니다. 그런 다음 승인된 STE 단어를 사용해야 합니다.

단어를 대체하는 경우, 선택한 대체 단어가 문장의 의미를 바꾸지 않는지 항상 확인해야 합니다. 의미가 바뀔 경우 다른 문장 구성을 사용해야 합니다.

승인된 의미(Approved Meaning)

규칙 1.3	승인된 의미를 가진 승인된 단어만 사용하라.

사전에 수록된 각 승인 단어는 표준 영어가 가지는 의미보다 제한된 특정 의미만을 승인하고 있습니다. 이러한 단어들은 항상 승인된 의미로만 사용해야 합니다.

"follow"라는 단어의 승인된 의미는 "obey(따르다)"의 의미가 아닌, "come after(따르다)"의 의미를 가집니다.

> *Non-STE* : *Follow the safety instructions.*
> STE : Obey the safety instructions.

단, 다음과 같이 문장을 작성할 수 있습니다.

> STE : Do the instructions that follow :

> STE : Follow the green lights to the nearest staircase.

동사 및 형용사 형태(Forms of Verbs and Adjectives)

규칙 1.4	승인된 형태의 동사 및 형용사만 사용하라.

사전에 수록된 각 승인 동사는 승인된 형태가 함께 명시하였습니다. 승인된 형용사는 해당하는 경우 괄호 안에 비교급 형태 및 최상급 형태를 명시하였습니다.

REMOVE (v),

REMOVES,

REMOVED,

REMOVED

이 단어는 승인된 동사 "remove"를 다음과 같이 사용할 수 있습니다.

부정사/명령형	현재 시제	단순 과거 시제	과거 분사 (형용사로 사용)
(To) Remove / Remove	Remove(s)	Removed	Removed

동사의 과거 분사는 종종 단순 과거 시제와 동일한 경우가 있습니다. 이러한 경우, 동일한 단어를 사전에 두 번 수록하였습니다.

SLOW (adj)

(SLOWER, SLOWEST)

이 단어는 승인된 형용사 "slow"를 다음과 같이 사용할 수 있음을 나타냅니다.

기본형	비교급 형태	최상급 형태
Slow	Slower	Slowest

비교급 및 최상급 형태가 각각 "more" 및 "most"를 가지는 형용사의 경우, "more"와 "most"가 승인 단어로 분류되어 있기 때문에 사전에는 이러한 형태의 형용사를 수록하지 않았습니다.

기술명칭(Technical Names)

규칙 1.5	기술명칭 범주에 포함시킬 수 있는 단어를 사용하라.

  기술명칭은 본 규칙 내 지정된 범주와 관련된 단어입니다. 다양한 기술명칭이 존재하고 각 제작업체에서 서로 다른 기술명칭을 사용하고 있기 때문에 사전에는 기술명칭을 승인 단어로 포함시키지 않고 있습니다. STE는 기술명칭을 정확하게 사용할 수 있도록 예제와 함께 기술명칭 범주 목록을 제공합니다.

  수록된 기술명칭은 예제일 뿐이며, 모든 기술명칭에 대한 전체 목록은 아닙니다. 목록에 수록된 일부 단어(예를 들면, 측정 단위, 제목, 공식 명칭 또는 인용된 텍스트 등)는 대문자를 사용해야 합니다.

  아래 20개 범주 중 한 가지 이상 범주에 포함시킬 수 있는 단어는 기술명칭에 해당합니다.

1. 공식 부품 정보(예를 들면, 부분품 도해 명세서 또는 기술도면)에 사용된 용어

> bolt, cable, clip, conductor, contact, engine, ferry tank, filter, hatch, indicator, light, logo, oil seal, prelubricated seal, pipe, propeller, retractor link, screw, switch, transceiver

2. 차량 또는 장비의 명칭과 이들 상의 특정 지점에 해당하는 명칭

> aircraft, aircraft carrier, airframe, airplane, bicycle, cabin, car, cargo compartment, cargo hold, cockpit, deck, engine room, fuselage, helicopter, galley, lifeboat, overhead panel, ship, submarine, tank, train, truck, wing, wing root

3. 공구, 지원장비 및 관련 부품의 명칭과 이들 부품 상의 특정 지점에 해당하는 명칭

> access ladder, blade, brush, cap, chock, clamp, cover, display, file, gauge (gage), handle, jack, label, rigging pin, roller, rope, rung, shaft, stand, tag, test rig, torque wrench, trestle

4. 물자, 소모성 물자 및 이물질에 대한 명칭

> acid, adhesive, aluminum alloy, ammunition, compound, copper, debris, detergent, dirt, disinfectant, dust, foam, foreign object, fuel, grease, oil, paint, penetrant spray, plastic, primer, sealant, sealing, soap, stainless steel, tape, waste, water, wire

5. 설비, 기반시설 및 군수 절차 명칭

> airport, apron, base, building, camp, dock, engine shop floor, flight simulator, gate, handling, hangar, packaging, packing, port, service bay, shipping, shop, store, storage, transport

6. 시스템, 구성품 및 회로 명칭과 그 기능, 형상 및 부품 명칭

air conditioning, amplifying circuit, armament, audio, aural warning system, collapsed position, exhaust, flight management, hardware, inhibiting signal, injection, inlet, input frequency, latch, pedal, power unit, pump, reverse mode, reverse position, standby mode, upright position, vent

7. 수학, 과학, 토목공학 용어 및 공식

acceleration, allowance, astronomy, atom, average, biochemistry, biology, biome, burr, capacitance, carbon, category, cavitation, center, circle, coefficient, configuration, conversion, count, critical temperature, curve, cycle, defect, degree, deceleration, density, diameter, displacement, duty cycle, elapsed time, electricity, energy, exponent, failure, ferry flight, flutter, force, fumes, genetics. geology. geophysics, graph, gravity, hardness, heat treatment, idle speed, ignition, incidence, inhibition, instrumentation, interference, issue, light, line replaceable unit, load, loss, measurement, modification, momentum, motoring, overhaul, oversized hole, oxygen, performance, phase, polarity, power, pressure, process, radius, rating, ratio, reduction, resistance, scan, shutdown, signal, specific gravity, stall, standard, steam, stiffness, strength, suction, temperature, tension, thread, tightness, torque, toxic property, vapor, voltage, water vapor, "C = (A - B) - 0.063 mm"

8. 항공학 및 지리학 용어

air, altitude, attitude, axis, bank, clearance, climb, coordinates, critical approach, datum, delay, deviation, drag, east, France, glideslope, gradient, heading, landing, leeway, Lima, north, pitch, roll, skid, south, west

9. 측정 및 시간 수(Numbers)와 단위(Units)(해당 기호)

92, 303, ½, ¼, ampere (A), degree (°), first, half, hour (h), kilogram (kg), knot, liter (L or l), meter (m), mile, minute ('), month, ohm (Ω), one, one-quarter, second ("), second (s), second, square inch (sq.in.), spring, third, three, year, winter, zero

10. 꼬리표, 라벨 표지, 표식 및 시현장치 상의 인용 문구

abort button, EXIT sign, INOP system, OXYGEN pushbutton switch, ON position, NEXT button, FAULT legend, NO STEP marking, FASTEN SAFETY BELT sign, WEAR PROTECTIVE CLOTHING sign

11. 사람, 단체 또는 조직명

air traffic control, captain, commander, copilot, crew, crew chief, European Aviation Safety Agency (EASA), Federal Aviation Administration (FAA), manufacturer, operator, Transport Canada Civil Aviation (TCCA)

12. 신체의 일부

blood, digestive system, ear, eyes, hair, hand, head, lung, mouth, respiratory tract, skin, stomach

13. 개인 소지품, 음식 및 음료

beans, bread, cigarette lighter, clothing, coffee, flour, footwear, high-heeled shoes, jewelry, lipstick, matches, milk, mineral water, nail scissors, perfume, pizza, shampoo, wine

14. 의학 용어

allergy, aspirin, asthma, blood poisoning, breathing, circulation, dermatitis, diabetes, dizziness, female, headache, heart rate, irritation, male, medication, nausea, pneumonia, pregnancy, pulse, skin irritation, virus

15. 공식 문서 및 문서의 일부명(매뉴얼, 기술 성적서, 표준서, 규격서 및 규정 포함)

Acceptance Test, Allowable Damage, attention, caution, chapter, Checklist, Class, Cleaning, Compass Correction Card, danger, data module, Description and Operation, diagram, engine logbook, Federal Aviation Regulations, Fault Isolation, figure, flow chart, font, Functional Test, Ice and Rain Protection, Inspection/Check, issue, letter, maintenance planning, maintenance practice, maintenance records, Normal Braking, note, notice, packaging, page, paragraph, parentheses, post-flight report, post-mod, pre-mod, preservation, reference, Removal/Installation, Repair Scheme, revision, section, Service Bulletin, Standard Practices Manual, storage, Structural Repair Manual, table, test procedure, Transportation, valid welding certificate, warning

16. 환경 및 작업 조건

atmosphere, cloud, day, daylight, ice, hail, humidity, lightning, moisture, night, rain, sand, snow, storm, turbulence, volcanic ash, wind

17. 색상

beige, black, cyan blue, dark brown, gray, green, magenta, light green, orange, red, white, yellow

> 주(註) : 색상 용어는 형용사이지만, STE에서는 이를 기술명칭으로 정의합니다. 이 용어의 비교급 및 최상급 형태(예를 들면, "blacker" 또는 "the reddest")는 STE에서 허용되지 않습니다.

18. 손상 용어

buckle, chafing, corrosion, crack, crack propagation, deformation, dent, discoloration, distortion, erosion, fracture, fraying, galling, kink, nick, score, scratch, stain, spurious fault message

19. 정보기술 및 정보통신 용어

add-in, add-on, arrow, authentication, backup, backup file, bookmark, content, cursor, database, dialog check box, e-mail, field, file, firewall, HTML, icon, interface, internet, laptop, local operation, memory, menu, mouse, network, operating system, phone, plug-in, pre-loaded software, preset value, remote operation, screen, smartphone, status bar, store, tablet, toolbar, touchscreen, tweet, update, voice mail, XML

20. 군사 용어

armed forces, assault, bomb, bullet, checkpoint, combat plan, deployment, echelon, ejection seat, evacuation, formation, general, ground zero, gun, lieutenant, machine gun, mission, patrol, rank

---

규칙 1.6	사전에서 승인되지 않은 단어는 기술명칭이거나 기술명칭 일부일 때만 사용하라.

사전에는 해당 기술명칭 범주에 포함시킬 수 있을 경우 기술명칭으로 사용할 수 있는 비승인된 단어들도 포함되어 있습니다.

"base"는 사전에서 승인되지 않은 단어입니다. 하지만, 이 단어를 기술명칭으로 사용할 수는 있습니다.

STE : The base of the triangle is 5 cm.

(이 경우 "base"는 범주 7, 수학, 과학, 토목공학 용어 및 공식에 해당되는 기술명칭입니다.)

Non-STE : *Make sure that the two spigots at the base of the unit engage.*

(이 경우 "base"는 표면과 관련이 있는 비승인된 단어입니다.)

STE : Make sure that the two spigots at the bottom of the unit engage.

동일어 "base"는 다른 문맥에서 다른 의미로 사용될 때 다른 기술명칭 범주로 구분될 수 있습니다.

STE : Access to the base is permitted between 9 a.m. and 6 p.m.

(이 경우 "base"는 범주 5, 설비, 기반시설 및 군수 절차에 해당하는 명칭입니다.)

"backup"은 승인되지 않은 단어입니다. 하지만, 이 단어를 기술명칭으로는 사용할 수 있습니다.

STE : Do the backup of the computer at regular intervals.

(이 경우 "backup"은 기술명칭으로 범주 19, 정보기술 및 정보통신 용어에 해당합니다.)

"backup"은 한 단어로 구성된 기술명칭입니다. 하지만, "backup file"과 같이 비승인된 단어 "backup"이 포함된 두 단어로도 사용할 수 있습니다.

STE : Keep the backup file in a safe area.

(이 경우 "backup file"은 기술명칭으로 범주 19, 정보기술 및 정보통신 용어에 해당합니다.)

Non-STE : *For this procedure, make sure that one person is available as backup.*

(이 경우 "backup"은 비승인된 단어로 사용할 수 없습니다.)

STE : Two persons are necessary to do this procedure.

"main"은 비승인된 단어로 사용 승인된 대체어는 "primary"입니다. 하지만, 이 단어를 기술명칭의 일부로 사용할 수 있습니다.

Non-STE : *The laptop has these main parts :*

(이 경우 "main part"는 기술명칭이 아니며 "main"을 "primary"로 대체하여 사용해야 합니다.)

STE : The laptop has these primary parts :

STE : Retract the main landing gear.

(이 경우 "main landing gear"는 기술명칭입니다. 예를 들어 "primary landing gear"는 업체 품명집에 수록된 공식 명칭이 아니므로, "main"을 "primary"로 대체할 수 없습니다.)

ASD STE 100

규칙 1.7	기술명칭인 단어를 동사로 사용하는 것을 금지한다.

기술명칭은 기술명칭의 일부에 해당하는 명사 또는 형용사로만 사용해야 합니다. 동일한 단어를 동사로 사용하지 않습니다.

"oil"은 기술명칭(범주 4, 물자, 소모성 물자 및 이물질에 대한 명칭)에 해당합니다. 따라서, "oil"을 동사로 사용해서는 안됩니다. "oil"을 명사로 사용할 수 있는 다른 문장으로 재구성해야 합니다.

> *Non-STE :* *Oil the steel surfaces.*
> STE : Apply oil to the steel surfaces.

"snow"는 기술명칭(범주 16, 환경 및 작업 조건)에 해당합니다. "snow"를 동사로 사용하지 않도록 합니다. "snow"를 명사로 사용할 수 있는 다른 문장으로 재구성해야 합니다.

> *Non-STE :* *If you think it will snow, make sure that the vehicle is in the applicable configuration.*
> STE : If you think that snow will fall, make sure that the vehicle is in the applicable configuration.

기술명칭으로 사용 가능한 동시에 기술동사로도 사용 가능한 단어

동일한 단어를 기술명칭 범주와 기술동사 범주에 동시에 포함시킬 수 있는 경우 해당 단어를 기술명칭과 기술동사로 모두 사용할 수 있습니다(규칙 1.12).

> Remove the rivets from the flange.

(여기서 "rivet"은 규칙 1.12, 범주 1, 공식 부품 정보에 해당하는 기술명칭입니다.)

> Rivet the panel in its position.

(여기서 "rivet"은 범주 1의 다) 제작 공정, 부착 물질에 해당하는 기술동사입니다.)

규칙 1.8	승인된 품명에 일치하는 기술명칭을 사용하라.

특정 시스템, 구성품, 부품 또는 공정에 대해 별도 지정된 기술명칭이 존재하는 경우 해당 기술명칭을 사용합니다. 통상적으로 이러한 기술명칭은 공식 부품 데이터, 업체 문서 등에 포함되어 있습니다.

> STE : The front panel of the phone has a touchscreen and a home button.
>
> (여기서 "touchscreen"과 "home button"은 업체 품명집에 수록되어 있는 기술명칭에 해당합니다.)

승인된 업체 품명집에 수록된 기술명칭은 긴 단어 그룹(명사 집단)의 형태일 수 있습니다. 가능한 경우 이러한 기술명칭은 짧게 구성할 수 있습니다(제1장 제2절 명사 집단 참조).

규칙 1.9	기술명칭을 선정해야 하는 경우 짧고 이해하기 쉬운 명칭을 사용하라.

승인된 품명집에 해당 기술명칭이 정의되어 있지 않은 경우, 짧고 이해하기 쉬운 명칭을 선택해야 합니다. 선택하는 기술명칭은 일반적으로 잘 알려진 단어여야 합니다.

> *Non-STE :* *Remove the four stainless steel pan head machine screws (10) that attach the metallic machined flange (15) to the front housing cover (20).*
>
> STE : Remove the four screws (10) that attach the flange (15) to the cover (20).

상기 예에서는 단어 "screws", "flange" 및 "cover"만 사용해도 충분합니다. 해당 부품을 지시하는 색인 번호가 있으며 관련 도해 상에 명확하게 식별되어 있기 때문입니다.

규칙 1.10	속어나 은어를 기술명칭으로 사용하는 것을 금지한다.

일부 단어의 경우 특정 지역에서만 사용됩니다. 이러한 단어는 그 지역 외의 사람들이 이해하는데 상당히 어려울 수 있습니다. 대부분의 사람들이 알 수 있는 단어를 항상 사용하도록 합니다. 이는 전문 용어에도 적용됩니다. 특정 기술 분야에 있는 소수의 사람들만 해당 단어를 이해한다고 할 경우 의사 소통에 방해가 될 수 있습니다.

> *Non-STE :* *Make a sandwich with two washers and the spacer.*
> STE : Install the spacer between the two washers
> *Non-STE :* *Remove your gear from the work area.*
> STE : Remove your tools and equipment from the work area.

규칙 1.11	동일한 품목에 대해 다른 기술명칭을 사용하는 것을 금지한다.

기술명칭 선택 시, 동일한 품목을 언급하기 위해 기존 사용한 명칭과 다른 명칭을 사용하지 않도록 합니다. 예를 들어, "actuator"를 기술명칭으로 사용하는 경우, 항상 동일한 명칭을 사용해야 합니다. 동일한 품목을 "servo control unit" 또는 다른 기술명칭으로 사용하지 않도록 합니다.

> Non-STE : 1. Make sure that the servo control unit is in the open position.
> 2. Do the operational test of the actuator.
> 3. Disconnect the control unit from the test rig.
>
> STE : 1. Make sure that the actuator is in the open position.
> 2. Do the operational test of the actuator.
> 3. Disconnect the actuator from the test rig.

위의 Non-STE에 대한 예제에서 "servo control unit", "actuator" 및 "control unit"은 동일한 품목을 나타냅니다. 업체 품명집을 참조하여 해당 품명집에 수록되어 있는 단어를 사용해야 합니다. 위의 STE에 대한 예제에서 보는 바와 같이 품명집에 수록된 단어가 "actuator"인 경우 관련 절차 및 해당 문서 내에서 이 단어를 동일하게 사용해야 합니다.

기술동사(Technical Verbs)

규칙 1.12	기술동사 범주에 포함시킬 수 있는 동사를 사용하라.

기술동사는 기술 및 운용 정보와 같은 특정 문맥에서 지침과 정보를 제공하기 위해 사용하는 단어입니다. 다수의 기술동사가 존재하며 각각의 제작업체들은 동일한 동작에 대해 서로 다른 단어를 사용하기 때문에 본 사전에는 기술동사를 포함하지 않습니다. STE는 기술동사를 정확하게 사용할 수 있도록 예제와 함께 범주 목록을 제공합니다.

아래 수록된 단어들은 단순 예제용으로만 수록하며 완벽한 수준의 기술동사 목록을 제시하지 않습니다. 기술동사는 STE에 수록된 다른 승인된 동사에 대한 규칙과 동일한 규칙을 따라야 합니다(제1장 제3절 참조).

아래 네 가지 범주 중 어느 한 가지 이상에 해당할 경우 특정 단어를 기술동사로 사용할 수 있습니다.

1. 제작 공정

아래 기술동사는 본 범주에 해당하는 각 제작 공정에 대한 구체적인 방법을 나타냅니다.

가) 물질 제거

> drill, grind, mill, ream

나) 물질 추가

> flame, insulate, remetal, retread

다) 물질 부착

> braze, crimp, rivet, solder, weld

라) 물질의 기계적 강도, 구조 또는 물리적 특성 변화

> anneal, cure, decay, freeze, heat-treat, magnetize, normalize, vaporize

마) 물질의 표면마감 변화

> buff, burnish, dress, passivate, plate, polish

바) 물질의 형태 변화

> flame, insulate, remetal, retread

2. 컴퓨터 프로세스 및 적용

아래 기술동사는 본 범주와 관련된 부분에서만 사용할 수 있습니다.

가) 입/출력 프로세스

> click, digitize, enter, press, print, swipe, tap, type

나) 사용자 인터페이스 및 적용 프로세스

> clear, close, copy, cut, delete, deselect, disable, drag, drag and drop, enable, encrypt, erase, filter, highlight, maximize, minimize, navigate, open, paste, save, scroll, sort, store, tweet, zoom in, zoom out

다) 시스템 운용

> abort, boot, communicate, debug, download, format, install, load, manage, process, reboot, update, upgrade, upload

3. 설명

아래 기술동사는 일반 정보, 시스템 설명 및 작동, 기술회보(Service Bulletin)의 설명 부분, 기술 보고서, 기술 및 법률 문서 등의 설명 부분에서만 사용할 수 있습니다. 절차를 작성할 때 이러한 동사는 사용하지 않습니다. 동사는 다음을 참조합니다.

가) 수학, 과학 및 공학적 프로세스

> bisect, compensate for, convert, detect, emit, modulate, radiate, transform

나) 군사 프로세스

> aim, arm, detect, disable, enable, explode, fire, intercept, load, lock on, parachute, unload

다) 통제적 언어

> waive (검사 및 요구조건에 대한 포기), comply with, conform to, supersede,
> meet (요구사항에 대한 충족)

4. 운용 언어

아래 기술동사는 사용자에게 무언가를 정확하게 작동하고 사용하는 방법을 설명하는 운용 정보와 같은 매뉴얼(예를 들어, 전화, 태블릿, 의료 기기, TV, 승무원 매뉴얼 및 지상/해상 정보 문서 등)에서만 사용할 수 있습니다.

> airdrop, alert, approach, authorize, brief, call, contact, crank, descend, deviate, disembark, drift, dry-motor, enable, evacuate, fasten, ferry, fly, hover, inform, inhibit, land, load, maintain, navigate, observe, provide, reach, respond, retard, retrim, return, rotate, serve, sanitize, shut down, sideslip, sit, sleep, sterilize, switch off, switch on, take off, take over, taxi, tie, trigger, trim, unfasten, unlatch, unload, verify, wet-motor

지침과 정보를 정확하게 제공하는 승인된 동사가 사전에 수록되어 있으면 해당 단어를 사용해야 합니다. 사전에서 승인된 단어를 이용하여 동일한 문장을 작성할 수 있을 경우, 기술동사를 사용하지 않습니다.

> Non-STE : *If you detect broken wires, repair them*
> STE : If you find broken wires, repair them.

단, 다음과 같이 문장을 작성할 수 있습니다.

> STE : The security scanner detects metallic objects.

기술동사를 사용해야 하는 경우, 명확한 의미를 가진 동사만 사용해야 합니다. 일반적이고 모호한 의미를 가진 동사를 사용하지 않습니다.

Non-STE :	*Machine the hole until it has a diameter of 8.00 +/- 0.003 mm*
STE :	Ream the hole until it has a diameter of 8.00 +/- 0.003 mm.

특별히 필요한 경우가 아니라면, 다른 기술동사를 추가로 생성하지 않습니다. 가능한 경우, 사전에서 승인된 단순 동사와 해당 기술명칭을 사용합니다.

"clamp"는 범주 1, 공식 부품 정보에 사용된 용어에 해당하는 기술명칭입니다. "clamp"를 기술동사로 사용해서는 안됩니다.

Non-STE :	*Clamp the cable in position.*
STE :	Put clamps on the cable to hold it in position.

"grease"는 범주 4, 물자, 소모성 물자 및 이물질에 해당하는 기술명칭입니다. "grease"를 기술동사로 사용해서는 안됩니다.

Non-STE :	*Grease the fasteners.*
STE :	Apply grease to the fasteners.

"wire"는 범주 1, 공식 부품 정보에 사용된 용어에 해당하는 기술명칭입니다. "wire"를 기술동사로 사용해서는 안됩니다.

Non-STE :	*Wire the cable to the structure.*
STE :	Attach the cable to the structure with wire.

<u>기술동사로 사용 가능한 비승인 단어</u>

사전에는 규정된 범주에 포함시킬 수 있을 경우 기술동사로 사용할 수 있는 승인되지 않은 단어들이 포함되어 있습니다.

STE :	Enter your password.

(이 경우 "enter"는 범주 2의 가) 입/출력 프로세스에 해당하는 기술동사입니다.)

Non-STE :	*Do not enter the engine test area without approval.*

(여기서 "enter"는 다른 의미를 가진 미승인 단어입니다.)

STE :	Do not go into the engine test area without approval.

STE : If the tower does not respond, use a different channel.

(이 경우"respond"는 범주 4 운용 언어에 해당하는 기술동사입니다.)

Non-STE : If the instrument fails to respond, do a test.

(여기서 "respond"는 다른 의미를 가진 승인되지 않은 단어입니다.)

STE : If the instrument does not operate correctly, do a test.

규칙 1.13	기술동사를 명사로 사용하는 것을 금지한다.

각 단어는 일반적으로 하나의 의미만을 가지고 있고 오직 하나의 품사로만 승인됩니다. 기술동사는 명사가 아닌 동사로만 사용해야 합니다.

Non-STE : Give the hole 0.20-inch over-ream.
STE : Ream the hole 0.20 inch larger than the standard.

STE : Lubricate the reamed hole.

(형용사 "reamed"는 기술동사 "ream"의 과거분사입니다. "reamed hole"은 기술명칭입니다.)

기술동사로 사용 가능한 동시에 기술명칭으로 사용 가능한 단어

동일한 단어를 기술동사 범주와 기술명칭 범주에 동시에 포함시킬 수 있는 경우 해당 단어를 기술동사와 기술명칭으로 모두 사용할 수 있습니다.

Make sure that the plate is not damaged.

(여기서 "plate"는 범주 1, 공식 부품 정보에 해당하는 기술명칭입니다.)

There are two methods to plate the ring nut (2).

(여기서 "plate"는 범주 1의 다) 제작 공정, 부착 물질에 해당하는 기술동사입니다.)

철자(Spelling)

규칙 1.14	(공식적인 지침에 별도의 명시가 없는 한) 미국식 철자를 사용하라.

STE 사전에 지정된 미국식 철자를 사용해야 합니다. 기타 기술 규격서, 스타일 가이드, 계약서 또는 기타 공식 지침서에 명시되어 있을 경우에만 다른 철자를 사용할 수 있습니다.

Non-STE : *The door is made of carbon fibre reinforced plastic.*

("fibre"는 영국식 철자입니다.)

STE : The door is made of carbon-fiber-reinforced plastic.

("fiber"는 미국식 철자입니다.)

Non-STE : *Change the colour of the display.*

("colour"는 영국식 철자입니다.)

STE : Change the color of the display.

("color"는 미국식 철자입니다.)

2 ▎명사 집단 (Noun Cluster)

규칙 요약

명사 집단(Noun Cluster)

규칙 2.1   3개 이상의 명사로 이루어진 명사 집단을 만들지 말라.

규칙 2.2   3개 이상의 단어로 이루어진 기술 명칭의 경우, 기술명칭 전체(Full name)을 작성한 후
아래와 같이 단순화하라.

  - 짧은 명칭(Shorter Name)을 사용한다.

  - 단일 단위로 사용되는 단어 사이 하이픈(-)을 사용한다.

관사 및 지시 형용사(Articles and demonstrative adjectives)

규칙 2.3   해당되는 경우, 명사 또는 명사구 앞에 관사(the, a, an)나 지시 형용사(this, these, that,
those)를 사용하라.

명사 집단(Noun Cluster)

규칙 2.1	3개 이상의 명사로 이루어진 명사 집단을 만들지 말라.

영어에서는 다른 명사를 설명 또는 수식하기 위해 하나 이상의 명사를 사용할 수 있습니다.

기술 문서에는 문장 내 품사의 기능을 하는 긴 단어 그룹이 자주 수록됩니다. 이러한 단어 그룹은 명사 집단(Noun Cluster)이라고 하는데 주로 명사 및/또는 형용사로 구성되며 문장 내 주어 또는 목적어가 됩니다.

일반적 예 :

> *Horizontal cylinder pivot bearing*

> *Stainless steel corrosion protection strips*

> *Actuator operating rod*

긴 명사 집단은 이해하기가 어려운데 명사 집단 내 단어가 서로 다양한 방식으로 관련될 수 있기 때문입니다. 명사 집단 내 "핵심 명사" 또는 "핵심어"는 주로 마지막에 위치합니다. 단어가 다양한 방식으로 만들어 질 때 모호성이 발생하므로 짧은 명사 집단이 이해하기에 더 수월합니다.

일반적 예 :

> *Runway light connection*

(이 문장은 짧은 명사 집단(3 단어) 입니다. 핵심 명사는 "connection"입니다.)

> *Runway light connection resistance calibration*

(이 문장은 긴 명사 집단(5 단어) 입니다. 핵심 명사는 "calibration"입니다.)

이 예문에서 "runway"와 "calibration"의 관계를 파악할 수 없으므로 독자는 핵심 명사 "calibration"에 도달하기 위해 4개의 수식 단어를 이해해야 합니다.

긴 명사 집단은 비영어권 독자들에게 혼란을 주기도 하는데 일부 언어에서는 명사 집단에서 첫번째 명사가 핵심 명사인 경우도 있기 때문입니다. 그러므로, 명사 집단 내 단어가 많으면 많을수록 이해하기 어렵습니다.

독자의 이해를 돕기 위해 명사 집단은 최대 세 개의 단어로 구성해야 합니다.

명사 집단의 이해를 돕기 위해 전치사(예: of, on, in, for)를 사용할 수 있습니다. STE에서는 관사 및 전치사는 명사 집단 내 단어로 포함하지 않습니다.

> *Non-STE :* *Runway light connection resistance calibration.*
> STE : Calibration of the resistance of the runway light connection.

> *Non-STE :* *Install the forward turbine overheat thermocouple terminal tags.*
> STE : Install the terminal tags on the forward overheat thermocouple of the turbine.

> *Non-STE :* *Remove the engine transmission housing attachment bolts.*
> STE : Remove the bolts that attach the transmission housing to the engine.

> *Non-STE :* *Adjust to obtain door operating rod alignment with the attachment point.*
> STE : Adjust the door operating rod until it aligns with the attachment point.

규칙 2.2	3개 이상의 단어로 이루어진 기술 명칭의 경우, 기술명칭 전체(Full Name)를 작성한 후 아래와 같이 단순화하라.
	- 짧은 명칭(Shorter Name)을 사용한다.
	- 단일 단위로 사용되는 단어 사이에는 하이픈(-)을 사용한다.

긴 명사 집단은 그 자체로 기술 명사가 되거나 더 짧은 기술 명사의 조합을 통해 만들어 질 수 있습니다. 긴 명사 집단을 더 작은 단위로 나누는 것이 불가능한 경우가 많은데, 이는 회사의 공식 명칭에 해당하기 때문입니다. 이 경우에는 회사의 공식 명칭을 그대로 사용하는 것이 가능합니다.

짧은 명사(Shorter Name)

공식 문서(예: 기술도면 또는 부분품 도해 명세서)에서 긴 기술 명사를 차용할 경우, 본문에 해당 명사를 최초 수록 시 이를 모두 기재해야 합니다. 전체 명사(Full Name)으로 수록 후 가능하다면 더 짧은 명사나 승인된 약어로 사용합니다.

Before you do this procedure, engage the ramp service door safety connector pin (the pin that holds the ramp service door, referred to in this procedure as the "safety connector pin").

The Main Fuel Metering Unit (MFMU) is an aluminum alloy unit that includes a Main Engine Control Unit (MECU) and a Distribution Block (DB). The MFMU is installed in the engine bypass duct and operates in the engine fuel system. The function of the MFMU is to meter and distribute the fuel from the Main Engine Fuel Pump (MEFP) to the fuel manifolds and the starter jets. The Digital Engine Control Unit (DECU) sends electrical signals to operate the MFMU.

첫 번째 예와 같이 "ramp service door safety connector pin"으로 모두 작성합니다. 전체 명칭 이후에는 "safety connector pin"과 같이 더 짧은 형태로 작성합니다. 이 짧은 명칭은 규칙 2.1에 의거하여 3개의 단어로 구성된 것입니다.

두 번째 예의 본문에서는 장치에 대한 모든 필요한 정보가 포함되어 있으므로 추가 설명이 필요없습니다. 3개 이상의 명사로 이루어진 모든 공식적인 기술 명칭은 최초 수록 시 전체 명칭으로 수록합니다. 이후 나머지 본문에는 해당되는 승인 약어를 사용합니다.

하이픈(-)

하이픈은 단어나 단어 일부를 연결하는 구두점입니다. 단어 사이에 하이픈을 사용하여 관련 단어가 하나의 단위로 기능하는 방식을 나타냅니다.

> Make sure that the cutoff-switch power connection is safe.

> Inspection of the lavatory rapid-decompression device.

명사 집단의 의미를 변경할 수 있으므로 관련 없는 단어는 하이픈으로 연결하지 않습니다. 하이픈 사용이 불확실할 경우, 명사 집단만으로 작성한 후 더 짧은 형태 또는 공식적인 승인 약어로 작성합니다.

회사의 공식 명칭에서 차용된 기술 명칭에 하이픈이 포함된 경우에는 이를 변경하지 않습니다. 해당 명칭이 너무 긴 경우, 최초 수록 시 전체 명칭으로 작성하고 그 이후에는 본 규칙에서 추천하는 방법(짧은 명칭)으로 작성합니다.

3개 이상의 단어를 하이픈으로 연결하지 않습니다. 독자가 명사 집단을 이해하는데 어려움이 있으므로 아래와 같이 모든 단어 사이에 하이픈으로 연결하지 않습니다.

> Non-STE : *Main-gear-door-retraction-winch handle.*
> STE : Main-gear-door retraction-winch handle.

관사 및 지시 형용사(Articles and demonstrative adjectives)

규칙 2.3	해당되는 경우, 명사 또는 명사구 앞에 관사(the, a, an)나 지시 형용사(this, these, that, those)를 사용하라.

관사 및 지시 형용사는 명사 및 명사구의 위치를 나타냅니다. 관사 및 지시 형용사는 정확하게 사용해야 하며 문장 길이를 줄이기 위한 목적으로 이를 생략해서는 안됩니다.

> Non-STE : *Turn shaft assembly.*
> STE : Turn the shaft assembly.

> Non-STE : *Data module tells you how to operate unit.*
> STE : This data module tells you how to operate the unit.

영어에서 명사 앞에 관사를 붙이는 경우가 항상 옳은 것은 아닙니다. 일반적인 서술문에서는 관사를 붙이지 않습니다.

> STE : Solvents can cause damage to paint.

짧은 문장의 경우, 모든 명사 앞에 관사를 붙이는 것이 더 명확할 수 있습니다.

> STE : Install the nuts (2) and the bolts (3).

단, 일련의 품목으로 구성된 문장일 경우 관사를 반복해서 붙이지 않는 것이 더 정확합니다.

> STE : Discard the O-rings (3), gaskets (4), seals (7), and washers (9).

또한, 품명 뒤에 품번이 올 때 정관사를 품명 앞에 붙이지 않습니다.

> Incorrect : Tag the circuit breaker 36L7.
> CORRECT: Tag circuit breaker 36L7.

3 ▎동사 (Verbs)

규칙 요약

동사의 형태 및 시제(Forms and Tenses of Verbs)

규칙 3.1 자체 사전에 수록되어 있는 동사의 형태만 사용하라.

규칙 3.2 다음과 같이 문장을 만드는 경우에 한하여 승인된 동사 형태를 사용하라.

  - 부정사

  - 명령문

  - 단순 현재 시제

  - 단순 과거 시제

  - 형용사로서의 과거분사

  - 미래 시제

규칙 3.3 과거분사는 형용사로만 사용하라.

규칙 3.4 조동사를 사용하여 복합 동사를 만들지 마라.

규칙 3.5 기술 명칭 또는 기술 명칭 수식어에 한해 동사의 "-ing" 형태를 사용하라.

능동태(Active Voice)

규칙 3.6 절차문 작성(Procedural Writing)에서는 반드시 능동태 형태를 사용하고,

      서술문 작성(Descriptive Writing)에서는 가능한 한 능동태를 사용하라.

동작서술 방법(How to Describe an Action)

규칙 3.7 특정 동작을 서술할 수 있는 승인된 동사를 사용하라(명사 또는 그 외 다른 품사 사용

      금지).

동사의 형태 및 시제(Forms and Tenses of Verbs)

규칙 3.1	자체 사전에 수록되어 있는 동사의 형태만 사용하라.

자체 사전에는 각 승인 동사의 사용 가능 형태를 담고 있습니다.

부정사 / 명령형	단순 현재 시제	단순 과거 시제	과거 분사 (형용사로 사용)
To decrease / Decrease	Decrease(s)	Decreased	Decreased
To give / Give	Give(s)	Gave	Given

규칙 3.2	다음과 같이 문장을 만드는 경우에 한하여 승인된 동사 형태를 사용하라.
	- 부정사
	- 명령문
	- 단순 현재 시제
	- 단순 과거 시제
	- 형용사로서의 과거분사
	- 미래 시제

승인된 동사 형태만 사용해야 합니다.

부정사	명령형	단순 현재 시제	단순 과거 시제	과거 분사 (형용사로 사용)	단순 미래 시제
(To) Adjust	Adjust + object	You/we/they adjust It adjusts	You/we/they adjusted It adjusted	The adjusted linkage	You/we/they will adjust It will adjust

아래와 예와 같이 승인되지 않은 동사 형태를 사용하지 않습니다.

- 현재완료(have/has adjusted)
- 과거완료(had adjusted)
- 현재/과거 진행(is/was adjusting)
- 기타 모든 복합 동사 형태

규칙 3.3	과거분사는 형용사로만 사용하라.

동사의 과거분사는 다음과 같이 형용사로서 사용할 수 있습니다.

- 명사 앞
- 동사 "to be" 또는 "to become" 형태 뒤

과거분사를 형용사로 사용할 경우, 이는 사물의 상태를 나타내는 것으로써 수동태를 의미하는 것은 아닙니다.

자체 사전에 수록되어 있지 않은 과거분사는 사용하지 않도록 합니다. "to be" 동사의 과거분사 "been"의 경우와 같이 일부 불규칙 동사의 과거분사는 허용되지 않습니다. 과거분사 "been"은 형용사가 아니라 복합 동사 형태의 일부입니다.

> STE : Connect the disconnected wires.

("Disconnected"는 명사인 "wires" 바로 앞에서 형용사로 사용되었습니다.)

> STE : The wires are disconnected.

("Disconnected"는 "to be" 동사 뒤에서 wires의 상태를 나타내는 형용사로 사용되었습니다.)

승인되지 않은 동사의 과거분사에서 파생된 승인된 형용사가 자체 사전에 수록되어 있는데 "specified", "permitted", "completed" 및 "damaged"가 이러한 예입니다.

승인된 부분은 자체 사전에 "(adj)"으로 표기되어 있으므로 이러한 단어는 사용할 수 있습니다.

> STE : These areas have the specified damage limits.
> STE : Do not put more than the permitted weight on the trolley.
> STE : Send the completed report to the supervisor for approval.
> STE : Make sure that the mating surfaces are not damaged.

ASD STE 100

규칙 3.4	동사를 사용하여 복합 동사를 만들지 마라.

과거분사와 조동사 "to have"를 함께 사용할 경우 승인되지 않은 시제를 만들 수 있으므로 이를 함께 사용하지 않습니다.

> Non-STE : *The operator has adjusted the linkage.*
>
> (현재완료는 승인되지 않은 시제입니다.)

> STE : The operator adjusted the linkage.
>
> (단순 과거 시제는 승인된 시제입니다.)

일부 복합 동사 구조에는 조동사("can", "must", "will" 또는 "to be")와 "to be"의 부정사 및 과거분사가 포함됩니다. 이러한 문장은 복합 수동태입니다.

> Non-STE : *The volume control can be adjusted.*
> STE : You can adjust the volume control.

> Non-STE : *The temperature must be adjusted.*
> STE : Adjust the temperature.

> Non-STE : *The sleeve will be adjusted.*
> STE : You will adjust the sleeve.

> Non-STE : *The seat is to be installed before you install the cushion.*
> STE : Before you install the cushion, install the seat.

규칙 3.5	기술 명칭 또는 기술 명칭 수식어에 한해 동사의 "-ing" 형태를 사용하라.

영어에서 "-ing"로 끝나는 단어는 문장 내에서 다른 기능(다른 품사)을 할 수 있습니다.

"-ing"로 끝나는 단어는 현재 동작을 나타내기 위해 <u>동사의 일부</u>가 될 수 있습니다.
일반적 예 :

> *Be careful while the door <u>is opening</u>.*

"-ing"로 끝나는 단어는 또한 <u>형용사</u>도 될 수 있습니다.
일반적 예 :

> *An <u>opening</u> door can be dangerous.*

"-ing"로 끝나는 단어는 <u>명사 또는 명사구의 일부</u>가 될 수 있습니다.

일반적 예 :

> *<u>Opening a door</u> can be dangerous.*

이런 단어는 <u>수식어, 명사구 및 종속절</u>로 이루어진 긴 문자열을 만들기 위해 사용할 수 있습니다.

일반적 예 :

> *A mechanic <u>opening a door</u> without obeying the specified safety precautions can easily cause injury to persons <u>standing near the door</u>.*

문장 내에서 이러한 다양한 기능으로 인해 종종 모호성이 생기거나, 길고 복잡한 문장으로 이어질 수 있기 때문에 STE에서는 일반적으로 "-ing"로 끝나는 단어의 사용은 허용하지 않습니다.

> *Non-STE :* *When you are doing this procedure, obey all the safety precautions.*
> STE : When you do this procedure, obey all the safety precautions.

> *Non-STE :* *Mechanics wearing insufficient protective clothing and opening containers containing hazardous materials in areas where there is a lack of ventilation, using inappropriate tools without observing the manufacturer's instructions, are in danger of coming into contact with these materials and thus suffering from skin irritation and breathing problems.*
>
> STE : Before you use dangerous materials, obey these precautions:
> (1) Read the manufacturer's instructions.
> (2) Make sure that there is sufficient airflow in the work area.
> (3) Put on a face mask and protective clothing.
> (4) Get the correct tools to open the containers for these materials.
> If you do not obey these precautions, injury to your skin and lungs can occur.

<u>기술 명칭 또는 기술 명칭의 일부인 "-ing"로 끝나는 단어</u>

"-ing"로 끝나는 단어는 절차 제목(Procedural Title)에서와 같이 기술 명칭으로 사용할 수 있습니다.

Cleaning, Testing and Fault Isolation, Handling, Packaging, Shipping, Troubleshooting

기술 명칭에서 수식어로서 동사의 "-ing" 형태를 사용할 수 있는데 이는 장치, 구성품, 부품, 도구 또는 장비의 기능을 서술하는 형용사입니다.

> Air-conditioning system, degreasing agent, grinding wheel, polishing disc, sanding machine, switching relay, welding torch

"-ing"로 끝나는 승인된 단어

사전에는 다음과 같이 "-ing"로 끝나는 소수의 승인된 단어가 있습니다.

- 명사(lighting, opening, routing, and servicing)
- 형용사(mating, missing, and remaining)
- 대명사(something)
- 전치사(during)

능동태(Active Voice)

규칙 3.6	절차문 작성(Procedural Writing)에서는 반드시 능동태 형태를 사용하고, 서술문 작성(Descriptive Writing)에서는 가능한 한 능동태를 사용하라.

기술문서는 절차문 작성과 서술문 작성으로 구성됩니다. STE에 따라 작성할 경우, 절차문 작성에서는 반드시 능동태를 사용하고 서술문 작성에서는 가능한 한 능동태를 사용해야 합니다.

"능동태" 또는 "수동태"란 무엇인가?

능동태에서 문장의 주어는 그 문장의 행위 주체가 됩니다("A"는 "B"를 수행함).
즉, 문법적 주어(A)는 논리적 주어(행위자)가 됩니다.

수동태에서 문장의 주어는 행위("B"는 "A"에 의해 수행됨)를 받는 대상이 됩니다. 문법적 주어는 B이고 논리적 주어 또는 행위자는 A입니다.
일반적 예 :

> Active : The manufacturer supplies the safety procedures.
> *Passive : The safety procedures are supplied by the manufacturer.*

> Active : The side stay holds the main gear leg.
> *Passive : The main gear leg is held by the side stay.*

문장이 수동태라는 것을 어떤 근거로 알 수 있는가?

수동태 문장을 알 수 있는 가장 적절한 방법은 "누구에 의해서 또는 무엇에 의해서" (행위자)에 해당되는 질문을 해보는 것입니다. 이 질문에 대한 대답을 문장에서 알 수 있는 경우 그 문장은 수동태로 작성된 것임을 알 수 있습니다. 문장에 전치사 "by"가 포함되어 있다면 이는 수동태임을 나타내는 좋은 근거가 될 수 있습니다. 전치사 "by"의 목적어는 행위자이고 능동태에서는 이를 주어로 사용할 수 있습니다. 다음의 예에서 행위자는 밑줄 친 부분입니다.

아래의 수동태 예에서 "누구에 의해서 또는 무엇에 의해서?"라는 질문을 할 수 있습니다.

The safety procedures are given <u>by the manufacturer</u>.
The main gear leg is held <u>by the side stay</u>.

단, 수동태 구문이 항상 행위자를 포함하고 있는 것은 아닙니다.

The dimensions are given in the table.
The main gear leg is held in its position.

일반적으로 서술문에서 능동태를 원활하게 사용할 수 있습니다. 하지만, 장치의 제작과정 및 작동법을 기술할 때 정확한 내용 전달을 위해 수동태가 필요한 경우도 있습니다. 수동태는 꼭 필요한 경우에만 사용하도록 합니다.

수동태 문장을 능동태 문장으로 바꾸는 방법

수동태 구조를 능동태 구조로 바꾸기 위해 아래의 4가지 방법을 이용할 수 있습니다.

방법 1

행위자(행위를 수행하는 사람 또는 사물)가 일반적으로 전치사 "by"의 목적어로서 문장 내에서 확인이 가능한 경우, 그 행위자를 문장 맨 앞부분에 주어를 옮깁니다. 아래 그림과 같이 주어는 문장 내에서 행위를 수행하는 명사가 되어야 합니다.

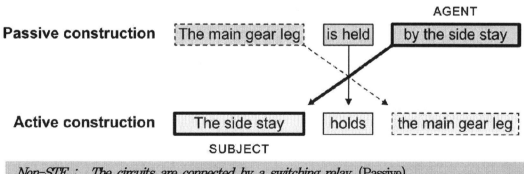

Non-STE : *The circuits are connected by a <u>switching relay</u>.* (Passive)
STE : A <u>switching relay</u> connects the circuits. (Active)

방법 2

부정사형 동사(Infinitive Verb)를 능동태의 동사(Active Verb)로 바꿉니다.

> *Non-STE :* *These values are used by the computer to calculate the energy consumption.*
> *(Passive)*
>
> STE : The computer calculates the energy consumption from these values. (Active)

"are used by" 구문은 중요한 정보를 제공하고 있지 않으므로 "calculate"를 본동사로 사용하여 능동태로 문장을 작성할 수 있습니다.

방법 3

절차문에서는 해당 동사를 명령형으로 바꿉니다.

> *Non-STE :* *The test can be continued by the operator.* *(Passive)*
> STE : Continue the test. (Active)

> *Non-STE :* *Oil and grease are to be removed with a degreasing agent.* *(Passive)*
> STE : Remove oil and grease with a degreasing agent. (Active)

방법 4

문장에서 행위자(행위를 수행하는 사람 또는 사물)를 확인할 수 없을 때 그 행위자가 독자("you") 또는 제작사("we")에 해당하는 경우에 한하여 대명사 "you" 또는 "we"를 주어로 사용하여 능동태 문장을 만들 수 있습니다.

> *Non-STE :* *On the ground, the valve can be opened with the override handle.* *(Passive)*
> STE : On the ground, you can open the valve with the override handle. (Active)

> *Non-STE :* *Oil and grease are to be removed with a degreasing agent.* *(Passive)*
> STE : Remove oil and grease with a degreasing agent. (Active)
>
> 또는
>
> STE : Remove oil and grease with a degreasing agent. (Active)

동작 서술 방법(How to Describe an Action)

규칙 3.7	동작을 서술할 수 있는 승인된 동사를 사용하라.
	(명사 또는 그 외 다른 품사 사용 금지).

동일한 정보를 제공할 수 있는 다양한 방법들이 존재하는 경우, 승인된 동사를 사용하여 해당 동작을 나타내야 합니다. 명사는 동작을 추상적으로 표현하나 동사는 동작을 더 명확하게 표현할 수 있습니다.

> *Non-STE : The ohmmeter gives an indication of 450 ohms.*
> STE : The ohmmeter shows 450 ohms.

> *Non-STE : Make sure that the 600 Hz tone is audible when the GPW GND ACT switch is pushed.*
> STE : (a) Push the GPW GND ACT switch.
> (b) Make sure that you can hear the 600 Hz tone at the same time.

단어가 자체 사전에서 동사로 승인되지 않은 경우에는 이를 동사로 사용하지 않습니다. 동일한 정보를 제공하기 위해 다른 품사를 사용하여 문장을 완성합니다.

> *Non-STE : Check the laptop battery.*
> STE : Do a check of the laptop battery.

ASD STE 100

4 ┃ 문장 (Sentences Verbs)

규칙 요약

단문(Short Sentences and Simple Sentence Structure)

규칙 4.1   짧고 명확한 문장을 작성하라.

규칙 4.2   문장을 짧게 만들기 위해 단어를 생략하거나 축약형을 사용하는 것을 금지한다.

수직적 배열(Vertical Lists)

규칙 4.3   복잡한 문장의 경우 수직적 배열 형태를 사용하라.

접속어 및 접속어구(Connecting Words and Phrases)

규칙 4.4   관련 주제를 포함하고 있는 문장들을 접속어 및 접속어구를 사용하여 연결된 문장으로 만들어라.

단문(Short Sentences and Simple Sentence Structure)

STE의 기본 철학은 문장을 읽고 이해하기 쉽게 작성하는 것입니다. 다시 말해, 이는 문장을 짧고 간결한 구조로 작성해야 한다는 것을 의미합니다.

STE에서는 절차문 작성(제5절) 및 서술문 작성(제6절)에 대한 다양한 방법을 수록하고 있습니다.

규칙 4.1	짧고 명확한 문장을 작성하라.

기술문서는 구체적인 정보를 제공하는 짧고 명확한 문장으로 작성해야 합니다.

<u>절차문 작성</u>은 짧고 명확한 지시사항과 더불어 독자가 취할 행위를 직접적으로 제시해야 합니다.

> *Non-STE :*   *To remove the cover assembly (9), first remove the four screws (10) that attach the cover (11) to the housing (12), and then, after taking the cover (11) off the housing (12), remove the preformed packing (13) and throw it away.*
>
> STE :   1. Remove the cover assembly (9) as follows:
>
>   A. Remove the four screws (10) that attach the cover (11) to the housing (12).
>
>   B. Remove the cover (11) from the housing (12).
>
>   C. Remove and discard the preformed packing (13).

서술문 작성의 경우, 각 문장에는 1개의 주제만 담고 있어야 합니다. 이후 이어지는 문장에서 점진적으로 정보를 제공하여 해당 주제를 발전시킵니다.

> **Non-STE :** *The side stay assembly has two folding toggles hinged together __and__ attached with hinges between the main gear strut and the side stay bracket.*

(이 문장에는 밑줄 친 접속사 "and"로 연결된 2개의 주제가 있습니다. 이 정보를 더 명확하게 하기 위해 각 주제에 대해 새로운 문장으로 작성할 수 있습니다.)

> **STE :** <u>The side stay assembly</u> has two folding toggles. <u>The folding toggles</u> are attached together with hinges. <u>These toggles</u> are also attached with hinges between the main gear strut and the side stay bracket.

절차문과 서술문 이 두가지 유형의 문장은 작업수행 방법 및 장치의 작동방법을 명확하게 제시해야 합니다. 문장의 내용이 모호하거나 불명확하고 일반적인 내용으로 작성하지 않습니다.

> **Non-STE :** *No leaks permitted.*

(이 문장은 독자가 취할 행동의 정보를 제공하고 있지 않아 큰 도움이 되지 않습니다.)

> **STE :** Make sure that there are no leaks.

(이 문장은 독자가 취할 행위를 직접적으로 제시하고 있습니다.)

> **Non-STE :** *Different temperatures will change the cure time.*

(이 문장은 시간 감소에 대한 어떠한 정보도 제공하고 있지 않으므로 추상적입니다.)

> **STE :** When the temperature increases, the cure time will decrease.

(이 문장은 시간 감소에 대한 정확한 정보를 제공하고 있습니다. 문장을 명확하게 하기 위해 구체적인 온도와 경화 관련 시간을 제공해야 합니다.)

규칙 4.2	문장을 짧게 만들기 위해 단어를 생략하거나 축약형을 사용하는 것을 금지한다.

각 문장에는 모든 요소가 있어야 합니다. 문장 작성 시, 단어를 생략하거나 축약형(예: don't, isn't, aren't)을 사용하지 않습니다. 단어를 생략하거나 축약형을 사용하면 문장은 더 짧아질 수 있지만 이해하기가 더 어려울 수 있습니다. 모든 단어는 완전한 형태로 작성합니다.

문장을 짧게 만들기 위해 <u>명사</u>를 생략하지 않습니다. 명사를 생략할 경우, 독자는 말하고자 하는 대상을 모르게 됩니다.

Non-STE :	*Can be a maximum of five inches long.*
STE :	Cracks can have a maximum length of five inches.

<u>동사</u>를 생략하지 않습니다. 동사를 생략할 경우, 독자는 취할 행위를 모르게 됩니다.

Non-STE :	*Rotary switch to INPUT.*
STE :	Set the rotary switch to INPUT.

<u>주어</u>를 생략하지 않습니다. 독자들은 무엇을 나타내고자 하는지 그 대상을 알지 못합니다.

Non-STE :	*If installed, remove the shims.*
STE :	If shims are installed, remove them.

Non-STE :	*WARNING : MAKE SURE THAT THE POTABLE WATER SYSTEM IS NOT PRESSURIZED. IF NOT, THIS CAN CAUSE INJURY TO PERSONS.*
STE :	WARNING : MAKE SURE THAT THE POTABLE WATER SYSTEM IS NOT PRESSURIZED. A PRESSURIZED SYSTEM CAN CAUSE INJURY TO PERSONS.

관사를 생략하지 않습니다. 그럴 경우, 문장을 불명확하게 할 수 있습니다.

Non-STE :	*Remove the bolt and stop.*
STE :	Remove the bolt and the stop.

단어의 일부를 <u>축약형</u>으로 만들지 않습니다. 그럴 경우, 문장을 이해하기 어려울 수 있습니다.

Non-STE :	*If your hands are wet, don't touch the USB power adapter.*
STE :	If your hands are wet, do not touch the USB power adapter.

수직적 배열(Vertical Lists)

규칙 4.3	복잡한 문장의 경우 수직적 배열 형태를 사용하라.

문장이 길고 상이한 항목(예를 들어, 구성품, 부품 또는 문서 등) 또는 상황을 많이 써야 할 경우, 수직적 배열 형태로 문장을 작성해야 합니다. 수직적 배열 형태의 문장은 더 쉽게 읽고 이해할 수 있습니다.

<u>수직적 배열을 이용하여 문장을 구성하는 경우, 아래 규칙을 준수합니다.</u>

- 수직적 배열 형태에서 첫 번째 항목 앞의 첫 번째 문장 끝에 콜론(:)을 찍습니다.

- 수직적 배열 형태에서 각 항목은 숫자, 문자, 구두점 또는 기호로 식별합니다.

예를 들어, 다음과 같이 사용할 수 있습니다.

- · 대시(–)

- · 글머리 기호(·)

- · 문자(가, 나, 다...)

- · 숫자(1, 2, 3...)

사용해야 할 표시 및 심볼은 기술 규격서, 스타일 가이드 및 기타 공식 지침서에 대한 해당 규격을 참조합니다.

- 수직적 배열 형태에서 각 항목의 첫 글자는 대문자로 작성합니다.

- 해당하는 경우, 수직적 배열 형태에서 각 항목의 주제가 되는 명사 앞에 관사를 사용합니다.

- 문장이 완전한 문장으로 끝났을 경우, 문장 끝에 마침표를 찍습니다.

- 문장이 완전한 문장으로 끝나지 않았을 경우, 문장 끝에 마침표를 찍지 않습니다.

- 문장이 완전한 문장으로 끝나지 않았을 경우, 문장 끝에 쉼표를 찍지 않습니다.

- 마침표는 수직적 배열 형태의 마지막 항목 끝에 찍습니다.

아래 두 가지 예에서는 부품 및 문서 목록을 수직적 배열 형태로 수록하고 있습니다. 대시 및 글머리 기호를 활용하여 이러한 부품 이나 문서를 구분합니다.

> *Non-STE :* *The wheel assembly comprises the tire, the tube, the spokes, the spoke fittings, the valve, and the hub.*
>
> STE : The wheel assembly has these parts :
>
> - The tire
> - The tube
> - The spokes
> - The spoke fittings
> - The valve
> - The hub

> *Non-STE :* *The report must include each of the following: a completed REC-1 form, a three-view drawing of the unit, a photograph of the unit, a copy of the source data.*
>
> STE : The report must include :
>
> - A completed REC-1 form
> - A three-view drawing of the unit
> - A photograph of the unit
> - A copy of the source data.

아래 두 가지 예에서는 절차 및 설명을 수직적 배열 형태로 수록합니다. 문자 및 숫자로 각 작업 단계를 식별합니다. 앞에서 언급한대로, 사용해야 할 표시 및 심볼은 기술 간행물, 스타일 가이드 및 기타 공식 지침서에 대한 해당 규격을 참조합니다.

Non-STE : *If the RAT is retracted, remove the tag, open the isolating valves and, ensuring that there is no possibility of fouling, slowly extend the RAT to its full stroke. Close the isolating valves; tag "DO NOT OPERATE." Release the DOWN pressure.*

STE : If the Ram Air Turbine (RAT) is retracted :

    (a) Remove the tag.

    (b) Open the isolating valves.

    (c) Slowly and fully extend the RAT and make sure that it does not touch other parts.

    (d) Close the isolating valves.

    (e) Tag the isolating valves with "DO NOT OPERATE."

    (f) Release the DOWN pressure.

Non-STE : *During the final movement of the landing gear retraction, the door operating bar located on the leg contacts and turns the latch, withdrawing the roller from the slot and the second roller entraps the door operating bar.*

STE : When the landing gear retracts:

    (1) The door operating bar on the leg touches and turns the latch.

    (2) The roller moves out of the slot.

    (3) The second roller keeps the door operating bar in position.

특히 안전 지침(예를 들어, 경고 또는 주의)에서 수직적 배열 형태를 사용할 경우, 부정적인 정보를 숨기지 않아야 합니다. 수직적 배열 형태의 해당 항목에 모두 부정형 명령을 사용해야 합니다.

Non-STE : <u>*CAUTION*</u> *: WHEN YOU GET ACCESS TO THE REAR FUSELAGE THROUGH THE ACCESS PANEL, DO NOT:*

    - PUT YOUR FEET ON THE APU LINE

    - USE THE APU LINE AS A HANDLE.

STE : <u>CAUTION</u> : WHEN YOU GET ACCESS TO THE REAR FUSELAGE THROUGH THE ACCESS PANEL:

    - DO NOT PUT YOUR FEET ON THE APU LINE.

    - DO NOT USE THE APU LINE AS A HANDLE.

　수직적 배열 형태의 각 항목은 수직적 배열 형태의 첫 번째 부분(콜론 앞의 문장)과 명확하고 정확하게 연결되어야 합니다.

Non-STE :　*Do not use acetone for cleaning these parts after the repair:*

　　　　　- the service cabinet,

　　　　　- the toilet shrouds with the supports,

　　　　　- parts made of polycarbonate.

STE :　After the repair, do not use acetone to clean:

　　　　- The service cabinet

　　　　- The toilet shrouds

　　　　- The toilet shroud supports

　　　　- Parts made of polycarbonate.

　　수직적 배열 형태의 레이아웃은 항상 가독성이 좋아야 합니다. 아래 두 가지 예에서는 1차 수직적 배열 형태에 2차 수직적 배열 형태가 포함되는 경우를 나타냅니다. 가능하다면, 수직적 배열 형태에서 모든 항목에 동일한 들여쓰기 레벨을 사용합니다.

Non-STE :　Remove these parts :
- *The four screws (3)*
- *The four washers (4)*
- *The flange (2) that includes :*
- *The two O-rings (6)*
- *The seals (7)*
- *The shims (8)*
- *The spring (9).*

STE :　Remove these parts :
- The four screws (3)
- The four washers (4)
- The flange (2) (that includes the two O-rings (6) and the seals (7))
- The shims (8)
- The spring (9).

접속어 및 접속어구(Connecting Words and Phrases)

규칙 4.4	관련 의미를 포함하고 있는 연속된 문장들은 접속어 및 접속어구를 사용하여 연결된 문장으로 만들어라.

　　접속어는 어느 한 가지 개념과 그 이후에 나타나는 또 다른 개념을 상호 연결해 주는 단어나 어구를 말합니다.

　　서술문에서, 접속어 및 접속어구는 문장 구조를 논리적으로 구성하고 이해하기 쉬운 방식으로 정보를 전달합니다. 승인된 접속어는 "and", "but" "then" 및 "thus" 등이 있습니다. "As a result" 및 "at the same time"은 사용할 수 있는 접속어구입니다.

　　(접속어 또는 접속어구에 밑줄을 표시하였습니다.)

The localizer course aligns with the centerline of the runway. <u>And</u> the glideslope path is at a constant angle to the threshold of the runway.

These safety precautions are the minimum necessary for work in the pit lane. <u>But</u> the local regulations can give other necessary safety precautions.

If the pressure increases, it changes the electrical currents in the transmitter. <u>Thus</u>, the power unit supplies currents to the indicator on the related panel.

When the hydraulic pressure is released, the sequence valve moves to the open position. <u>As a result</u>, the actuators are connected to the hydraulic return.

대명사 및 지시 형용사를 사용하여 관련 문장에서 개념을 연결할 수 있습니다.

Identify the disassembled parts with tags. <u>This</u> method will help you during the subsequent assembly procedures.

(지시 형용사에 밑줄을 표시하였습니다.)

CAUTION : WHEN YOU REMOVE THE PROBES, DO NOT LET <u>THEM</u> TOUCH EACH OTHER. IF THE PROBES TOUCH, <u>THEY</u> CAN BECOME DEMAGNETIZED.

(대명사에 밑줄을 표시하였습니다.)

5 ▌절차 (Procedures)

규칙 요약

문장(Sentences)

규칙 5.1   짧은 문장을 써라. 각 문장은 최대 20 단어를 사용하라.

규칙 5.2   하나 이상의 동작이 동시에 행해지는 경우라도 한 문장 당 한 지시사항만 기록하라.

동사(Verbs)

규칙 5.3   지시문(Instruction)에서 동사는 명령형으로 작성하라.

지시문 내 서술문(Descriptive Statements in Instructions)

규칙 5.4   서술문이 있는 지시문을 나타낼 경우, 콤마(,)를 이용해 해당 서술문과 지시문의 나머지
            부분을 구분해야 한다.

주(註)(Notes)

규칙 5.5 주(註) 내용은 지시문이 아닌 정보 제공용으로 서술하라.

문장(Sentences)

규칙 5.1	짧은 문장을 써라. 각 문장은 최대 20 단어를 사용하라.

절차는 작업을 수행 방법을 알려줍니다. 문장이 길면 이해하기 어렵습니다.

STE에서, 절차문을 작성하는 경우 허용되는 문장의 최대 길이는 20 단어입니다

(단어 수 세는 방법은 제8절 참조).

경고, 주의 및 기타 안전 지침도 이 규칙을 준수해야 합니다.

Install the three auxiliary screws (2) in the flange of the motor assembly (9).

(14 단어)

CAUTION : WHEN YOU REMOVE THE SHROUD (26), BE CAREFUL NOT TO CAUSE DAMAG
            E TO THE SURFACE OF THE FLANGE ASSEMBLY (22).

(20 단어)

ASD STE 100

Non-STE :	*Put preservation oil into the unit through the vent hole until the oil level is approximately 6 mm (0.24 inches) below the surface of the flange cover.* (25 단어)
STE :	Put preservation oil into the unit through the vent hole. (10 words) Continue until the oil level is approximately 6 mm (0.24 in) below the surface of the flange cover. (16 단어)

STE에서 긴 문장은 더 읽기 쉬운 2개의 짧은 문장으로 나누어 씁니다. 이러한 지침은 두 가지 작업이 동시에 진행되기 때문에 2개의 작업 절차 단계로 나눌 수는 없습니다.

규칙 5.2	한 가지 이상의 동작이 동시에 행해지는 경우라도 한 문장 당 한 가지 지시사항만 기록하라.

한 문장에 지시 사항이 너무 많으면 문장을 이해하기 어렵습니다. 각 문장에 한 가지 지시 사항만 쓰고, 작업 단계 순서를 명확하게 수록합니다(일반적으로 숫자 또는 문자를 사용). 작업 단계는 해당 작업을 완료하는데 필요한 만큼 구분하여 사용할 수 있습니다.

STE :	(1) De-energize the system.
	(2) Make sure that all of the switches on the control panel are in their correct positions.

Non-STE :	*Set the TEST switch to the middle position and release the SHORT-CIRCUIT TEST switch.*
STE :	A. Set the TEST switch to the middle position.
	B. Release the SHORT-CIRCUIT TEST switch.

복수의 동작이 동시에 진행될 경우 문장에 1개 이상의 지시사항을 수록할 수 있습니다.
STE에서의 예 :

Hold the panel in its open position and install the fastener.

Slowly extend the rod fully and make sure that it does not touch other parts.

Cut and remove the wire.

Remove and discard the seal.

아래의 경우, 하나의 작업 단계에서 1개 이상의 문장을 수록할 수 있습니다.

- 작업 행위가 동시에 일어날 경우, 또는
- 작업 행위 직후에 결과가 발생할 경우

STE에서의 예 :

Make sure that the locking torque of each of the four bolts (6) is a minimum of 0.30 Nm.
Then, torque each of the four bolts (6) to 4.20 Nm.

Measure the leakage from the outlet port.
The leakage must not be more than 0.5 cc/minute.

동사(Verbs)

규칙 5.3	지시문(Instruction)은 명령형 형태로 작성하라.

지시문은 독자가 수행해야 할 작업을 알려줍니다. 그래서, 동사를 명령형으로 작성합니다.

STE에서의 예 :

Set the switch to ON.

Remove the four bolts

Increase the pressure to 60 psi.

Inflate the tires.

Install the new O-ring.

명령형은 독자에게 지시사항을 명확하게 제시합니다. 더 복잡한 구조의 문장을 사용할 경우, 내용을 모호하게 받아들일 수 있습니다. 그러면 독자는 아래 사항들을 모르게 될 것입니다.

- 작업 단계를 수행하는 것이 일반적으로 중요한 경우에만
- 작업 단계가 이미 완료된 경우
- 향후 다른 사람이 작업 단계를 수행해야 하는 경우

Non-STE : The test can be continued
    STE : Continue the test.

Non-STE : Oil and grease are to be removed with a degreasing agent.
    STE : Remove oil and grease with a degreasing agent.

ASD STE 100

지시문 내 서술문(Descriptive Statements in Instructions)

규칙 5.4	서술문이 있는 지시문을 나타낼 경우, 콤마(,)를 이용해 해당 명령문에서 서술문과 지시문을 구분해야 한다.

특정 조건 하에서 작업 단계를 수행하는 것이 가능할 때가 있습니다. 이러한 경우, 독자는 먼저 특정 조건에 대해 알아야 합니다.

문장 서두에 조건을 먼저 수록하고 콤마(,)를 사용하여 조건이 끝나는 부분과 지시가 시작되는 부분을 표시합니다.

Non-STE : *Set the switch to NORMAL when the light comes on.*
STE : When the light comes on, set the switch to NORMAL.

Non-STE : *Apply the primer when the surface is dry.*
STE : When the surface is dry, apply the primer.

Non-STE : *Disconnect the constant speed drive (CSD) from the gearbox, if it does not operate correctly.*
STE : If the constant speed drive (CSD) does not operate correctly, disconnect it from the gearbox.

콤마(,)는 중요합니다. 문장의 뜻을 변경시킬 수 있기 때문에 정확하게 사용하도록 주의해야 합니다.
STE에서의 예 :

If the constant speed drive (CSD) does not operate correctly, disconnect it from the gearbox.

If the constant speed drive (CSD) does not operate, correctly disconnect it from the gearbox.

위의 예에서 볼 수 있듯이, 두 문장은 맞는 문장이지만 두 가지의 의미로 해석됩니다.

주(Notes)

규칙 5.5	NOTE 내용은 지시문이 아닌 정보 제공용으로 서술하라.

독자들이 작업 진행 과정에서 이해할 수 있도록 NOTE 내용에는 서술문이나 정보 제공용 내용만 수록합니다.

NOTE 내용에는 지침사항이나 요구조건을 담지 않아야 합니다.

STE에서의 예 :

NOTE : The gyroscope will become stable after approximately 15 seconds.

NOTE : It is not necessary to remove the nameplate (33) from the flange (27).

NOTE : You can use equivalent alternatives for these items.

NOTE 내용에는 1개 이상의 문장을 포함할 수 있으며, 각 문장은 최대 25 단어를 사용해야 합니다.

STE에서의 예 :

NOTE : During the subsequent test, you get the cracking pressure when the fuel flow from the CROSS FEED port is more than 5 cc/minute.

(1 문장, 22 단어)

NOTE : The data collection is not completed. Thus, the statistics module can give incorrect results.

(2 문장, 6 단어 및 8 단어)

명령형을 쓰지 않습니다. 명령형을 사용하면, NOTE는 작업 단계에 대한 지침사항이 됩니다.

Non-STE : NOTE : *Make sure that the avionics ventilation system continues to operate correctly.*

(이 문장은 명령문 형태라서 주(NOTE) 내용에 해당하지 않습니다).

STE : (6) Make sure that the avionics ventilation system continues to operate correctly.

NOTE 내용에 지침사항을 수록하면 독자가 정보를 보지 않을 수도 있습니다. 주(NOTE) 내용에 제공된 정보가 손상 또는 상해를 방지하는데 중요한 내용이라면 안전 지침에 이러한 정보를 담아야 합니다.

> *Non-STE* : *NOTE* : *When you connect the lines, do not bend them too much. If you bend the lines too much, you can cause damage to them.*

(이 문장은 주(NOTE) 내용이 아닌 안전 지침 내용에 해당합니다.).

> STE : CAUTION : WHEN YOU CONNECT THE LINES, DO NOT BEND THEM TOO MUCH. IF YOU BEND THE LINES TOO MUCH, YOU CAN CAUSE DAMAGE TO THEM.

> *Non-STE* : *NOTE* : *Before closing the hatch, it is mandatory to ensure that no persons are in the crew rest compartment. When the hatch is closed, there is no airflow to the compartment and therefore there is a risk of suffocation.*

(이 문장은 명령형은 아니지만 주(NOTE) 내용이 아니라 안전 지침 내용입니다.).

> STE : WARNING : BEFORE YOU CLOSE THE HATCH, MAKE SURE THAT NO PERSONS ARE IN THE CREW REST COMPARTMENT. WHEN THE HATCH IS CLOSED, THERE IS NO AIRFLOW TO THE COMPARTMENT AND THERE IS A RISK OF SUFFOCATION.

절차를 작성하고 이 절차에 NOTE가 포함되면 다음과 같이 테스트를 수행합니다.
- 주(NOTE) 내용없이 절차를 주의하여 읽습니다.
- 독자가 주(NOTE) 내용없이 절차를 올바르게 수행하는지 확인합니다.

결과가 만족스럽다면 당신은 이러한 NOTE 내용을 정확하게 사용한 것입니다.

절차에 중요한 정보가 빠져 있고, 이 정보가 NOTE 내용에 포함된 경우 다음 조치를 취합니다.
- NOTE 내용에서 정보를 삭제합니다.
- 작업 단계에서 빠진 정보를 담습니다.
- 절차에 해당하는 경우, 이 새로운 작업 단계를 포함시킵니다.
- 독자가 NOTE 내용 없이 절차를 수행할 수 있다고 확신할 때까지 테스트를 반복 수행합니다.

STE에서 NOTE는 절차 부분에 사용합니다. 설명 부분의 일부인 그림 또는 표에서 NOTE 내용이 필요한 경우에만 설명 부분에 NOTE 내용을 포함할 수 있습니다.

6 ▌ 서술문 작성(Descriptive Writing)

규칙 요약

내용 구조(Content Structure)

규칙 6.1   정보를 이해하기 쉽도록 천천히 제공하라.

규칙 6.2   핵심어 또는 어구를 사용해 텍스트를 논리적으로 구성하라.

문장(Sentences)

규칙 6.3   문장을 짧게 작성하라. 각 문장은 최대 25 단어를 사용하라.

문단(Paragraphs)

규칙 6.4   관련된 정보를 작성할 경우 문단을 사용하라.

규칙 6.5   각 문단에는 하나의 주제만을 담아라.

규칙 6.6   여섯 문장 이상으로 구성된 문단이 없도록 하라.

내용 구조(Content Structure)

서술문은 지침이 아닌 정보를 제공하기 위하여 작성합니다. 서술문은 아래의 경우 사용합니다.

- 품목, 생산품, 계통, 또는 구성품의 기능, 제작법 및 운용방법에 대한 설명
- 일반적인 정보(예를 들어, 보고서, 브로셔, 논문 등)를 제공하는 텍스트
- 절차 내 주(NOTE)

ASD STE 100

규칙 6.1	정보를 이해하기 쉽도록 천천히 제공하라.

서술문에서는 정보를 천천히 제공하고 각 문장에는 하나의 주제만 수록합니다. 과도한 양의 정보를 성급하게 제공하면 텍스트를 이해하기 어렵고 독자는 이해하기 위해 텍스트를 반복해서 읽게 될 것입니다.

Non-STE : Instrument Landing System

During the approach to the runway, deviation pointers in the course indicators give commands to fly up or down and left or right. This information comes from the VHF transceivers, which are part of the Instrument Landing System. This helps the pilot during the landing approach. When the pilot responds to the commands, the aircraft can be flown over the runway centerline (localizer) and at a fixed angle (glideslope) to the runway threshold. The localizer signals are processed by the transceiver and data are transmitted to Air Traffic Control.

STE에서는 짧은 문장 및 핵심어를 사용하여 텍스트를 명확하게 작성하는 방법을 수록합니다.

STE : Instrument Landing System

The Instrument Landing System (the system) on the aircraft shows data that helps the pilot during the approach to the runway. This system shows the pilot the deviations from the localizer course and the glideslope path. The localizer course aligns with the centerline of the runway. And the glideslope path is at a constant angle to the threshold of the runway. During the approach to the runway, deviation pointers in the course indicators show the pilot in which direction the aircraft must go:

- Left or right (for the localizer)
- Up or down (for the glideslope).

This data about deviations from the localizer course and glideslope path comes from two VHF transceivers. These transceivers transmit this data to Air Traffic Control.

STE 버전은 두 문단으로 분리되고 논리적 구조로 작성되어 있습니다.

- 첫 번째 문단은 5문장입니다.
- 두 번째 문단은 2문장입니다.

규칙 6.2	핵심어 또는 어구를 사용해 문장을 논리적으로 구성하라.

핵심어 및 어구는 문장에 논리적 구조를 제공합니다. 핵심어는 서로 상이한 개념을 연결하기 위해 문장에서 자주 나타나는 단어입니다. 핵심 어구는 핵심어와 동일한 기능을 합니다. 이러한 단어 및 구는 문장의 정보가 어떻게 관련되어 있는지 보여주고 문장에 논리적 구조를 제공합니다.

또한 연결단어 및 어구를 사용하여 독자가 문장에서 개념의 진행 상황을 이해하도록 도움을 줍니다. 연결단어 및 어구는 교통 표지판의 기능을 하고 문장의 정보가 새로운 것인지, 다른지 또는 선행 사실에 기초한 결론인지를 독자에게 알려줍니다.

다음 예는 규칙 6.1에 대한 STE 버전의 예입니다. 텍스트에서 핵심어 및 어구에 밑줄을 표시하였습니다. 핵심어 및 어구가 어떻게 문장을 연결하고 개념을 연결하는지를 알 수 있습니다. 이런 방식을 사용하면 텍스트를 훨씬 쉽게 읽을 수 있습니다.

문장 1	문장 2
The Instrument Landing System (the system) on the aircraft shows data that helps the pilot during the approach to the runway.	This system shows the pilot the deviations from the localizer course and the glideslope path.

문장 2에는 "system", "show", 및 "pilot"이라는 핵심 단어를 반복 사용하여 문장 1에 수록한 정보를 추가 및 확장시킵니다.

문장 2	문장 3 및 4
This system shows the pilot the deviations from the localizer course and the glideslope path.	The localizer course aligns with the centerline of the runway. And the glideslope path is at a constant angle to the threshold of the runway.

문장 3과 4에는 "localizer course" 및 "glideslope path"라는 핵심 단어를 반복 사용하여 새로운 정보를 추가합니다.

문장 3	문장 4
The localizer course aligns with the centerline of the runway.	And the glideslope path is at a constant angle to the threshold of the runway.

문장 3과 4에는 문장 1에서 언급한 "runway"도 포함하고 있습니다.

문장 3 및 4	문장 5
The localizer course aligns with the centerline of the runway. And the glideslope path is at a constant angle to the threshold of the runway.	During the approach to the runway, deviation pointers in the course indicators show the pilot in which direction the aircraft must go : - Left or right (for the localizer) - Up or down (for the glideslope).

문장 5에서도 "runway"라는 단어를 사용하여 이전 문장 3과 4를 다시 연결하고 localizer 및 glideslope용 지시기 기능에 관한 정보를 추가로 제공합니다.

문장 2	문장 5
This system shows the pilot the deviations from the localizer course and the glideslope path.	During the approach to the runway, deviation pointers in the course indicators show the pilot in which direction the aircraft must go : - Left or right (for the localizer) - Up or down (for the glideslope).

문장 2와 5는 핵심어와 어구를 사용하여 논리적으로 연결됩니다.

문장 1	문장 5
The Instrument Landing System (the system) on the aircraft shows data that helps the pilot during the approach to the runway.	During the approach to the runway, deviation pointers in the course indicators show the pilot in which direction the aircraft must go : - Left or right (for the localizer) - Up or down (for the glideslope).

문장 1과 5는 논리적 문단을 구성하기 위해 서로 연결됩니다.

문장 5에서도 문장 1에서 수록한 "during the approach to the runway" 어구를 반복하여 원래의 상황을 언급하고 이를 확장시킵니다. 동일한 핵심어와 핵심 어구를 반복하면 문장이 논리적으로 연결됩니다. 다른 단어를 많이 사용하면 문장의 내용을 이해하기가 어려울 것입니다.

또한 두 문단은 논리적으로 연결됩니다.

문단 1 : (문장 1 ~ 5) : deviation, data, localizer, glideslope

문단 2 : (문장 6, 7) : This data about deviations from the localizer course and glideslope path comes from two VHF transceivers. These transceivers transmit this data to Air Traffic Control.

문장(Sentences)

규칙 6.3	문장을 짧게 작성하라. 각 문장은 최대 25 단어를 사용하라.

간단하거나 복잡한 주제에 대하여 기술 문서를 잘 쓰는 방법은 짧은 문장을 사용하는 것 입니다. 짧은 문장은 명료한 구조로 글을 쓸 수 있게 하고, 정보를 이해하기 쉽게 만듭니다.

서술문 작성에서 문장은 최대 25 단어까지 사용합니다. 왜냐하면, 서술문은 절차문보다 더욱 복잡한 내용을 다루기 때문입니다.

> STE : During the approach to the runway, deviation pointers in the course indicators show the pilot in which direction the aircraft must go. (22 단어)

> *Non-STE : A smartphone is a cellular telephone that has an integrated computer and many other functions, such as an operating system, internet browsing as well as the ability to run software applications. (31 단어)*
>
> STE : A smartphone is a cellular telephone that has an integrated computer and many other functions.(15 단어) It includes an operating system and an internet browser, and it can also operate software applications.(16 단어)

문단(Paragraphs)

규칙 6.4	관련된 정보를 작성할 경우 문단을 사용하라.

절차문에는 작업 단계에 그 순서를 식별하는 숫자 및 문자가 포함되어 있습니다. 서술문 작성에서 문단은 관련 정보를 함께 수록하고 본문의 논리적 순서를 구성하는 역할을 합니다.

STE에서 문단의 첫 문장은 독자에게 해당 문단의 주제가 무엇인지 알려주는 "주제문(Topic Sentence)"으로 시작합니다. 주제문이 제시되고 난 후, 뒤에 오는 문장은 해당 내용을 설명하거나 뒷받침하는 추가 정보를 제공합니다.

새 문단이 시작될 경우, 독자는 해당 문단에 새로운 정보 또는 다른 정보가 수록된다는 것을 알 수 있습니다.

> STE : 1. Lightning Strike
>
> A. General
>
> (1) A lightning strike can cause damage to the aircraft. The damage usually occurs at the attachment points. The attachment points include:
>
> - The nose of the fuselage
> - The tail section
> - The propellers
> - The wing tips
> - The tips of the stabilizer
> - The tips of the stabilizer
> - The trailing edge of the stabilizer
> - The antennas
> - The static dischargers.
>
> (2) From the attachment points, the lightning strike usually goes aft through the structure of the aircraft. The high current of the lightning strike can cause damage to the mechanical systems of the aircraft. Thus, a permanent or a temporary malfunction of the electrical and electronic equipment and the systems can occur.
>
> (3) If a lightning strike occurs, it is necessary to do an inspection of the aircraft for damage. The maintenance personnel must do this inspection before the next flight.

본 예시는 본문의 명확한 구조를 나타내고 이해기 쉽도록 세 개의 짧은 문단으로 구성하였습니다.

규칙 6.5	각 문단 당 하나의 주제만 담아라.

주제문은 문단의 처음이자 가장 중요한 문장입니다. 주제문은 새로운 정보를 제공하고 이전 문단에서 다루었던 내용과 해당 문단을 논리적으로 연결합니다. 이를 위해 주제문은 일반적으로 핵심어(Keywords) 및 연결 단어나 구를 포함하고 있습니다.

주제문에서 독자는 본문의 내용을 이해하고 특정 정보를 빠르게 찾을 수 있습니다. 독자는 본문에서 각 주제문만 기록하더라도 내용의 대략적인 윤곽을 이해할 수 있습니다. 문단의 나머지 문장들은 주제를 뒷받침하거나 발전시키는 추가 정보를 제공합니다.

규칙 6.1 및 6.2의 예시에서 STE 버전을 다시 참조하자면, 본문이 두 문단으로 나누어 짐을 알 수 있습니다.
문단 1(문장 1부터 5까지) - "Data to help the pilot."
문단 2(문장 6 및 7) - "How this data is transmitted."

다음 예시에서 각 문단의 시작 부분에 있는 주제문은 독자가 앞으로 논의될 내용을 파악할 수 있도록 도와주는 역할을 합니다. 그런 다음 더 많은 정보가 점진적으로 추가되고 본문이 논리적으로 연결됩니다.

STE : Instrument Landing System

The Instrument Landing System (the system) on the aircraft shows data that helps the pilot during the approach to the runway. This system shows the pilot the deviations from the localizer course and the glideslope path. The localizer course aligns with the centerline of the runway. And the glideslope path is at a constant angle to the threshold of the runway. During the approach to the runway, deviation pointers in the course indicators show the pilot in which direction the aircraft must go :

- Left or right (for the localizer)
- Up or down (for the glideslope).

This data about deviations from the localizer course and glideslope path comes from two VHF transceivers. These transceivers transmit this data to Air Traffic Control.

ASD STE 100

규칙 6.6	여섯 문장 이상으로 구성된 문단이 없도록 하라.

문단은 본문을 논리적 단위로 구성하고 독자의 주의를 끄는 데 도움을 줍니다. 문단이 너무 길면 논리적 구성이 어렵거나 흥미를 떨어뜨릴 수 있습니다. 같은 문단에 다른 주제를 수록해서는 안됩니다. 또한 문단에 여섯 개 이상의 문장이 있는 경우, 작은 문단 두 개로 나누어 본문의 가독성을 높여 줍니다.

STE : Description of the fuel manifold (refer to figure 10001)
The fuel manifold (1) has these primary parts:
- Two motorized fuel shut-off valves (referred to in this manual as "shut-off valve")
- A pressure transducer (2)
- Three fittings (10), (13) and (15).   (one paragraph, 1 sentence)
The shut-off valve operates in the valve body (21). The valve body (21) has:
- An aluminum alloy ball (27)
- A retaining ring (31)
- Two seals (26)
- A spring (25).   (one paragraph, 1 sentence)
The spring (25) holds the ball (27) in position to prevent internal leakage. The preformed packings (18), (2) and (30) are installed on the seals (26), the shaft (28), and in the valve body. They prevent external leakage. One of the two seals (26), on which the spring (25) operates, has the function of a relief valve. It operates when the pressure applied in the opposite direction is more than a set value.

                    (one paragraph, 5 sentences)
The actuator assembly (4) is of a rotary type. A DC motor, which has a permanent high-speed magnet, supplies power to the actuator. Micro-switches in the actuator de-energize it at the end of travel. They also send signals to the fuel control panel to show the operation condition of the valve. A micro-relay controls the direction of shaft rotation and an electrical connector connects the actuator assembly to the aircraft electrical supply.

                    (one paragraph, 4 sentences)
The pressure transducer (2) is installed downstream of the shut-off valve (in the RH engine line). The fitting (10) connects the pressure transducer (2) to the fuel manifold (1). A lockwire safeties the pressure transducer (2). The pressure transducer (2) has an electrical connector that connects it to the Fuel Management System of the aircraft.   (one paragraph, 4 sentences)
Three fittings (10), (13), and (15) connect the two shut-off valves and the pressure transducer (2). They attach the fuel manifold (1) to the aircraft structure.   (one paragraph, 2 sentences)

본 예시는 본문의 명료한 구조를 제공하고 쉽게 이해할 수 있도록 짧은 문단들로 이루어져 있습니다.

7 ▐ 안전 지침(Safety instructions)

규칙 요약

정의(Definitions)

안전 지침 작성 방법(How to write safety instructions)

규칙 7.1   위험 수준을 식별할 수 있도록 적절한 단어(예: "경고(warning)", 또는 "주의(caution)")
를 사용하라.

규칙 7.2   안전 지침은 간단하고 명확한 명령문 또는 조건문 형태로 시작하라.

규칙 7.3   특정 위험 또는 발생 가능한 결과를 알리기 위한 설명을 제공하라.

정의(Definitions)

안전 지침(Safety instructions)은 절차 또는 절차의 단계에 위험 또는 손상 유발 요인이 있음을 독자에게 알려 줍니다.

다음의 단어 및 정의는 항공우주 및 방위분야에 적용되는 정의입니다.

- 경고(Warning)는 독자에게 상해 또는 사망의 위험이 있음을 알려줍니다.
- 주의(Caution)는 독자에게 물체의 손상 위험이 있음을 알려 줍니다.

다른 산업에서는 안전 지침에 대해 다른 단어 또는 범주를 사용할 수 있습니다.

다른 단어(예 : "danger", "attention", 또는 "notice") 또는 그래픽 기호를 사용할 경우에도 규칙 7.1 ~ 7.3의 원칙을 준수해야 합니다. 자세한 내용은 다음을 참조합니다.

- ISO 45001 - Occupational Health and Safety
- ANSI Z535 - Safety Alerting Standards(sub-standard 1부터 6까지)
- ISO 3864 - International Standards for Safety Signs(part 1부터 4까지).

ASD STE 100

안전 지침 작성 방법(How to write safety instructions)

규칙 7.1	위험 수준을 식별할 수 있도록 적절한 단어(예: "경고(warning)", 또는 "주의(caution)")를 사용하라.

위험 수준을 독자가 즉시 인지할 수 있도록 적절한 단어(예: "경고(warning)", 또는 "주의(caution)", 해당할 경우에는 기호)를 사용합니다.

STE에서의 예 :

모든 예시는 대문자로 수록하였습니다. STE에는 글쓰기 서식에 대한 규정이 명시되어 있지 않으므로 본 규격은 관련 기술 도서 규격서, 스타일 가이드 또는 공식 지침서들과 함께 참고하여 활용해야 합니다.

WARNING : BEFORE YOU FILL THE LIQUID OXYGEN SYSTEM, PUT ON A FACE MASK AND PROTECTIVE CLOTHING. LIQUID OXYGEN CAN CAUSE IRRITATION OF THE RESPIRATORY TRACT AND EYE IRRITATION.

WARNING : ALWAYS KEEP YOUR HANDS AND FEET AWAY FROM THE BLADE. WHEN THE MOTOR OPERATES, THE BLADE TURNS AND CAN CAUSE INJURY.

CAUTION : BEFORE YOU OPERATE THE GROUND TEST UNIT, MAKE SURE THAT THE PRESSURE REGULATOR IS SET TO ZERO. THIS WILL PREVENT DAMAGE TO THE UNIT.

CAUTION : DO NOT USE BLEACH OR CLEANSERS THAT CONTAIN CHLORINE TO CLEAN THE UNIT. THESE CLEANING AGENTS CAN CAUSE CORROSION.

위험을 정확하게 분석하여 위험 수준을 식별해야 합니다.
 - 상해 또는 사망의 위험이 있는 경우 "경고(WARNING)"를 사용합니다.
 - 기계, 공구 또는 장비 손상의 위험이 있는 경우 "주의(CAUTION)"를 사용합니다.
 - 두 가지 수준의 위험이 함께 있는 경우 "경고(WARNING)"를 사용합니다.

Non-STE : *CAUTION* : *EXTREME CLEANLINESS OF OXYGEN TUBES IS IMPERATIVE*

STE : WARNING : MAKE SURE THAT THE OXYGEN TUBES ARE FULLY CLEAN. OXYGEN AND OIL OR GREASE MAKE AN EXPLOSIVE MIXTURE. AN EXPLOSION CAN CAUSE INJURY OR DEATH TO PERSONNEL.

Non-STE에 대한 예제에서, 본 안전 지침은 "주의(CAUTION)"로 수록되어 있습니다. 그러나, 산소가 다른 물질과 혼합될 경우 폭발을 일으킬 수 있습니다. 폭발이 발생하게 되면, 상해 또는 사망의 위험이 있으므로 본 안전 지침은 "경고(WARNING)"로 식별되어야 합니다.

두 가지 안전 지침을 비교해보면 Non-STE는 추상적이며 일반적인 설명만을 제공하고 STE로 작성된 경고는 폭발 위험을 예방하는 법에 대해 훨씬 더 구체적인 정보를 제공하고 있습니다. STE의 경고에서는 독자가 본 안전 지침이 얼마나 중요한지에 대하여 명확하게 이해할 수 있도록 "explosion", "injury" 및 "death"라는 단어를 사용합니다.

규칙 7.2	안전 지침은 간단하고 명확한 명령문 또는 조건문 형태로 시작하라.

안전 지침은 간단하고 명확한 명령문 또는 조건문 형태로 시작해야 합니다. 독자는 사고를 예방하고 고수준의 안전을 유지하기 위해 반드시 취해야 할 조치가 무엇인지를 알아야 합니다.

STE에서의 예 :

　　　　(밑줄 친 부분은 명령문에 해당함)

WARNING : DO NOT SWALLOW THE SOLVENT. ALWAYS MAKE SURE THAT YOU KNOW THE SAFETY PRECAUTIONS AND FIRST AID INSTRUCTIONS FOR SOLVENTS. SOLVENTS ARE POISONOUS AND CAN CAUSE INJURY OR DEATH TO PERSONNEL.

CAUTION : DO NOT USE BLEACH OR CLEANSERS THAT CONTAIN CHLORINE TO CLEAN THE UNIT. THESE CLEANING AGENTS CAN CAUSE CORROSION.

독자가 절차 또는 작업 단계를 시작하기 전, 특정 조건에 대해 알아야 할 경우에는 해당 조건문을 먼저 써야 합니다.

STE에서의 예 :

　　　　(밑줄 친 부분은 조건문에 해당함)

WARNING : WHILE YOU USE THE SPRAY PAINT, POINT THE SPRAY AWAY FROM YOUR FACE. THE SPRAY PAINT CAN CAUSE INJURY TO YOUR EYES.

CAUTION : WHEN YOU ASSEMBLE THE UNIT, DO NOT LET THE PARTS FALL. IF THEY FALL, PERMANENT DAMAGE TO THE PARTS CAN OCCUR.

규칙 7.3	특정 위험 또는 발생 가능한 결과를 알리기 위한 설명을 제공하라.

가능한 경우, 안전 지침을 준수하지 않을 경우 발생할 수 있는 위험을 독자에게 항상 알려줘야 합니다. 위험이 명확하게 명시되어 있을 경우, 작업자는 위험을 이해하고 더 주의를 기울일 것입니다. 다음은 규칙 7.2의 예제로, 밑줄 친 부분에서 특정 위험 또는 발생 가능한 위험 요소를 명확하게 나타냅니다.

(밑줄 친 부분은 위험 또는 결과에 해당함)

WARNING : DO NOT SWALLOW THE SOLVENT. ALWAYS MAKE SURE THAT YOU KNOW THE SAFETY PRECAUTIONS AND FIRST AID INSTRUCTIONS FOR SOLVENTS. SOLVENTS ARE POISONOUS AND CAN CAUSE INJURY OR DEATH TO PERSONNEL.

CAUTION : DO NOT USE BLEACH OR CLEANSERS THAT CONTAIN CHLORINE TO CLEAN THE UNIT. THESE CLEANING AGENTS CAN CAUSE CORROSION.

WARNING : WHILE YOU USE THE SPRAY PAINT, POINT THE SPRAY AWAY FROM YOUR FACE. THE SPRAY PAINT CAN CAUSE INJURY TO YOUR EYES.

CAUTION : WHEN YOU ASSEMBLE THE UNIT, DO NOT LET THE PARTS FALL. IF THEY FALL, PERMANENT DAMAGE TO THE PARTS CAN OCCUR.

8 ▍구두점 및 단어 수 계산(Punctuation and Word Counts)

규칙 요약

구두점(Punctuation)

규칙 8.1 세미콜론(;)을 제외한 모든 표준 영어의 구두점 부호를 사용할 수 있다.

규칙 8.2 밀접한 관련 단어들을 연결할 경우 하이픈(-)을 사용하라.

규칙 8.3 다음과 같은 경우, 괄호를 사용할 수 있다.

- 도해 또는 본문을 참조할 경우
- 도해 또는 본문의 항목을 식별하는 문자나 숫자를 수록할 경우
- 절차문의 단계를 식별할 경우
- 약어를 수록할 경우
- 명사의 단수형 및 복수형을 동시에 제공할 경우
- 문장의 단어 또는 일부를 설명할 경우
- 대체 단어를 수록할 경우

단어 수 계산(Word count)

규칙 8.4 수직적 배열의 콜론(:)은 마침표와 동일하게 단어 수에 영향을 미치며 문장의 끝을 나타낸다.

규칙 8.5 괄호 안의 내용은 해당 문장에서 한 단어로 계산한다.

규칙 8.6 다음과 같은 경우 한 단어로 계산한다.

- 숫자, 측정 단위, 약어, 식별자(문자, 숫자 조합), 인용문, 제목, 플래카드, 라벨

규칙 8.7 하이픈으로 연결한 단어는 한 단어로 계산한다.

구두점(Punctuation)

구두점을 사용하면 본문의 다른 부분과 서로 어떻게 연관되어 있는지 확인할 수 있고 모호성을 방지할 수 있기 때문에 정확하게 사용하는 것이 중요합니다.

STE에서는 구두점에 관한 일반적인 지침이 수록되어 있지 않으므로 상세한 정보는 공식 참고 서적을 참조하시기 바랍니다. 예를 들면 다음과 같습니다.

- The Chicago Manual of Style,   - The Gregg Reference Manual
- U.S. Government Printing Office Style Manual
- John Kirkman: Punctuation Matters
- Advice on punctuation for scientific and technical writing.

규칙 8.1	세미콜론(;)을 제외한 모든 표준 영어의 구두점 부호를 사용할 수 있다.

세미콜론(;)은 매우 긴 문장을 작성할 수 있도록 하며 바르게 사용하는 것 또한 어렵기 때문에 STE에서는 인정되지 않습니다. 세미콜론을 사용하는 대신 다른 두 개의 문장으로 작성해야 합니다.

예 :

> *Non-STE :*   *(1) Examine the removed parts; replace the damaged ones.*
> STE :   (1) Examine the removed parts for damage.
>   (2) Replace the damaged part(s).

> *Non-STE :*   *The battery is not user-replaceable; it can only be replaced by an approved service provider.*
> STE :   Do not replace the battery. Only an approved service provider can replace it.

규칙 8.2	밀접한 관련 단어들을 연결할 경우 하이픈(-)을 사용하라.

하이픈(-)은 단어 또는 단어의 부분을 연결하는 문장부호입니다. 하이픈을 사용하여 두 개 이상의 단어가 밀접하게 관련되어 있음을 표시합니다. 이로 인해 독자는 단어 및 구를 더 쉽게 이해할 수 있습니다. 다음의 예는 하이픈을 사용하여 밀접한 관련 단어들을 연결하는 방법을 나타냅니다.

1. 명사 전에 오는 형용사로 두 개 이상의 단어를 가진 용어

> low-altitude flight, high-pressure chamber, air-conditioned compartment, transmitter-receiver system, quick-release fastener, clamshell-type flap, eighteen-inch monitor, cast-aluminum bracket, three-to-one ratio, trial-and-error method, air-to-air refueling, soap-and-water solution, up-to-date information, run-on torque, break-away torque, cut-in speed, in-flight entertainment system, stiff-bristled brush, fire-resistant material, self-sealing hose

2. 두 개의 단어가 조합되어 분수 또는 숫자로 쓰이는 경우

> forty-seven, ninety-ninth, one hundred and sixty-two, three-sixteenths, one thirty-second

3. 대문자나 숫자와 합쳐진 명사로 일반적으로 어떠한 것의 형태이나 구성을 설명하는 용어

> L-shaped bracket, O-ring, T-shirt, U-beam, Y-coupling, V-band clamp, 3-prong connector, 180-grit abrasive cloth

4. 명사 또는 다른 품사가 첫 번째 요소로 수록되는 동사

> die-cast, arc-weld, fusion-bond, stop-drill, vacuum-pack, heat-treat, jump-start, air-condition, short-circuit, fast-forward, cold-roll, dry-clean, blow-dry

5. 모음으로 끝나는 접두사와 모음으로 시작하는 접미어로 구성한 용어

de-energize, pre-amplifier, de-ice, anti-icing, pre-engage

하이픈은 단어를 분리하거나 범위 또는 중단을 나타내는 대시와 다릅니다. 일반적으로 대시는 하이픈
보다 길지만 양쪽에 공백이 있는 하이픈으로도 표시할 수 있습니다.

규칙 8.3   다음과 같은 경우, 괄호를 사용할 수 있다.
               - 도해 또는 본문을 참조할 경우
               - 도해 또는 본문의 항목을 식별하는 문자나 숫자를 수록할 경우
               - 절차문의 단계를 식별할 경우
               - 약어를 수록할 경우
               - 명사의 단수형 및 복수형을 동시에 제공할 경우
               - 문장의 단어 또는 일부를 설명할 경우
               - 대체 단어를 수록할 경우

STE에서는 다음과 같은 경우 괄호를 사용할 수 있습니다.

1. 도해 또는 본문을 참조할 경우

Remove the valve (10, Figure 1).

Install the cover (refer to paragraphs 2 thru 5.)

2. 도해 또는 본문의 항목을 식별하는 문자나 숫자를 수록할 경우

Disconnect the hoses (2) and (12) from the suction ejector (8).

Remove the nuts (74), the washers (76), the bolts (68), the seals (70), and the bonding
straps (72).

3. 절차문의 단계를 식별할 경우

(1) Install the locking cap (4) on the body (8).
(2) Safety the locking cap (4) with the cotter pin (5).
(3) Install a new retaining ring (6).

4. 약어를 수록할 경우

A Liquid Crystal Display (LCD) is a flat-panel display that uses the light-modulating
properties of liquid crystals.

---

5. 명사의 단수형 및 복수형을 동시에 제공할 경우

A. Before you do the test(s), install the component(s).

B. Do the applicable test(s).

6. 문장의 단어 또는 일부를 설명할 경우

Increase the pressure slowly (not more than 10 psi each minute.)

Make sure that the BLEED pushbutton switch is released (the ON legend is off.)

7. 대체 단어를 수록할 경우

Open the left (right) access panel L42 (R42).

단어 수 계산(Word count)

규칙 8.4	수직적 배열의 콜론(:)은 마침표와 동일하게 단어 수에 영향을 미치며 문장의 끝을 나타낸다.

수직적 배열에서 콜론(:)은 문장의 첫 부분을 수직적 배열의 후속 항목들과 구분하는 역할을 합니다. 이 콜론은 마침표의 기능을 수행합니다.

- 절차문에서는 콜론 앞에 최대 20개의 단어를 사용할 수 있습니다.
- 서술문에서는 콜론 앞에 최대 25개의 단어를 사용할 수 있습니다.

콜론 뒤에 오는 수직적 배열의 각 항목은 새로운 문장으로 계산됩니다. 따라서 수직적 배열의 각 항목에 대한 제한은 다음과 같습니다.

- 절차문을 위한 20개의 단어
- 서술문을 위한 25개의 단어

STE에서의 예

To extinguish a possible fire, portable fire extinguishers are installed in these areas :	(13 words)
- The cockpit	(2 words)
- The cabin	(2 words)
- The cabin sub-compartment	(3 words)
- The crew rest compartment.	(4 words)

규칙 8.5	괄호 안의 내용은 해당 문장에서 한 단어로 계산한다.

문장 길이로서 단어를 셀 때, 괄호 안의 본문은 해당 문장의 한 단어로 계산됩니다. 하지만 괄호 사이에 들어가는 단어 또한 새로운 문장을 생성하기 때문에 또 다른 문장으로 계산해야 합니다.

STE에서의 예 :

Make sure that the EMER pushbutton switch is released (the EMER legend is off.)

(괄호 안의 문장을 한 단어로 계산하기 때문에 본 문장은 10개의 단어로 구성되어 있습니다.

괄호 안의 문장은 다섯 개의 단어로 구성되며 다른 문장으로 계산됩니다.)

괄호 안에 식별자(숫자, 문자, 또는 문자 및 숫자를 조합한 식별자)가 수록될 경우, 해당 식별자는 문장에서 한 단어로 계산합니다. 괄호 안의 약어 또한 한 단어로 계산합니다.

ASD STE 100

STE에서의 예

Remove the safety pin (10).	(5 words)

Installation of a Business Class (B/C) Seat	(7 words)

Hardware and Software Configuration Check of the In-Flight Entertainment (IFE) System	
	(11 words)

규칙 8.6	다음과 같은 경우, 하나의 단어로 계산한다.
	- 숫자, 측정 단위, 약어, 식별자(문자, 숫자 조합), 인용문, 제목, 플래카드, 라벨

문장의 길이로서 단어를 셀 경우 다음은 각각 하나의 단어로 계산합니다.

1. 숫자

Do steps 13 thru 16 a minimum of three times.	(10 words)

("13" 및 "16"은 숫자이며 각각 한 단어로 계산합니다.)

The spar box has twenty-one ribs.	(6 words)

("Twenty-one"은 숫자이며 한 단어로 계산합니다.)

2. 측정 단위

일반적으로 기술 문서에서 측정 단위는 관련 숫자 다음에 수록됩니다(예: 10 mA). 측정 단위에 대한 약어 또는 기호를 쓸 경우 그 단위와 숫자를 한 단어로 계산합니다. 단위나 기호를 모두 풀어 쓸 경우에는 각각 한 단어로 계산합니다.

Make sure that the temperature in the room is 10 °C.	(10 words)
Make sure that the temperature in the room is 10 degrees Celsius.	(12 words)

The unit weighs 20 kg.	(4 words)
The unit weighs 20 kilograms.	(5 words)

The resistance must be 10 Ω.	(5 words)
The resistance must be 10 ohms.	(6 words)

3. 약어

기술 문서에서는 약어(두문자어 및 이니셜)를 사용하여 문장을 더 짧고 읽기 쉽게 작성할 수 있습니다. 그러나, 이러한 약어는 독자가 알고 있는 경우에만 도움이 됩니다. 각 약어는 하나의 단어로 계산됩니다.

We do a test of this system each day at 10 a.m.	(12 words)

("a.m."은 약어이며 한 단어로 계산됩니다.)

Make sure that the unit has the NATO code. (9 words)

(NATO는 약어(두문자어)이며 한 단어로 계산됩니다.)

4. 문자 및 숫자를 조합한 식별자

문자 및 숫자를 조합한 식별자는 어떠한 것을 식별하는 문자와 숫자의 조합입니다. 각 식별자는 하나의 단어로 계산됩니다.

Examine the No. 1 bearing installation. (5 words)

("No. 1"은 문자 및 숫자를 조합한 식별자이며 한 단어로 계산됩니다.)

Tag circuit breaker 36L7. (4 words)

("36L7"은 문자 및 숫자를 조합한 식별자이며 한 단어로 계산됩니다.)

5. 인용문

인용문은 일반적으로 인용 부호("....")로 구분합니다. 인용 부호 사이의 단어는 문장에서 한 단어로 계산합니다. 때로는 대문자 또는 다른 글꼴을 사용하여 인용문을 나타낼 수도 있으며 마찬가지로 해당 문구 또한 한 단어로 계산합니다.

Touch the "Service Overview" arrow to select the function page. (9 words)

("Service Overview"는 인용문이며 한 단어로 계산합니다.)

Release the SHORT-CIRCUIT TEST switch. (4 words)

(SHORT-CIRCUIT TEST는 인용문이며 한 단어로 계산합니다.)

C = (A - B) - 0.063 mm. (1 word)

(STE에서 공식은 인용문이며 한 단어로 계산합니다.)

6. 제목, 표제, 플래카드(placard) 및 라벨

일부 내용에는 변경할 수 없는 단어 또는 단어 집단이 포함되며 다음과 같습니다.

- 제목 및 표제
- 플래카드(예를 들어, 작업장이나 공공장소의 경고 문구)
- 라벨(예를 들어, 물체에 부착되어 있는 주의 및 경고 라벨)

Refer to Testing and Fault Isolation, page block 1001. (6 words)

("Testing and Fault Isolation"은 장의 제목이며 한 단어로 계산합니다.)

Refer to Requirements after Job Completion for the applicable procedures. (7 words)

("Requirements after Job Completion"은 데이터 모듈의 표제이며 한 단어로 계산합니다.)

This procedure is for the inspection of SSI No. 57-21-16, "Outer wing bottom skin lower surface spanwise skin joints at stringer 13 and stringer 20 between Rib 12 and Rib 27 excluding areas covered by flap track fairings 3, 4, and 5." (9 words)

("This procedure is for the inspection of"은 일곱 단어입니다. "SSI No. 57-21-16"는 구조적 주요 품목(Structurally Significant Item, SSI)의 참조 번호이며 하나의 단어로 계산합니다. 인용 부호로 묶인 내용은 SSI의 제목이며, 본 문서는 STE로 작성되지 않아 변경할 수 없습니다. 따라서 본 후속 내용은 하나의 단어로 간주합니다. 결과적으로 전체 문장은 총 아홉 개의 단어로 계산합니다.)

"Interior hazards exist to such a degree that interior operations may be conducted only after full examination, and with extreme caution." (1 word)

(인용 부호 안의 내용은 STE에 준하여 작성하지 않았지만 플래카드에서 가져온 것으로 변경이 불가능합니다. 한 단어로 계산합니다.)

"FRAGILE - Please handle with care." (1 word)

(인용 부호 안의 내용은 STE에 준하여 작성하지 않았지만 선적 컨테이너의 라벨에서 가져온 것으로 변경이 불가능합니다. 한 단어로 계산합니다.)

규칙 8.7	하이픈으로 연결한 단어는 한 단어로 계산한다.

일반적으로 형용사는 아니지만 명사 앞에서 함께 형용사 역할을 하는 단어 집단은 하이픈으로 연결합니다. 이러한 단어 집단은 하나의 단어로 계산합니다.

Clean the surface with a soap-and-water solution. (7 words)

Use the trial-and-error method. (4 words)

독자에게 더 명확하게 하기 위해 긴 기술 명칭을 하이픈으로 연결할 경우, 하이픈으로 연결된 단어 집단 또한 해당 명사 집단 내에서는 한 단어로 계산합니다.

Cutoff-switch power connection (3 words)

Main-gear-door retraction-winch handle (3 words)

9 작성 지침(Writing Practices)

규칙 요약

상이한 문장 구조(Different Sentence Constructions)

규칙 9.1   단어를 일대일로 바꿀 수 없는 상황일 경우 다른 문장 구조를 이용하여 서술하라.

승인된 단어의 정확한 사용(Correct Use of Approved Words)

규칙 9.2   승인된 각 단어를 올바르게 사용하라.

규칙 9.3   두 단어를 함께 사용할 경우 구동사(phrasal verb)를 만들어서는 안된다.

일관된 스타일(Consistent Style)

규칙 9.4   용어 및 단어 선택 시, 항상 일관된 스타일을 사용하라.

일반 추천 사항(General Recommendations)

GR-1   접속사 "that"

GR-2   전치사 "with"

GR-3   대명사 사용법

GR-4   대명사 "this"

GR-5   비슷해 보이지만 뜻이 다른 단어

GR-6   라틴어 축약형

다른 문장 구조(Different Sentence Constructions)

규칙 9.1	단어를 일대일로 바꿀 수 없는 상황일 경우 다른 문장 구조를 이용하여 서술하라.

승인된 단어를 정확하게 사용할 수 있도록 하기 위하여, STE 사전은 비승인 단어를 대체할 승인된 단어를 담고 있습니다. (승인된 단어는 비승인 단어와 같은 품사이거나, 또는 다른 품사일 수 있습니다.) 만일 사전에서 비승인 단어와 동일한 품사의 대체할 수 있는 단어를 찾는다면, 문장에서 비승인 단어를 대신해서 사용할 수 있습니다(일대일 단어 대체).

> *Non-STE : A value of 2 mm is <u>acceptable</u>.*

("Acceptable" 은 비승인 형용사입니다.)

> STE : A value of 2 mm is <u>permitted</u>.

단어를 대체해서 사용할 경우, 항상 선택한 대체 단어로 인해 문장의 의미가 달라지지 않도록 확인해야 합니다. 대체 단어로 인해 문장의 의미가 달라지거나 대체 단어의 품사가 다를 경우, 다른 문장 구조를 사용해야 합니다.

다른 문장 구조는 다음과 같은 네가지 이유로 사용합니다.

1. 선택한 대체 단어를 사용할 때 문법 구조를 변경해야 하는 경우, 다른 문장 구조를 사용합니다. 이러한 방법은 승인된 예시들을 통해 알 수 있습니다.

> *Non-STE :*   *The oil level on the sight gauge <u>must be visible</u> during the test.*
> STE :   During the test, <u>make sure that you can see</u> the oil level on the sight gauge.

본 예문에서는 비승인 형용사인 "visible"은 승인된 동사 "see"로 바꾸었습니다. 그러나, "see"를 이용하기 위해서는 "must be"를 "make sure that you can"으로 바꾸어야 합니다.

> *Non-STE :*   *<u>Cycle</u> the unit <u>twice</u> to remove air from the lines.*
> STE :   <u>Operate the unit</u> for two <u>cycles</u> to remove air from the lines.

본 예문에서는 비승인 동사 "cycle"이 승인된 명사 "cycle"로 바꾸었습니다. 또한, 비승인 부사 "twice"가 기술명칭인 "two"로 바꾸었습니다.

다른 문장 구조를 사용할 경우, 항상 선택한 승인된 단어로 인해 문장의 의미가 달라지지 않도록 확인해야 합니다.

2. 비승인 단어의 단어 대 단어 교체가 의미가 없는 경우, 다른 문장 구조를 이용합니다.

> *Non-STE :*   *Without this modification, the service life of the unit <u>can be uncertain</u>.*

"Uncertain"이란 단어는 사전에 없는 단어이지만 "not sure" 또는 "not known"과 같은 의미를 가집니다. 그러므로, 사전에서 "sure" 및 "know"를 참조할 수 있습니다. 이 단어들은 승인된 단어들이며, 각각 "not sure" 및 "not known"으로 사용할 수 있습니다("not"+ 승인된 단어.)

그러나, 다음과 같이 사용하면 안됩니다.

> *Non-STE :*   *Without this modification, the service life of the unit cannot be uncertain.*

    또는

> *Without this modification, the service life of the unit cannot be known.*

이러한 문장들은 의미가 부적절하고 올바른 영어 문장이 아닙니다.

문장이 정확히 어떤 의미를 가지고 있는지 생각하면서 다른 문장 구조를 사용해야만 합니다.

> *Non-STE :*   *Without this modification, the service life of the unit <u>can be uncertain</u>.*
> STE :   Without this modification, <u>it is possible that the service life of this unit will be shorter than usual</u>.

STE 문장은 같은 정보를 명확하게 전달하기 위해서 다양한 방법으로 승인된 단어를 사용합니다. 항상 전달하려는 말을 정확하게 인지하고, 사용하려는 단어들이 전달하고자 하는 의미를 정확하게 제공하는지 확인해야 합니다.

3. 선택한 승인된 대체 단어가 문장의 의미를 바꿀 수도 있는 경우, 다른 문장 구조를 이용합니다.

> *Non-STE :* *Just apply very light pressure to the surface.*
> STE : Only apply very light pressure to the surface.
> *Non-STE :* *Immediately apply very light pressure to the surface.*

"Immediately"는 "just"의 승인된 대체 단어입니다. 그러나 이 문맥상에서 "immediately"라는 단어를 쓸 경우, 지시문의 의미를 바꾸게 됩니다.

4. 대체해야 할 단어가 사전에 없는 경우, 다른 문장 구조를 이용합니다.

> *Non-STE :* *The incidence of water in fuel is dangerous.*
> STE : Water in fuel is dangerous.

"Incidence"란 단어는 사전에 없는 단어이기 때문에 "presence"와 같은 동일한 의미를 가진 다른 단어를 사용해야 합니다. 그러나 "presence"는 비승인된 단어입니다. 그러므로, 대체할 수 있는 단어는 "be"입니다. 다른 구조를 이용하여 같은 의미를 유지할 수 있습니다.

다른 문장 구조를 사용하는 방법

단어를 대체할 수 없다면 다른 단어들을 사용하여 같은 의미의 문장을 만들 수 있습니다.

> *Non-STE :* *If the air intake flap has failed, deactivate air inlet valve.*
> STE : *If the air intake flap is not serviceable, lock the air inlet valve in the fully open position.*
> *Non-STE :* *If the air intake flap is not serviceable, disconnect (or stop, or isolate) the air inlet valve.*

본 예문에서 "deactivate"는 승인되지 않습니다. 자체 사전에서는 "disconnect," "stop," 및 "isolate"를 대체 단어로 제안합니다. 이러한 승인된 대체 단어의 사용은 좋은 방법입니다.

그러나, 상기 예문에서는
- "Disconnect"는 기술적으로 부적절한 단어입니다.
- "Stop" 및 "isolate"는 의미가 정확하지 않습니다.

ASD STE 100

문장을 작성하기 전에 다음 사항을 생각해봐야 합니다.
- 본 맥락에서 "deactivate"가 무엇을 의미하는 가요?

  또는
- 독자가 해야 하는 행동은 무엇인가요?

그러고 나면 "deactivation(비활성화)"가 다음과 같은 특정 작업의 결과라는 것을 알 수 있습니다.
- 공기 흡입구 밸브를 완전히 개방된 위치에서 잠금

따라서, 독자에게 작업 내용을 알려주면 그 지시사항은 정확할 것이고, 독자는 올바른 작업을 할 수 있습니다.

본 예문에 다음을 확인할 수 있습니다.
- 문장에서 승인되지 않은 단어를 변경하는 방법.
- 같은 의미를 가진 새로운 문장을 작성하는 방법.

문장을 작성할 때는 종종 다른 단어를 선택하거나, 다른 동사 형태를 사용하거나, 완전히 새로운 문장 구조를 써야 합니다. 때로는 긴 문장을 짧은 문장들로 쪼개거나, 필요하지 않은 정보를 삭제하거나, 엔지니어에 추가 설명을 요청해야 하기도 합니다. 종종 문장을 완전히 재구성해야 하기도 합니다. 그리고 나서, 문장의 한 부분을 변경할 때 해당 문장의 다른 부분에 부정적인 영향을 미치지 않도록 해야 합니다.

Non-STE : *If cracks are <u>detected</u> during this procedure, the operator must <u>perform</u> the repair <u>within</u> a <u>certain</u> number of flight hours <u>depending</u> on crack length. Refer to <u>following</u> table:*

Crack length detected	Time before repair
L> ...	*1000 flight hours*
L= ...	*2000 flight hours*
L< ...	*3000 flight hours*

STE : If you find cracks, refer to the table that follows :

If the crack is of this length	Do the repair before
L> ...	1000 flight hours
L= ...	2000 flight hours
L< ...	3000 flight hours

앞에 제시한 "Non-STE"에 대한 설명은 다음과 같습니다.

    a) 밑줄 친 부분의 단어는 STE에서 승인되지 않은 단어입니다.

    b) 첫 번째 동사 "are detected"는 수동태입니다.

    c) 첫 문장은 24 단어로 되어있습니다.

    d) "crack length" 및 "following table" 앞에 관사가 없습니다.

    e) 지시문 문장임에도 불구하고 동사가 명령형 형태가 아닙니다.

STE 사전에 제시된 단어로 단어들을 바꿀 수 있습니다.

    - "perform"은 "do"로 바꿀 수 있습니다.

    - "within"은 "in"로 바꿀 수 있습니다.

    - "certain"은 "some"로 바꿀 수 있습니다.

    - "detect"는 "find"로 바꿀 수 있습니다.

관사까지 포함하여 문장을 바꾸면 다음과 같습니다.

If cracks are found during this procedure, the operator must do the repair in some flight hours depending on the crack length. Refer to the following table :

상기의 예는 기존 문장과 구조는 동일하나 부적절한 영어 문장 구조입니다.

"*are found*"(수동태 형태)를 대체하기 위해 문장 구조를 "If you find cracks ..."로 변경해야 하나 문장 구조의 나머지 부분은 변경되지 않습니다.

"*following*"은 구조가 약간 다른 "Refer to the table that follows:"로 변경해야 합니다.

"*the operator must do the repair*"는 "do the repair"로 변경해야 합니다.

"*depending*"은 사전에 제시된 대체 단어 "if"의 사용이 불가능하기 때문에 문장을 변경해야 합니다.

따라서 다음과 같이 첫번째 문장을 다시 쓸 수 있습니다.

If you find cracks during this procedure, do the repair before the number of flight hours applicable to the crack length.

그러나, 여전히 21개의 단어로 구성 되어있고 기술적인 의미는 쉽게 이해할 수 없습니다. 일부 정보 또한 표에 수록되어 있어서 반복할 필요가 없습니다. 가장 좋은 해결 방법은 상기의 STE 예문과 같이 표 앞 부분에 관련 내용을 담는 것입니다.

<u>STE의 주요 목표는 독자들이 각 문장을 읽고 즉시 이해하는 것이란 사실을 항상 기억해야 합니다.</u>

승인된 단어의 정확한 사용(Correct Use of Approved Words)

규칙 9.2	승인된 각 단어를 올바르게 사용하라.

일부 STE에서 승인된 단어는 "제한적" 의미를 가집니다.

단어를 선택하기 전에 사전에서 해당 단어의 승인된 정의를 확인해야 합니다. 영어 단어는 경우에 따라 하나의 단어가 여러가지 의미를 가지지만, STE에서 승인된 단어는 일반적으로 하나의 승인된 의미만 가집니다. 따라서, 일반적인 영어에서 단어가 가지는 모든 의미들은 승인되지 않습니다.

사용하는 단어가 문맥에 맞는 의미를 가지는지도 확인해야 합니다.

> *Non-STE :* *Wear protective clothing.*
> STE : Use (or put on) protective clothing.

"Wear"는 "마찰에 의해 손상되다" 라는 의미를 가진 승인된 동사입니다.

> *Non-STE :* *This regulation extends to all units.*
> STE : This regulation is applicable to all units.

동사 "extend"는 "차원이나 범위에서 증가하거나 증가하게 하다"라는 승인된 의미를 가지고 있으나, Non-STE 예문에서는 승인된 의미로 사용되지 않았습니다.

> *Non-STE :* *When the pressure goes down, lift the cover.*
> STE : When the pressure decreases, lift the cover.

"Goes down"은 지시기 값이 내려가는 경우를 설명하는 구입니다(예: 게이지 바늘 또는 플래그). 압력을 모니터링한 지시기가 아닌 압력을 설명할 경우에는 "Decrease"를 사용하는 것이 적절합니다.

> *Non-STE :* *Make sure that the probe went through more than 500 degrees C.*
> STE : Make sure that the temperature of the probe increased to more than 500 degrees C.

"Go through"는 무언가를 통과하여 물리적으로 움직이는 것에 대해서만 사용할 수 있습니다. 요구 사항 또는 조건을 나타내는 데에 사용할 수 없습니다.

> *Non-STE :* *Move the tube to see if the inner connection is tight.*
> STE : Move the tube to make sure that the inner connection is tight.

"See"는 "확인하다"라는 의미가 아니라 눈으로 볼 수 있는 것에 대해서만 사용할 수 있습니다.

> Non-STE : *The indicator turns green.*
> STE : The color of the indicator changes to green.

"Turn"은 "축, 점 주변으로 어떤 물체를 움직이거나 움직이게 하다"라는 의미로 사용할 수 있습니다.

> Non-STE : *Do not let the pressure go below (or above) 20 psi.*
> STE : Do not let the pressure become less than (or more than) 20 psi.

"Above" 및 "below"는 수적 한계가 아닌 물리적 위치를 나타낼 경우에만 사용됩니다.

또한, 승인된 단어를 사용할 때에는 승인된 품사의 형태로만 사용해야 합니다. 영어 단어는 보통 문장에서 어떤 품사로 사용되었는지 바로 알 수 있는 정해진 형태가 없습니다. 따라서, 독자들은 종종 같은 단어를 다르게 이해할 수도 있습니다. 문장을 더 명확하게 하기 위해서 승인된 단어는 일반적으로 하나의 기능(품사)만 가질 수 있기 때문에 승인된 단어는 승인된 품사로만 사용해야 합니다.

> Non-STE : *When you work with cleaning agents, use breathing equipment.*
> STE : When you do work with cleaning agents, use breathing equipment.

"Work"는 명사로는 승인되었으나 동사로는 승인되지 않았습니다.

> Non-STE : *Install the cover with the help of a second person.*
> STE : Install the cover with the aid of a second person.

"Help"는 동사로는 승인되었으나 명사로는 승인되지 않았습니다.

> Non-STE : *Be careful not to damage the sleeve.*
> STE : Be careful not to cause damage to the sleeve.

"Damage"는 명사로는 승인되었으나 동사로는 승인되지 않았습니다.

중요한 단어이거나 기술 영어에서 자주 쓰이는 단어들의 경우 하나 이상의 품사로 승인되거나 한 가지 이상의 의미를 가지기도 합니다. 예를 들어, "flush"라는 단어는 기술 영어에서 동사(물이 파이프를 통해 빠르게 흐르게 하다) 또는 형용사(한 표면이 다른 표면에 완전히 닿은)로 자주 사용됩니다.

> STE : Flush the pipes with a disinfectant solution.

> (본 예문에서 "Flush"는 동사로 사용되었습니다.)

> STE : Make sure that the door is flush with the adjacent surfaces.

> (본 예문에서 "Flush"는 형용사로 사용되었습니다.)

그러나, 동사와 형용사는 문장에서 위치가 다르고 다른 문맥에서 사용되어 쉽게 혼동되지 않습니다.

규칙 9.3	두 단어를 함께 사용할 경우 구동사(phrasal verb)를 만들어서는 안된다.

영어에서 동사와 하나 이상의 전치사는 때때로 함께 사용되어 "구동사(phrasal verb)"를 이룹니다. 구동사는 각 단어의 본래 의미와는 다른 의미를 가집니다. 구동사는 보통 기본적이고 구체적인 의미뿐만 아니라 좀 더 추상적인 의미도 가지고 있습니다.

일반적인 예 :

Put out the cat.

   (구체적인 의미: "고양이를 집 밖에 두세요.")

Put out the fire.

   (추상적인 의미: "불을 끄세요.")

STE에서는 이러한 애매함을 방지하기 위해 승인된 단어를 사용하여 또 다른 추상적인 의미를 가지는 새로운 구를 만드는 것을 허용하지 않습니다.

> *Non-STE : After you put out the fire, close the valve on the fire extinguisher.*
> STE : After you <u>extinguish</u> the fire, close the valve on the fire extinguisher.

"Put"과 "out"은 STE에서 승인된 단어들입니다. 그러나, 본 예문에서 "put out"은 STE 사전에 승인된 단어 "put"과 "out"의 의미와는 다른 의미를 가집니다. 이 경우, "불을 끄다."라는 승인된 의미를 가진 단어 "extinguish"를 기술 문서에서 가장 일반적으로 사용합니다.

> *Non-STE : This compound can give off poisonous fumes.*
> STE : This compound can <u>release</u> poisonous fumes.

"Give"와 "off"는 STE에서 승인된 단어들입니다. 그러나 본 예문에서 "give off"는 STE 사전에 승인된 단어 "give"와 "off"의 의미와는 다른 의미를 가집니다. 따라서, "give off"와 같은 의미를 가진 다른 승인된 단어를 사용해야만 합니다. 이 경우, 단어 "release"는 "자유롭게 하다" 또는 "놓아주다"라는 승인된 의미를 가지며, 문맥상 "give off"를 대체하여 사용할 수 있습니다.

일반적으로 사전에서는 비승인 된 구동사들을 일일이 열거하지 않습니다. 그러므로 STE로 문장을 다시 쓸 때에는 새로운 문장이 여전히 좋은 표준 영어인지 항상 확인해야 합니다.

일관된 스타일(Consistent Style)

규칙 9.4	용어 및 단어 선택 시, 항상 일관된 스타일을 사용하라.

절차에서 동일한 정보를 반복해서 사용하는 경우가 많습니다. 예를 들어, 대부분의 절차는 구성 요소나 부품을 제거 또는 설치하는 방법을 설명합니다. 이러한 작업 단계에 대한 특정 용어를 결정하면, 해당 유형의 단계가 발생할 때마다 동일한 용어를 사용해야 합니다. 동일한 용어를 사용하면 독자들은 용어를 인식하고 무엇을 해야 하는지 빠르게 알 수 있습니다. 각기 다른 단어와 용어를 사용하면 혼란을 일으켜 시간 낭비가 될 수 있습니다.

다음 두 문장은 각각 같은 지시를 내리고 모두 STE의 규칙을 정확하게 따릅니다.

> STE : Lubricate the two bolts with a small quantity of oil.
> STE : Apply a small quantity of oil to the threads of the two bolts.

그러나, 동일한 지시를 위의 두 문장을 사용하여 여러 다른 절차 단계에서 제공하는 것은 결코 독자에게 도움이 되지 않습니다. 여러 표현을 사용하기 보다는 하나의 문장 또는 문장 스타일을 선택한 다음 문맥과 의미가 동일할 때마다 반복해서 사용합니다.

> Non-STE :
> 1. Put the housing (8) in its installation position on the <u>main body (9)</u>.
> 2. Lubricate the two bolts (10) with oil.
> 3. Install the two bolts (10) in the <u>body (9)</u>.
> 4. <u>Torque-tighten</u> the two bolts to 4 Nm.
> 5. Put the transducer (11) on the <u>body assembly (9)</u>.
> 6. <u>Apply a small quantity of oil</u> to the threads of the four bolts (12).
> 7. Attach the transducer (11) to the <u>body assembly (9)</u> with the four bolts (12).
> 8. Torque each of the four bolts (12) to 0.8 Nm.
>
> STE :
> 1. Put the housing (8) in its installation position on the <u>body assembly (9)</u>.
> 2. <u>Apply a small quantity of oil</u> to the threads of the two bolts (10).
> 3. Install the two bolts (10) in the <u>body assembly (9)</u>.
> 4. <u>Torque</u> each of the two bolts to 4 Nm.
> 5. Put the transducer (11) on the <u>body assembly (9)</u>.
> 6. <u>Apply a small quantity of oil</u> to the threads of the four bolts (12).
> 7. Attach the transducer (11) to the <u>body assembly (9)</u> with the four bolts (12).
> 8. Torque each of the four bolts (12) to 0.8 Nm.

ASD STE 100

Non-STE 예문에서는 각각 다른 용어들이 사용되는 것을 알 수 있습니다.

- 항목(9)에 여러가지 용어가 사용되고 있습니다. ("*main body*", "*body*" 및 "*body assembly*")
- 볼트를 조일 때 서로 다른 용어가 사용됩니다. ("*torque*" 및 "*torque-tighten*")
- 윤활 단계에 대하여 다른 표현의 문장들이 사용됩니다. ("*Lubricate the XX bolts*" 및 "*Apply a small quantity of oil to the threads of the XX bolts.*")

STE 버전에서는 동일한 구성 요소가 언급될 때마다 동일한 이름을 가지며, 동일한 문맥에서는 항상 동일한 문구가 사용됩니다. 이러한 일관성은 글의 내용을 더욱 알아듣기 쉽게 만듭니다. 독자는 작업 단계를 한 번에 하나씩 읽고 해당 작업을 수행합니다. 내용을 빨리 인식하고 각 작업 단계를 올바르게 수행하는 것이 중요한 것입니다.

서술형 글쓰기에서 독자는 본문을 전체적으로 이해해야 합니다. 따라서 단어와 문장을 올바르게 사용하며 논리적인 구조를 바탕으로 글이 작성되어야 합니다. 해당 규칙이 지켜진다면 글을 읽고 내용을 기억하기가 더 쉬워집니다.

일반 추천 사항(General Recommendations)

본 장의 일반 추천사항(GR)은 STE 규칙은 아니지만, 글을 쓸 때 자주 하는 전형적인 실수를 피하는 데에 도움이 됩니다.

GR-1	접속사 "that"

영어에서는, 접속사 "that"을 종속절의 추가적인 정보를 주절에 연결할 때 사용할 수 있습니다. 접속사 "that"은 "make sure", "show" 및 "recommend"와 같은 동사 뒤에 사용할 수 있습니다. 영어 원어민들은 빠르게 말을 할 때나 글을 쓸 때 자주 접속사 "that"을 생략합니다. 그러나 이 접속사는 주절이 어디서 끝나고 종속절이 어디서 시작하는지에 대한 독자들의 이해를 도와줍니다. 그러므로, 애매함을 방지할 수 있도록 접속사 "that"을 생략하지 않는 게 좋습니다.

여러 외국어는 동등 단어를 생략할 수 없기 때문에 접속사 "that"을 사용하면 번역에도 도움이 됩니다.

> *Do not write* : *Make sure the valve is open.*
> WRITE : Make sure <u>that</u> the valve is open.

> *Do not write* : *The manufacturer recommends you prepare the mixture in an area with good airflow.*
> WRITE : The manufacturer recommends <u>that</u> you prepare the mixture in an area with good airflow.

> *Do not write* : *The gauge shows the reservoir is full.*
> WRITE : The gauge shows <u>that</u> the reservoir is full.

GR-2	전치사 "with"

STE에서 전치사 "with"는 세 가지 승인된 의미를 가집니다. 전치사 "with"는 "결합이나 관계", "도움이나 공유" 또는 "수단이나 도구"를 나타내는 기능 단어입니다. 이 단어는 애매함을 일으킬 수 있습니다. 예를 들어, "Install the panel with the green fasteners."라는 문장은 다음과 같은 의미들을 가질 수 있습니다.

- Install the panel that has green fasteners.
- Install the panel together with the green fasteners.
- Use the green fasteners to install the panel.

보통 문장의 맥락은 독자들이 올바른 의미를 알아내는 데에 충분한 정보를 제공합니다.

ASD STE 100

그러나, "with"라는 단어를 사용할 때는 문장을 다시 읽어보면서 애매한 부분이나 오류가 없는지 확인하고 말하고자 하는 바가 제대로 쓰여 있는지 확인하는 것이 좋습니다.

> *Do not write :* *Lift the aircraft at the maximum takeoff weight with passengers.*
> WRITE : Lift the aircraft at the maximum takeoff weight (passenger weight included.)

문맥(또는 경험)상 승객에게 항공기를 들어올리는 것을 도와 달라고 요청하지 않을 것임을 알고 있습니다. 하지만 이 문장이 두 가지 의미로 이해될 수 있기 때문에 농담이 되어버립니다. 이는 기술 문서의 기능이 아닙니다.

> *Do not write :* *Make sure that there is no contact with stop (1) with hydraulic pressure applied.*
> WRITE : When you apply hydraulic pressure, make sure that the lever does not touch the stop (1).

(조건을 먼저 씁니다.)

> *Do not write :* *Seal the opening with tool TS9867.*
> WRITE : Use tool TS9867 to seal the opening.
>
> (문장이 애매하다고 생각되는 경우에만 이 유형의 문장을 씁니다. STE에서는 동작 동사를 "use"가 아니라 "seal"로 사용해야 합니다.)
>
> 다음과 같이 작성할 수 있습니다.
>
> Seal the opening. To do that, use tool TS9867.

GR-3	대명사 사용법

대명사는 글에서 이미 언급한 사람, 장소 또는 사물을 다시 말합니다.

예를 들어 "it", "they", "that", "these" 및 "those"가 있습니다. 만약 대명사가 올바르게 사용된다면, 글은 더욱 읽기 쉬워집니다.

STE에서 승인된 대명사는 사전에 있습니다. 사전에 있지 않은 대명사의 경우 사용하지 말아야 합니다. (예: "she" 또는 "he").

만약 대명사가 글에서 하나 이상의 명사를 가리킨다면 문장이 애매해질 수 있습니다. 문장이 애매한 경우, 대명사가 가리키는 단어로 대명사를 변경함으로써 문장이 명확해지고 더 읽기 쉬워집니다.

> **Do not write :** *If you engage the pins incorrectly with the seats, they can become damaged*
>
> **WRITE :** If you engage the pins incorrectly with the seats, the pins can become damaged.
>
> 또는
>
> If you engage the pins incorrectly with the seats, the seats can become damaged.
>
> 또는
>
> If you engage the pins incorrectly with the seats, the pins and seats can become damaged.

GR-4   대명사 "this"

문장에서 대명사 "this"를 쓸 경우, 단어가 가리키는 대상을 분명히 해야 합니다. "This"가 하나 이상의 대상을 가리킬 수 있는 경우, 해당 문맥을 다시 설명해야 합니다.

> **Do not write :** *Make sure that the cover is not locked (this can cause damage to the probe.)*
>
> (무엇이 프로브를 손상시킬 수 있습니까? 뚜껑이 잠긴 상태입니까? 혹은 뚜껑이 잠기지 않은 상태입니까?)
>
> **WRITE :** Make sure that the cover is not locked. If the cover is locked, this can cause damage to the probe.
>
> 또는
>
> If the cover is locked, damage to the probe can occur.

> **Do not write :** *Do not use crocus cloth on aluminum parts. If you do this, you can cause corrosion on aluminum parts. Crocus cloth contains ferrous oxide.*
>
> **WRITE :** Do not use crocus cloth on aluminum parts. Crocus cloth contains ferrous oxide and can cause corrosion on aluminum parts.

GR-4   비슷해 보이지만 뜻이 다른 단어

"False friend"는 다른 나라의 모국어와 비슷한 형태를 가지고 있지만 다른 의미를 가진 단어나 표현을 의미합니다. 예를 들어, 영어 단어 "disposition"과 이탈리아어 단어 "disposizione" 또는 스페인어 단어 "disposición"이 있습니다.

영어 원어민이 아니라면, 문장에서 단어를 사용할 때 해당 단어가 영어로 올바른 의미를 가지는지 확인해야 합니다.(자국어의 유사한 단어를 의미하는 것이 아닙니다.)

> **Do not write :** *Obey the dispositions of the manufacturer when you use this adhesive.*
>
> (영어로 "disposition"은 "instruction"을 의미하지 않습니다.)
>
> **WRITE :** When you use this adhesive, obey the manufacturer's instructions.

GR-6	라틴어 축약형

영문으로 된 글에서 일부 라틴어 약어를 볼 수 있습니다(예: "e.g.", "i.e.", 및 "etc."). 독자에게 혼란을 줄 수 있으므로 STE에서는 사용하지 않는 것이 좋습니다. 항상 영어 단어를 사용하도록 합니다.

> *Do not write :*   *Discard the standard parts (e.g. washers, screws, bolts, and nuts) each time you remove them.*
>
> WRITE :   Discard the standard parts (for example, washers, bolts, and nuts) each time you remove them.

> *Do not write :*   *These wires can have insulation of different colors (blue, green, red, etc.)*
>
> WRITE :   These wires can have insulation of different colors. They can be blue, green, red, or other colors.

종종 이러한 약어는 필요하지 않기 때문에 생략할 수 있습니다.

> *Do not write :*   *These wires can have insulation of different colors (blue, green, red, etc.)*
>
> WRITE :   These wires can have insulation of different colors.

CHAPTER
02

Dictionary

—

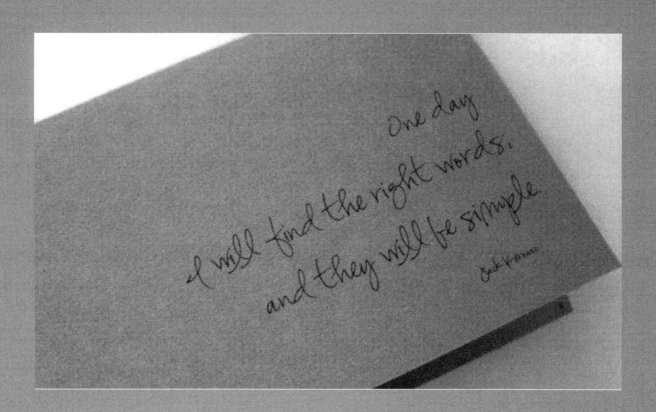

One day
I will find the right words,
and they will be simple.

Jack Kerouac

1 ｜ 소개(Introduction)

일반 사항

사전은 STE가 승인한 모든 단어와 각 단어를 바르게 사용하는 예를 수록하고 있습니다. STE에서 승인한 단어와 동등한 단어인 비승인 단어도 보여줍니다. 이 예를 통해 승인된 단어를 어떻게 사용하는지, 경우에 따라서 어떻게 다른 구문을 사용하는가를 보여줍니다.

사전의 단어 목록에는 기술 명칭이나 기술 동사를 수록하지 않았습니다. 기술 명칭이나 기술 동사의 일부는 비승인 단어의 대체어를 사용하기도 합니다.

사전 사용법

사전에는 4개의 칼럼이 있습니다.

- Word (part of speech) : 단어(품사)
- Approved meaning / ALTERNATIVES : 승인된 의미 / 대체어
- APPROVED EXAMPLE : 승인 예문
- Not approved example : 비승인 예문

Word (part of speech)	Approved meaning / ALTERNATIVES	APPROVED EXAMPLE	Not approved example
accuracy (n)	PRECISION (n)	THE PRECISION OF THE ADJUSTMENT CAN CHANGE.	The accuracy of the adjustment can vary.

Column 1	단어(품사)

모든 단어는 볼드체로 표시합니다.

알파벳 대문자로 나타나는 단어는 승인 단어이며, 사용할 수 있음을 나타냅니다.

Word (part of speech)	Approved meaning / ALTERNATIVES	APPROVED EXAMPLE	Not approved example
ABRASIVE (adj)	That can remove material by friction	DUST, WHEN MIXED WITH OIL, HAS AN ABRASIVE EFFECT.	
AID (n)	Help that is given	IF YOU GET THE SOLUTION IN YOUR EYES, GET MEDICAL AID IMMEDIATELY.	

알파벳 소문자로 표시하는 단어는 STE 승인 단어가 아니며, 다른 단어나 다른 구조를 사용해야 한다는 것을 나타냅니다.

ASD STE 100

Word (part of speech)	Approved meaning / ALTERNATIVES	APPROVED EXAMPLE	Not approved example
main (adj)	PRIMARY (adj)	THE PRIMARY CAUSE OF VALVE FAILURE IS CONTAMINATION OF THE HYDRAULIC FLUID.	The main cause of valve failure is contamination of hydraulic fluid.
build (v)	ASSEMBLE (v)	ASSEMBLE THE UNIT.	Build the unit.

각 단어의 품사는 괄호 안에 별도로 명시해 두었습니다. 승인 단어는 수록된 품사로만 사용해야 합니다(1부, 제 1 장 참조).

STE에는 8품사가 사용됩니다.

1. 명사(n) : 사람, 장소, 물건, 아이디어, 품질 또는 활동 등의 이름을 나타내는 단어

2. 동사(v) : 상태, 동작을 묘사하는 단어. 시제(현재형, 과거형, 미래형)가 동작 발생 시점을 알려 줍니다.

3. 형용사(adj) : 명사, 명사구를 수식하는 단어. 명사, 명사구의 종류, 크기, 색상, 수 등을 묘사합니다.

4. 부사(adv) : 동사, 형용사 또는 다른 부사를 수식하는 단어. "어떻게?", "어디서?", "언제?", "얼마나 자주?", "가격이 얼마?"등의 질문에 답합니다.

5. 대명사(pron) : 명사나 명사구를 대신하는 단어

6. 관사(adv) : 명사구가 이미 알고 있는 것(정관사 = the)인지, 새로운 것인지(부정관사= a, an)를 알려 주는 단어

7. 전치사(prep) : 대명사, 명사, 명사구와 문장의 나머지 부분의 관계를 나타내는 단어.

8. 접속사(conj) : 단어, 구 및 절을 연결하는 단어나 구.

승인된 단어의 형태

명사 : 명사는 단수형으로만 나타내나 셀 수 있는 명사의 복수형도(참고에서 다르게 설명하는 경우라도) 허용합니다.

예 :

Word (part of speech)	Approved meaning / ALTERNATIVES	APPROVED EXAMPLE	Not approved example
AGENT(n)	One of a group of materials made to do a specified task	DO NOT USE THESE CLEANING AGENTS ON HOT SURFACES	

동사 : 동사는 승인된 형태로만 나타냅니다(1부, 제 3 장 참조). 목록에 없는 동사 형태는 쓰지 않습니다. 동사의 뜻은 목적어가 있을 때(타동사)와 없을 때(자동사) 각각 다릅니다. 이런 동사는 하나 이상의 승인된 의미와 승인 예문이 있습니다.

Word (part of speech)	Approved meaning / ALTERNATIVES	APPROVED EXAMPLE	Not approved example
ADAPT(v), ADAPTS, ADAPTED, ADAPTED	To change or adjust to that which is necessary	ADAPT THE PRESSURE CONNECTION TO THE PITOT HEAD. THE SYSTEM INTERFACE CIRCUITS ADAPT TO THE PHYSICAL PROPERTIES OF THE CONNECTED SYSTEMS.	

형용사 : 형용사는 기본형으로 나타내고 비교급, 최상급도 괄호 안에 나타냅니다. 비교급과 최상급에 "more"나 "most"를 사용하는 형용사의 경우 "more" 및 "most"가 승인 단어이므로 따로 표시하지 않습니다.

Word (part of speech)	Approved meaning / ALTERNATIVES	APPROVED EXAMPLE	Not approved example
SLOW (adj) (SLOWER, SLOWEST)	At low speed	MAKE SURE THAT THE MOVEMENT OF THE ELEVATORS IS SLOW	

부사 : 항상 그렇지는 않지만 대개 형용사 끝에 "-ly"를 붙여서 형용사에서 부사로 만들 수 있습니다. 부사의 비교급과 최상급도 "more" 및 "most"를 사용합니다. 형용사와 마찬가지로 따로 표시하지 않습니다.

Word (part of speech)	Approved meaning / ALTERNATIVES	APPROVED EXAMPLE	Not approved example
SLOWLY (adv)	In a slow manner	TURN THE KNOB SLOWLY.	
briskly (adv)	QUICKLY (adv)	RUB THE SURFACE QUICKLY WITH A SOFT, DRY CLOTH.	Rub the surface briskly with a soft, dry cloth.

ASD STE 100

Column 2	승인된 의미 / 대체어

승인 단어

본 칼럼은 STE가 승인한 단어의 승인된 의미를 알려 줍니다. 두 번째 칼럼에 나오지 않는 의미로 그 단어를 사용할 수 없습니다. 이 경우 대체어를 사용해야 합니다.

Word (part of speech)	Approved meaning / ALTERNATIVES	APPROVED EXAMPLE	Not approved example
BEHIND (prep)	In a position at the rear of	THE PUMP IS INSTALLED BEHIND THE HYDRAULIC MOTOR.	

비승인 단어

비승인 단어는 이 칼럼에서 비승인 단어를 대체할 수 있는 승인 대체어를 나타냅니다. 이 대체어들은 대문자로 표기하며 사용자를 돕기 위한 제안일 뿐입니다.

Word (part of speech)	Approved meaning / ALTERNATIVES	APPROVED EXAMPLE	Not approved example
addition (n)	ADD (v)	TO GET THE CORRECT CLEARANCE, ADD SPECIAL SHIMS, AS NECESSARY.	Adjust the clearance by the addition of special shims, as necessary.

비승인 단어 대신 제안된 대체어가 다른 품사인 경우도 있습니다. 일반적으로, 첫 번째 제안 대체어는 비승인 단어와 같은 품사입니다.

Word (part of speech)	Approved meaning / ALTERNATIVES	APPROVED EXAMPLE	Not approved example
maintain (v)	KEEP (v)	KEEP THE FLUID TEMPERATURE AT 70°F.	Maintain the fluid temperature at 70°F
	HOLD (v)	TURN THE ROTATING TUBE 75 DEGREES. THEN HOLD THE TUBE IN THIS POSITION.	Turn the rotating tube 75 degrees. Then maintain the tube in this position.
	MAINTENANCE (v)	DO MAINTENANCE ON THE FUEL SYSTEM.	Maintain the fuel system.

사전에는 기술 명칭이나 기술 동사를 다루지는 않습니다. 기술 명칭이나 기술 동사가 제안 대체어로 사용하는 경우, 이 단어는 (TN) 기술 명칭 또는 (TV) 기술 동사로 규정합니다. 반의어는 사전에서 다루지 않습니다.

Word (part of speech)	Approved meaning / ALTERNATIVES	APPROVED EXAMPLE	Not approved example
uncovered (v)	COVER (TN)	DO NOT PUT A COVER ON THE CONTAINER.	Leave the container uncovered.

비승인 단어를 위한 대체어는 두 단어 이상으로 구성될 수도 있습니다. 이 경우에, 품사는 따로 기술하지 않습니다.

Word (part of speech)	Approved meaning / ALTERNATIVES	APPROVED EXAMPLE	Not approved example
simultaneously (adv)	AT THE SAME TIME	DO THESE TWO STEPS AT THE SAME TIME.	Do these two steps simultaneously.

도움말

몇몇 단어들은 전구 모양의 기호와 설명이 있고, 다른 승인 대체어나 다른 구문을 사용하도록 알려주고 있습니다. 이 기호와 텍스트는 "도움말"로 부릅니다. 이 도움말은 다음 네 가지 범주가 있습니다.

범주 1

추천은 승인 단어를 어떻게 사용해야 하는지에 대한 추가 정보와 지침을 안내합니다.

Word (part of speech)	Approved meaning / ALTERNATIVES	APPROVED EXAMPLE	Not approved example
PUSH (v) PUSHES, PUSHED, PUSHED	1. To apply a force to something to move it away from the source of the force. 2. To move with a force against something 💡 Use this word together with a preposition or an adverb to show direction.	PUSH THE INSERT DOWN UNTIL IT TOUCHES THE BOTTOM OF THE HOLE. THE SPRING UNIT PUSHES AGAINST THE BRAKE PEDAL	

범주 2

도움말 중 본 범주는 ABOUT(prep)과 같은 몇몇의 승인 단어들의 의미가 제한적임을 알려줍니다. 이 경우에는 반드시 제안된 대체어를 사용해야 합니다. 도움말에서 승인된 단어의 의미를 제한할 때, 사전은 칼럼 3과 칼럼 4에 "승인"된 예와 "비승인"예를 보여줍니다.

Word (part of speech)	Approved meaning / ALTERNATIVES	APPROVED EXAMPLE	Not approved example
ABOUT (prep)	Concerned with For other meanings, use:	FOR DATA ABOUT THE LOCATION OF CIRCUIT BREAKERS REFER TO THE WIRING LIST.	
	APPROXIMATELY (adv)	DRAIN APPROXIMATELY 2 LITERS OF FUEL FROM THE TANK.	Drain about 2 liters of fuel from the tank
	AROUND (prep)	TURN THE SHAFT AROUND ITS AXIS.	Rotate the shaft about its axis.

범주 3

도움말 중 본 범주는 한 가지의 문맥으로만 사용하도록 승인된 단어들의 사용에 관해 주의하도록 알려줍니다. 예를 들어, SWALLOW(v)는 안전 지침에서만 사용하도록 합니다. 그래서 SWALLOW(v)같은 단어는 승인된 뜻이 아닌 다른 뜻으로는 사용하면 안됩니다.

Word (part of speech)	Approved meaning / ALTERNATIVES	APPROVED EXAMPLE	Not approved example
SWALLOW (v) SWALLOWS, SWALLOWED, SWALLOWED	To take through the mouth and esophagus into the stomach Use this word for safety instructions only.	IF YOU SWALLOW NITRIC ACID, GET MEDICAL AID IMMEDIATELY.	

범주 4

도움말 중 본 범주는 주어진 정보에 관해 생각하도록 알려 줍니다. 예를 들어, BE(v)동사는 사전에 나열되어 있는 형태로만 사용할 수 있고, 다른 형태는 허용하지 않습니다.

Word (part of speech)	Approved meaning / ALTERNATIVES	APPROVED EXAMPLE	Not approved example
BE (v), IS, WAS (also ARE, WERE) 💡 No other forms of this verb.	1. To occur, exist	IF THERE IS CORROSION ON THE PUMP VANES, REPLACE THE PUMP.	
	2. To have a property to be equal to	ACID SOLUTIONS ARE DANGEROUS.	

Column 3   승인 예문

본 칼럼은 다음을 보여줍니다.

- 승인된 단어 사용하는 법, 또는

- 승인된 대체어 사용하는 법(대개 단어와 단어를 대체), 또는

- 다른 구문으로 같은 의미 유지하는 법

승인 예문에 나와 있는 표현은 필수는 아닙니다. 단지 승인된 단어로 같은 정보를 어떻게 쓰는지 한 가지 방법만을 보여줄 뿐입니다. 많은 경우에 같은 것을 말하기 위해 다른 승인된 단어를 가지고 다른 구문으로 사용할 수 있습니다.

Word (part of speech)	Approved meaning / ALTERNATIVES	APPROVED EXAMPLE	Not approved example
A (art)	Function word: Indefinite article	A FUEL PUMP IS INSTALLED IN ZONE 10.	
main (adj)	PRIMARY (adj)	THE PRIMARY CAUSE OF VALVE FAILURE IS CONTAMINATION OF THE HYDRAULIC FLUID.	The main cause of valve failure is contamination of hydraulic acid.
manufacture (v)	MAKE (v)	YOU CAN MAKE THE CLEARING TOOL LOCALLY.	The clearing tool can be manufactured,

Column 4	비승인 예문

4번째 칼럼은 어떻게 비승인 단어가 STE에서 사용되는지 예를 보여줍니다. 이 예는 같은 정보를 전달하기 위해 어떻게 승인 대체어 및/또는 다른 구문을 사용해야 하는지에 대한 이해를 돕습니다.

비승인 예문에서, 두 개 이상의 비승인 단어나 STE 미적용 구문이 있는 경우가 있습니다. 그래서, 승인 예문에서는 모든 비승인 단어를 대체하는 법과 STE 적용 구문 제대로 사용하는 법을 보여줍니다.

승인된 단어의 경우 다른 의미나 제한과 관련된 참고가 있는 경우를 제외하고 칼럼 4는 공란입니다. ABOVE(prep)의 경우 아래와 같이 칼럼 4에 비승인 예문을 찾을 수 있습니다.

Word (part of speech)	Approved meaning / ALTERNATIVES	APPROVED EXAMPLE	Not approved example
main (adj)	PRIMARY (adj)	THE PRIMARY CAUSE OF VALVE FAILURE IS CONTAMINATION OF THE HYDRAULIC FLUID.	The main cause of valve failure is contamination of hydraulic acid.
previous (adj)	BEFORE (conj)	REMOVE THE PLATE BEFORE YOU ADJUST THE CABLE.	Adjustment of the cable requires previous removal of the plate.
A (art)	Function word: Indefinite article	A FUEL PUMP IS INSTALLED IN ZONE 10.	
ABOVE (prep)	In (or to) a position farther up than something 💡 For other meanings, use:	LIFT THE CYLINDER ABOVE ITS INSTALLED POSITION.	
	MORE THAN	THE PRESSURE VALUE MUST BE MORE THAN 800 kPa.	The pressure value must be above 800 kPa.

올바른 단어 사용

STE는 제한된 단어로 쓰는 제한된 표현법입니다.

결과적으로, 사용자가 원하는 모든 단어를 사용할 수 없습니다. 사용하고자 하는 단어가 확실하지 않다면, 다음의 흐름도를 참조합니다.

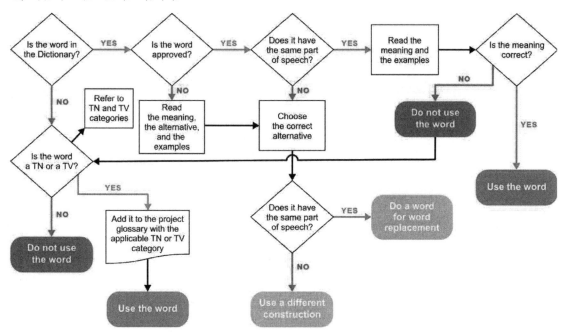

아래의 표는 사용자들이 STE를 적용할 때 가장 자주 범하는 오류를 보여줍니다. <u>사전에서 승인하는 단어가 아니면 사용하지 않습니다.</u>

Non-STE	STE
acceptable (adj)	PERMITTED (adj)
alternate (adj)	ALTERNATIVE (adj)
any (adj)	None or a different conjunction
avoid (v)	PREVENT (v)
both (adj)	THE TWO (TN)
check (v)	CHECK (n)
cover (v)	COVER (TN)
damage (v)	DAMAGE (n)
ensure (v)	MAKE SURE (v)
fit (v)	INSTALL (v)
follow (v)	OBEY (v)
further (adj)	MORE (adj)
further (adv)	MORE (adv)

ASD STE 100

02 Dictionary

Non-STE	STE
have to (v)	MUST (v)
insert (v)	PUT (v)
main (adj)	PRIMARY (adj)
may (v)	CAN (v)
need (v)	NECESSARY (adj)
now (adv)	AT THIS TIME
over (prep)	ABOVE (prep), ON (prep), ALONG (prep)
perform (v)	DO (v)
press (v)	PUSH (v)
reach (v)	GET (v)
repeat (v)	DO (v) ⋯ AGAIN
required (v)	NECESSARY (adj)
rotate (v)	TURN (v)
secure (v)	ATTACH (v), SAFETY (v)
shall (v)	MUST (v)
should (v)	MUST (v)
since (conj)	BECAUSE (conj)
test (v)	TEST (n)
therefore (adv)	THUS (adv), AS A RESULT

2 ▌사전 (Dictionary)

Word (part of speech)	Approved meaning / ALTERNATIVES	APPROVED EXAMPLE	Not approved example
A (art)	Function word: indefinite article	A FUEL PUMP IS INSTALLED IN ZONE 10.	
abaft (prep)	AFT OF (prep)	THE CONTROL UNIT IS INSTALLED AFT OF THE FLIGHT COMPARTMENT	The control unit is installed abaft the flight compartment.
abandon (v)	STOP (v)	STOP THE ENGINE START PROCEDURE.	Abandon the engine start procedure.
	GO (v)	IF THERE IS A FIRE, IMMEDIATELY GO TO A SAFE AREA.	If there is a fire, immediately abandon the area.
abate (v)	DECREASE (v)	WHEN THE WIND SPEED DECREASES TO LESS THAN 30 KNOTS, YOU CAN OPEN THE CARGO DOOR.	When the wind speed abates to less than 30 knots, you can open the cargo door.
ability (n)	CAN (v)	ONE GENERATOR CAN SUPPLY POWER FOR ALL THE SYSTEMS.	One generator has the ability to supply power for all the systems.
able (adj)	CAN (v)	IF YOU CAN START THE ENGINE, DO THE APPLICABLE TESTS.	If you are able to start the engine, do the applicable tests.
abnormal (adj)	UNUSUAL (adj)	LISTEN FOR UNUSUAL NOISES.	Listen for abnormal noises.
	INCORRECT (adj)	IF YOU FIND AN INCORRECT QUANTITY OF AIR FROM THE VENT MAST, DO A SYSTEM TEST.	If you find an abnormal quantity of air from the vent mast, do a system test.
abnormality (n)	DEFECT (TN)	EXAMINE THE SEAL FOR DEFECTS.	Examine the seal for abnormalities.

Word (part of speech)	Approved meaning / ALTERNATIVES	APPROVED EXAMPLE	Not approved example
ABOUT (prep)	Concerned with	FOR DATA ABOUT THE LOCATION OF CIRCUIT BREAKERS, REFER TO THE WIRING LIST.	
	For other meanings, use: APPROXIMATELY (adv)	DRAIN APPROXIMATELY 2 LITERS OF FUEL FROM THE TANK.	Drain about 2 liters of fuel from the tank.
	AROUND (prep)	TURN THE SHAFT AROUND ITS AXIS.	TURN THE SHAFT AROUND ITS AXIS.
ABOVE (prep)	In (or to) a position farther up than something	LIFT THE CYLINDER ABOVE ITS INSTALLED POSITION	
	For other meanings, use: MORE THAN	THE PRESSURE VALUE MUST BE MORE THAN 800 kPa	The pressure value must be above 800 kPa.
ABRASIVE (adj)	That can remove material by friction	DUST, WHEN MIXED WITH OIL, HAS AN ABRASIVE EFFECT.	
abrupt (adj)	SUDDEN (adj)	THE DAMPER PREVENTS SUDDEN MOVEMENT OF THE CONTROL	The damper prevents abrupt movement of the control.
	SUDDENLY (adv)	IF THE ROTORS STOP SUDDENLY, EXAMINE THE INTAKE FOR UNWANTED MATERIAL	If the rotors come to an abrupt stop, examine the intake for unwanted material.

Word (part of speech)	Approved meaning / ALTERNATIVES	APPROVED EXAMPLE	Not approved example
absence (n)	NONE (pron)	IF NONE OF THE BRACKETS ARE DAMAGED, CONTINUE THE PROCEDURE.	In the absence of damage to the brackets, continue the procedure.
	NOT (adv)	IF THE BRACKETS ARE NOT DAMAGED, CONTINUE THE PROCEDURE.	In the absence of damage to the brackets, continue the procedure.
	NO (adj)	IF THERE IS NO CONTAMINATION IN THE FUEL SAMPLE, CONTINUE THE PROCEDURE.	In the absence of contamination in the fuel, sample, continue the procedure.
absent (adj)	MISSING (adj)	F ONE OR MORE BLADES ARE MISSING, MAKE AN ENTRY IN THE ENGINE LOGBOOK.	If one or more blades are absent, make an entry in the engine logbook.
	NO (adj)	IF THERE IS NO CONTAMINATION IN THE FUEL SAMPLE, CONTINUE THE PROCEDURE.	If contamination is absent from the fuel sample, continue the procedure.
absolutely (adv)	FULLY (adv)	MAKE SURE THAT THE LATCH IS FULLY ENGAGED.	Ensure the latch is absolutely engaged.
ABSORB (v), ABSORBS, ABSORBED, ABSORBED	1. To take up or into	ABSORB THE FLUID WITH A CLEAN CLOTH.	
	2. To decrease the effect of	THE SHOCK MOUNT ABSORBS THE VIBRATION.	
absorption (n)	ABSORB (v)	MEASURE THE TIME THAT IS NECESSARY FOR THE SILICA GEL TO ABSORB THE MOISTURE.	Measure the rate of absorption of the moisture by the silica gel.
abundant (adj)	LARGE (adj)	CLEAN YOUR SKIN WITH A LARGE QUANTITY OF CLEAN WATER.	Clean your skin with abundant clean water.

ASD STE 100

Word (part of speech)	Approved meaning / ALTERNATIVES	APPROVED EXAMPLE	Not approved example
abut (v)	TOUCH (v)	THE BIN TOUCHES THE FORWARD HINGE SURFACE.	The bin abuts the forward hinge surface.
accelerate (v)	INCREASE (v)	A HIGHER TEMPERATURE INCREASES THE SPEED OF EVAPORATION.	Evaporation is accelerated by a higher temperature.
	FASTER (adj)	TO MAKE THE CURING PROCESS FASTER ,APPLY HEAT TO THE COMPOUND.	The curing process of, the compound can be accelerated by heating.
ACCEPT (v), ACCEPTS, ACCEPTED, ACCEPTED	To make a decision that something is satisfactory.	ACCEPT THE RELAY IF IT IS SERVICEABLE.	
acceptable (adj)	PERMITTED (adj)	A VALUE OF 2 mm IS PERMITTED.	A value of 2 mm is acceptable.
	SATISFACTORY (adj)	REPLACE THE CAP IF ITS CONDITION IS NOT SATISFACTORY.	Replace the cap if its condition is not. acceptable
	SERVICEABLE (adj)	BEFORE INSTALLATION, MAKE SURE THAT THE UNIT IS SERVICEABLE.	Before installation, make sure that the unit is acceptable.
acceptance (n)	ACCEPT (v)	BEFORE YOU ACCEPT THE UNIT, DO THE SPECIFIED TEST PROCEDURE.	Before acceptance of the unit, do the specified test procedure.
ACCESS (n)	The ability to go into or near	GET ACCESS TO THE ACCUMULATOR FOR THE No. 1 HYDRAULIC SYSTEM.	
accessible (adj)	ACCESS (n)	TURN THE COVER UNTIL YOU CAN GET ACCESS TO THE JACKS THAT HAVE + AND - MARKS.	Rotate the cover until the jacks marked by + and -are accessible.
ACCIDENT (n)	An occurrence that causes injury or damage	MAKE SURE THAT THE PINS ARE INSTALLED TO PREVENT ACCIDENTS.	

Word (part of speech)	Approved meaning / ALTERNATIVES	APPROVED EXAMPLE	Not approved example
ACCIDENTAL (adj)	That does not occur on purpose	TO PREVENT ACCIDENTAL OPERATION OF THE SYSTEM, INSTALL THE SAFETY LOCK.	
ACCIDENTALLY (adv)	That does not occur on purpose	IF YOU ACCIDENTALLY MOVE THE LEVER, SET THE SYSTEM TO THE NEUTRAL POSITION AGAIN.	
accommodate (v)	LET (v)	DO THIS TASK FIRST.	This task must be accomplished first.
	💡 You can use a more specific command verb. COMPLETE (v)	THE PERSONNEL MUST COMPLETE THE TASK IN THE GIVEN TIME.	The personnel must accomplish the task in the given time.
according to (prep)	REFER (v)	TO CALIBRATE THE TEST SET, REFER TO THE MANUFACTURER'S INSTRUCTIONS.	Calibrate the test set according to the manufacturer's instructions.
account for (v)	MAKE SURE (v)	MAKE SURE THAT YOU REMOVE ALL TOOLS AND EQUIPMENT.	All tools and equipment must be accounted for.
accumulate (v)	COLLECT (v)	IF WATER COLLECTS IN THE FILLER LINE, DRAIN IT.	If water accumulates in the filler line, drain it.
accumulation (n)	QUANTITY (n)	REMOVE LARGE QUANTITIES OF CONTAMINATION.	Large accumulations of contamination must be removed.
	COLLECT (v)	IF FUEL COLLECTS FREQUENTLY, EXAMINE FOR LEAKS.	If accumulation of fuel is frequent, examine for leaks.

Word (part of speech)	Approved meaning / ALTERNATIVES	APPROVED EXAMPLE	Not approved example
accuracy (n)	PRECISION (n)	THE PRECISION OF THE ADJUSTMENT CAN CHANGE.	The accuracy of the adjustment can vary.
ACCURATE (adj)	Exact	THE ADJUSTMENT MUST BE ACCURATE.	
ACCURATELY (adv)	Exactly	PUT THE REPAIR SHEET ACCURATELY ON THE DAMAGED AREA.	
achieve (v)	GET (v)	SET THE CONTROL TO GET MAXIMUM THRUST.	Set the control to achieve maximum thrust.
acquire (v)	GET (v)	THE COMPUTER GETS THIS DATA FROM FIVE SENSORS.	The computer acquires this data from five sensors.
acrid (adj)	DANGEROUS (adj)	THIS MATERIAL RELEASES DANGEROUS FUMES WHEN IT TOUCHES HOT SURFACES.	On contact with hot surfaces, this material produces acrid fumes.
ACROSS (prep)	From one side to the other side	SAFETY THE CLAMP BLOCK ACROSS THE CONTROL LEVER FORKS WITH SAFETY WIRE.	
act (v)	Use a specific action verb.	THE HYDRAULIC FLUID FLOW OPENS THE VALVE.	The hydraulic fluid flow acts on the inlet valve.
action (n)	STEP (n)	DO THE STEPS THAT FOLLOW:	Do the following actions :
	PROCEDURE (n)	DO NOT DO THIS PROCEDURE IN THE HANGAR.	This action must not be done in the hangar :

Word (part of speech)	Approved meaning / ALTERNATIVES	APPROVED EXAMPLE	Not approved example
activate (v)	START (v)	START THE MOTOR.	Activate the motor.
	OPERATE (v)	THE LEVERS OPERATE THE MICROSWITCHES.	Microswitches are activated by levers.
	CONNECT (v)	MAKE SURE THAT THE CIRCUIT IS CONNECTED.	Make sure the circuit is activated.
active (adj)	ON (adj)	WHEN THE SYSTEM IS ON, YOU WILL GET A REPORT.	When the system is active, you will get a report.
	OPERATE (v)	THE AUTOTHRUST SYSTEM IS ON BUT IT .DOES NOT OPERATE.	The autothrust system is on but not active.
activity (n)	WORK (n)	THIS WORK IS APPLICABLE TO VERTICAL INSTALLATIONS.	This activity is relevant to vertical installations.
actuate (v)	START (v)	START THE MOTOR.	Actuate the motor.
	OPERATE (v)	OPERATE THE HAND PUMP.	Actuate the hand pump.
	PUSH (v)	PUSH THE PUSHBUTTON SWITCH.	Monitor the actuation of the steering motor.
ADAPT (v), ADAPTS, ADAPTED, ADAPTED	To change or adjust to that which is necessary	ADAPT THE PRESSURE CONNECTION TO THE PITOT HEAD.	
		THE SYSTEM INTERFACE CIRCUITS ADAPT TO THE PHYSICAL PROPERTIES OF THE CONNECTED SYSTEMS.	
ADD (v), ADDS, ADDED, ADDED	To increase the number, dimension, or quantity	ADD 5 ml OF HARDENER TO THE COMPOUND.	

ASD STE 100

Word (part of speech)	Approved meaning / ALTERNATIVES	APPROVED EXAMPLE	Not approved example
addition (n)	ADD (v)	TO GET THE CORRECT CLEARANCE, ADD SPECIAL SHIMS, AS NECESSARY.	Adjust the clearance by the addition of special shims, as necessary.
additional (adj)	MORE (adj)	THIS CHAPTER GIVES MORE INFORMATION ABOUT SAFETY.	This chapter gives additional information about safety.
adequate (adj)	SUFFICIENT (adj)	MAKE SURE THAT CONTAINERS HAVE SUFFICIENT CAPACITY AND DIAMETER.	Make sure that containers have adequate capacity and diameter.
adhere (v)	BOND (v)	THE SEAL MUST BOND CORRECTLY.	The seal must adhere correctly.
	OBEY (v)	OBEY THE SAFETY INSTRUCTIONS.	Adhere to the safety instructions.
adhesion (n)	BOND (n)	CLEAN THE SURFACE TO MAKE SURE THAT THE BOND IS SATISFACTORY.	Clean the surface to ensure there will be good adhesion.
ADJACENT (adj)	That which is near to an object, with no other object of the same type between the two	MAKE SURE THAT YOU DO NOT OPERATE THE ADJACENT CONTROL.	
ADJACENT TO (prep)	To be near to an object, with no other object of the same type between the two	THE FUEL PUMP IS INSTALLED ADJACENT TO THE BULKHEAD.	
adjoining (adj)	ADJACENT (adj)	ALIGN THE BRACKETS WITH THE ADJACENT COMPONENTS.	Align the brackets with the adjoining components.
ADJUST (v), ADJUSTS, ADJUSTED, ADJUSTED	To put in or come to a specified position or value	ADJUST THE FREQUENCY TO THE VALUE GIVEN IN TABLE 1.	
		THE INTERNAL LOGIC ADJUSTS TO SUDDEN CHANGES IN TEMPERATURE.	
ADJUSTABLE (adj)	That you can adjust	THE TWO STOP BOLTS ARE ADJUSTABLE.	

Word (part of speech)	Approved meaning / ALTERNATIVES	APPROVED EXAMPLE	Not approved example
ADJUSTMENT (n)	The effect of adjusting	MAKE SURE THAT THE ADJUSTMENT IS IN THE LIMITS GIVEN IN TABLE 1.	
admit (v)	LET (v)	OPEN THE VALVE TO LET NITROGEN GO INTO THE OLEO STRUT.	Open the valve to admit nitrogen into the oleo strut.
adopt (v)	USE (v)	USE THIS PROCEDURE IF THE UNIT IS DAMAGED.	Adopt this procedure if the unit is damaged.
advance (n)	FORWARD (adj)	THE FORWARD MOVEMENT OF THE CONTROL LEVER MUST BE SLOW AND CONTINUOUS.	The advance of the control lever must be slow and continuous.
advance (v)	SET (v)	SET THE THROTTLE TO MAXIMUM POWER.	Advance the throttle to maximum power.
	FORWARD (adj)	MOVE THE LEVER FORWARD.	Advance the lever.
adverse (adj)	BAD (adj) 💡 Give accurate and correct conditions if possible.	REFER TO CHAPTER 6 FOR INSTRUCTIONS ABOUT HOW TO PARK THE AIRCRAFT IN BAD WEATHER CONDITIONS.	For parking aircraft in adverse weather conditions, refer to Chapter 6.
advisable (adj)	RECOMMEND (v)	WE RECOMMEND THAT YOU TORQUE THE BOLTS AGAIN AFTER 50 FLIGHT HOURS.	It is advisable to retorque the bolts after 50 flight hours.
advise (V)	TELL (v)		Advise Person B that the brakes are set.
	RECOMMEND (v)	WE RECOMMEND THAT YOU REFER TO THE REPAIR MANUAL.	We advise you to refer to the repair manual.
affect (v)	EFFECT (n) 💡 Be specific if possible.	MAGNETIC TOOLS HAVE AN UNWANTED EFFECT ON THE COMPASS SYSTEM.	Magnetic tools affect the compass system.
AFT (adj)	At or nearer to the rear of an air or sea vehicle	THE PUMP IS IN THE AFT CELL OF THE FUSELAGE TANK.	

ASD STE 100

Word (part of speech)	Approved meaning / ALTERNATIVES	APPROVED EXAMPLE	Not approved example
AFT (adv)	In the direction of the rear of an ai or sea vehicle.	MOVE THE THROTTLE AFT.	
AFTER (conj)	That follows a specified time, sequence, or operation.	DO A FUNCTIONAL TEST AFTER YOU INSTALL THE COMPONENT.	
AFTER (prep)	That follows a specified time, sequence, or operation	THE BAR MOVES DOWN AFTER 20 SECONDS.	
AFT OF (prep)	At a position nearer to the rear	THE CONTROL UNIT IS INSTALLED AFT OF THE FLIGHT COMPARTMENT.	
AGAIN (adv)	One more occurrence	MOVE THE CONTROL STICK BACK TO THE CENTER, AND THEN MOVE IT FORWARD AGAIN.	
AGAINST (prep)	In contact with	PUT THE ADAPTER IN POSITION AGAINST ITS SUPPORT.	
AGENT (n)	One of a group of materials made to do a specified task	DO NOT USE THESE CLEANING AGENTS ON HOT SURFACES.	
aggravate (v)	INCREASE (v)	TIRE WEAR INCREASES WITH HIGH SPEED.	Tire wear is aggravated by high speed.
agitate (v)	SHAKE (v)	SHAKE THE SOLUTION.	Agitate the solution.
agitation (n)	SHAKE (v)	IF YOU SHAKE THE SOLUTION, DO NOT USE IT FOR ONE HOUR.	After agitation, do not use the solution for one hour.
AGREE (v), AGREES, AGREED, AGREED	To be consistent with	THE INDICATIONS MUST AGREE WITH THE VALUES IN THE TABLE.	
ahead (adv)	FORWARD (adv)	WHEN YOU INSTALL THE ANTENNA, THE ALIGNMENT ARROW MUST POINT FORWARD.	When you install the antenna, the alignment arrow must point ahead.

Word (part of speech)	Approved meaning / ALTERNATIVES	APPROVED EXAMPLE	Not approved example
AID (n)	Help that is given	IF YOU GET THE SOLUTION IN YOUR EYES, GET MEDICAL AID IMMEDIATELY.	
aid (v)	HELP (v)	APPLY SAND TO THE PLANKS TO HELP WITH TIRE TRACTION.	
aim (v)	POINT (v)	DO NOT POINT THE HOSE AT PERSONS.	
AIRBORNE (adj)	In, or used in, flight	POSITION 2 OF THE SWITCH GIVES A SIGNAL OF THE AIRCRAFT AIRBORNE CONDITION.	
air-dry (v)	DRY (v)	DRY THE FILTER IN THE AIR.	
AIRFLOW (n)	A flow of air	MAKE SURE THAT THE AIRFLOW IS NOT MORE THAN 10 LITERS/MINUTE	
alert (v)	TELL (v)	TELL ALL PERSONNEL TO GO AWAY FROM THE AREA.	Alert all personnel to go away from the area..
ALIGN (v), ALIGNS, ALIGNED, ALIGNED	To put or come into a specified position in relation to a line	ALIGN THE FLANGE HOLES WITH THE STUDS.	
		ALL THREE BRACKET HOLES MUST ALIGN WITH THE FUEL TUBE.	
alignment (n)	ALIGN (v)	MAKE SURE THAT THE KEYWAY IS AT THE TOP AND ALIGNS WITH THE PEG.	Ensure that the keyway is at the top and in alignment with the peg.
ALL (adj)	Full quantity GIVE (v)	DRAIN ALL THE FLUIDS.	
allocate (v)	LET (v)	GIVE THE DIFFERENT MAINTENANCE TASKS TO THE TECHNICIANS.	Allocate the different maintenance tasks to technicians.
allow (v)	CABLE TOUCH THE FLOOR.	DO NOT LET THE CABLE TOUCH THE FLOOR	Do not allow the cable to touch the floor.

Word (part of speech)	Approved meaning / ALTERNATIVES	APPROVED EXAMPLE	Not approved example
allowable (adj)	PERMITTED (adj)	THE MAXIMUM PERMITTED DIFFERENCE IS 5 mm.	
	APPROVED (adj)	THE VALUES MUST NOT BE MORE THAN THE APPROVED DIFFERENCES.	
ALMOST (adv)	Near the limit or the value	MAKE SURE THAT THE PRESSURE IN THE CABIN IS ALMOST ZERO.	
ALONG (prep)	In a line parallel with the length or direction of	MOVE THE TENSIOMETER ALONG THE CABLE	
already (adv)	IN PROGRESS (adv)	THE DATABASE SYNCHRONIZATION IS IN PROGRESS.	The database is already synchronizing.
	NO OTHER	YOU CAN DO THIS PROCEDURE ONLY IF THERE IS NO OTHER REPAIR IN THE REPAIR AREA.	Only do this procedure if there is not already a repair in the repair area.
	Frequently, an alternative for this word is not necessary.	MAKE SURE THAT SOFTWARE IS INSTALLED IN THE REPOSITORY.	Make sure that the software is already installed in the repository.
ALSO (adv)	In addition	ALSO DO THE APPLICABLE STEPS OF THIS PROCEDURE.	
alter (v)	CHANGE (v)	IT IS POSSIBLE THAT THE INSTALLATION OF THE CONNECTOR PINS CHANGED THE ROUTING OF THE CABLE LOOM.	It is possible that the installation of the connector pins altered the routing of the cable loom.
alteration (n)	CHANGE (v)	IF YOU CHANGE THIS REPAIR PROCEDURE, GET APPROVAL OF THE DESIGN AUTHORITY.	The alteration to this repair procedure must get approval of the Design Authority.

Word (part of speech)	Approved meaning / ALTERNATIVES	APPROVED EXAMPLE	Not approved example
alternate (adj)	ALTERNATIVE (adj)	AN ALTERNATIVE REPAIR IS AVAILABLE	An alternate repair is available.
	EACH SECOND	EACH SECOND SQUARE IS RED.	Alternate squares are red.
alternate (v)	THEN (adv)	DO THE PILOT'S INSTRUMENT TEST AND THEN THE COPILOT'S TEST.	Alternate between pilot's and copilot's instrument test.
alternately (adv)	IN ONE (TN) ⋯ AND THEN THE OTHER	TO MAKE PIN REMOVAL EASIER, MANUALLY TURN THE CANOPY IN ONE DIRECTION AND THEN IN THE OTHER.	To make pin removal easier, manually turn the canopy alternately in the two directions.
ALTERNATIVE (adj)	That gives a choice	IT IS PERMITTED TO USE ALTERNATIVE MATERIALS.	
ALTERNATIVE (n)	One of two or more objects or processes that have the same or almost the same properties or functions	IN AN EMERGENCY YOU CAN USE FUEL F-43 AS AN ALTERNATIVE TO FUELS F-34 AND F-40	
alternatively (adv)	ALTERNATIVE (n)	DO TEST B AS AN ALTERNATIVE TO TEST A.	Alternatively, you can do test B.
ALTHOUGH (conj)	In spite of the fact that	ALTHOUGH THE PRESSURE DECREASES, THE VALVE MUST STAY CLOSED.	
ALWAYS (adv)	At all times	ALWAYS KEEP THE BRIGHTNESS CONTROL ON THE LCD DISPLAY AT MAXIMUM.	

ASD STE 100

Word (part of speech)	Approved meaning / ALTERNATIVES	APPROVED EXAMPLE	Not approved example
amend (v)	CHANGE (v)	IF IT IS NECESSARY TO CHANGE THE REPAIR SCHEME, GET THE APPROVAL OF THE DESIGN AUTHORITY.	If it is necessary to amend the Repair Scheme, get the approval of the Design Authority.
amendment (n)	CHANGE (n)	THE DESIGN AUTHORITY MUST GIVE APPROVAL TO CHANGES THAT YOU MAKE TO THE REPAIR SCHEME.	The Design Authority must approve the amendments that you make to the Repair Scheme.
	CHANGE (v)	IF IT IS NECESSARY TO CHANGE THE REPAIR SCHEME, GET THE APPROVAL OF THE DESIGN AUTHORITY.	If an amendment to the Repair Scheme is necessary, get the approval of the Design Authority.
among (prep)	IN (prep)	IF THERE ARE METAL PARTICLES IN THE SAMPLE SOLIDS, REPLACE THE PUMP.	If there are metal particles among the sample solids, replace the pump
amount (n)	QUANTITY (n)	MAKE SURE THAT THE QUANTITY OF FUEL IN THE TANK IS NOT MORE THAN 500 LITERS.	Make sure that the amount of fuel in the tank is not more than 500 liters.
AN (art)	Function word: indefinite article	MAKE AN ENTRY IN THE LOGBOOK.	
ANALOG (adj)	Of data given by pointers and dials	THE PRE-MOD UNIT HAS ANALOG INDICATORS	
analyze (v)	ANALYSIS (TN)	MAKE AN ANALYSIS OF THE OIL	Analyze the oil sample.
anchor (v)	ATTACH (v)	THE STRAPS ARE ATTACHED TO A FULL-LENGTH RAIL	The straps are anchored to a full-length rail.

Word (part of speech)	Approved meaning / ALTERNATIVES	APPROVED EXAMPLE	Not approved example
ancillary (adj)	AUXILIARY (adj)	THE ENGINE AND ALL UXILIARY EQUIPMENT USE THE SAME LUBRICANT.	The engine and all ancillary equipment use the same lubricant.
	SECONDARY (adj)	DO AN OPERATIONAL CHECK OF THE SECONDARY0 CONTROLS	Do an operational check of the ancillary controls.
AND (conj)	Function word used to connect words, phrases, or clauses	MAKE SURE THAT THE FLAPS ARE RETRACTED AND THE AILERON TRIM HANDWHEEL IS IN THE ZERO POSITION	
ANGULAR (adj)	That has one or more angles	MAKE SURE THAT THE ANGULAR POSITION IS CORRECT.	
annotation (n)	WRITE (v)	WRITE THE TEMPERATURE ON THE ENGINE RECORD CARD	Make an annotation of the temperature on the Engine Record Card.
annunciate (v)	SHOW (v)	THE DISPLAY SHOWS A FAULT MESSAGE.	The display annunciates a fault message.
another (adj)	ONE (TN) MORE	INSTALL ONE MORE WASHER ON THE LINE.	Install another washer on the line.
	DIFFERENT (adj)	REFER TO DETAIL C ON FIG. 4 FOR A DIFFERENT PROCEDURE TO ATTACH THE CABLE.	Refer to detail C on Fig. 4 for another way of attaching the cable.
	ADD (v)	ADD A WASHER IF NECESSARY.	Use another washer if necessary.
	AGAIN (adv)	REMOVE THE FUEL FROM THE GROUND BEFORE YOU TRY TO START THE ENGINE AGAIN.	Remove the fuel from the ground before you try another start.
anticlockwise (adv)	COUNTERCLOCKWISE	TURN THE CAP) COUNTERCLOCKWISE	Turn the cap anticlockwise.

ASD STE 100

Word (part of speech)	Approved meaning / ALTERNATIVES	APPROVED EXAMPLE	Not approved example
any (adj)	Frequently, an alternative for this word is not necessary.	IF YOU HAVE QUESTIONS ABOUT THIS DOCUMENT, SEND AN E-MAIL TO THE ADDRESS THAT FOLLOWS:	If you have any questions about this document, send an email to the address that follows:
any (pron)	ONE (TN)	REMOVE ONE OF THE FOUR BOLTS.	Remove any of the four bolts.
anytime (adv)	WHEN (conj)	WHEN YOU USE THE EMERGENCY PUMP, RECORD THE TIME OF OPERATION.	Anytime you use the emergency pump, record the time of operation.
APART (adv)	At a distance (not specified) from	MOVE THE CABLE STRANDS APART.	
aperture (n)	OPENING (n)	GET ACCESS TO THE CONTROL UNIT THROUGH THE OPENING IN THE SIDE OF THE TANK.	Get access to the control unit through the aperture in the side of the tank.
apparent (adj)	SEE (v)	IF YOU SEE DISCOLORATION, REPLACE THE PART.	If discoloration is apparent, replace the part.
	FIND (v)	IF YOU FIND A CRACK, DO THE APPLICABLE REPAIR PROCEDURE.	If a crack is apparent, do the applicable repair procedure.
appear (v)	SHOW (v)	A WARNING FLAG SHOWS IN THE WINDOW.	A warning flag appears in the window.
	VIEW (n)	THE LOWER SEAL COMES INTO VIEW WHEN YOU PULL THE LOWER BEARING DOWN.	The lower seal appears when you pull the lower bearing down.
	THINK (v)	IF YOU THINK THAT THE ENGINE IS TOO HOT, TURN THE SWITCH TO "OFF".	If the engine appears to be too hot, turn the switch to off.
	POSSIBLE (adj)	IF IT IS POSSIBLE THAT THE TEMPERATURE VALUES ARE INCORRECT, DECREASE THE POWER.	If it appears that the temperature values are incorrect, decrease the power.

Word (part of speech)	Approved meaning / ALTERNATIVES	APPROVED EXAMPLE	Not approved example
APPLICABLE (adj)	Correct or satisfactory for the task	REFER TO THE TABLE THAT FOLLOWS FOR THE APPLICABLE TORQUE VALUES.	
application (n)	APPLY (v)	APPLY THE SEALANT WITH A WOODEN SPATULA.	The application of sealant must be carried out with a wooden spatula.
APPLY (v), APPLIES, APPLIED, APPLIED	To put or spread something on	APPLY A FORCE OF 100 N ON THE END OF THE LEVER. APPLY THE SEALING COMPOUND	
appoint (v)	TELL (v)	TELL TWO PERSONS TO BE PREPARED TO OPERATE THE FIRE EXTINGUISHERS.	Appoint two persons to be prepared to operate the fire extinguishers.
approach (v)	GO NEAR	IF IT IS NECESSARY TO GO NEAR THE ENGINE EXHAUST, USE EAR PROTECTION.	If it is necessary to approach the engine exhaust, use ear protection.
appropriate (adj)	APPLICABLE (adj)	LOCK THE WASHER WITH THE APPLICABLE TABS.	Lock the washer with the appropriate tabs.
APPROVAL (n)	That which permits a person or a thing to do something	GET THE APPROVAL OF THE MANUFACTURER BEFORE YOU REPAIR THIS UNIT.	
approve (v)	APPROVAL (n)	GET APPROVAL FROM All THE DESIGN AUTHORITY FOR ALL MODIFICATIONS.	All modifications must be approved by the Design Authority.
APPROVED (adj)	Permitted by an authority	DO THE PROCEDURE IN AN APPROVED AREA.	
APPROXIMATE (adj)	Almost correct or accurate	AN APPROXIMATE VALUE IS SATISFACTORY.	
APPROXIMATELY (adv)	Almost correct or accurate	DRAIN APPROXIMATELY 2 LITERS OF FUEL.	

ASD STE 100

Word (part of speech)	Approved meaning / ALTERNATIVES	APPROVED EXAMPLE	Not approved example
AREA (n)	A specified surface or location	DO NOT SMOKE IN THE WORK AREA.	
arise (v)	OCCUR (v)	SHOCK LOADING OF THE ENGINE CAN OCCUR DURING A HEAVY LANDING.	Shock loading of the engine can arise from a heavy landing.
	CAUSE (v)	A HEAVY LANDING CAN CAUSE SHOCK LOADING OF THE ENGINE.	Shock loading of the engine can arise from a heavy landing.
ARM (v), ARMS, ARMED, ARMED	1. To install armaments	ARM THE AIRCRAFT.	
	2. To prepare for automatic operation	SWITCH TO "CLOSE" TO ARM THE CIRCUIT.	
AROUND (prep)	On all sides of	PUT THE STRAP CLAMPS AROUND THE CYLINDER.	
arrange (v)	PUT (v)	PUT THE COMPONENTS IN THIS SEQUENCE:	Arrange the components in this order.
arrangement (n)	CONFIGURATION (TN)	THE CONFIGURATION OF THE INSERTS IS RELATED TO THE DIMENSIONS OF THE CONNECTOR SHELL.	The arrangement of the inserts is related to the dimensions of the connector shell.
	PREPARE (v)	PREPARE FOR THE LEAK TEST.	Make the arrangements for the leak test.
arrest (v)	STOP (v)	STOP THE FLOW FOR 10 SECONDS.	Arrest the flow for 10 seconds.
	HOLD (v)	A COTTER PIN HOLDS THE GIRT BAR.	A cotter pin arrests the girt bar.
arrive (v)	GET (v)	TO GET THE CORRECT VALUE, SET THE SWITCH TO POSITION 2.	To arrive at the correct value, set the switch to position 2.
ARROW (n)	A mark that has a point to show direction	MAKE SURE THAT THE ARROW POINTS IN THE DIRECTION OF THE FUEL FLOW.	

Word (part of speech)	Approved meaning / ALTERNATIVES	APPROVED EXAMPLE	Not approved example
article (n)	OBJECT (n)	MAKE SURE THAT THERE ARE NO LOOSE OBJECTS IN THE ENGINE AIR INTAKES.	Ensure that there are no loose articles in the engine air intakes.
AS (prep)	In the manner of, to the same quantity, equally	DO NOT USE THE CYLINDER AS A SUPPORT.	
as (conj)	BECAUSE (conj)	THE PUMP DID NOT OPERATE BECAUSE THE SHAFT WAS BROKEN.	The pump did not operate as the shaft was broken.
	WHILE (conj)	WHILE YOU DO EACH STEP OF THE VALVE TEST, MAKE SURE THAT THERE IS NO LEAKAGE.	As you do each step of the valve test, make sure that there is no leakage.
	You can use: AS FOLLOWS	ASSEMBLE THE VALVE AS FOLLOWS:	
	AS NECESSARY	SET THE LENGTH OF THE CONTROL ROD AS NECESSARY.	
	AS SHOWN	MEASURE THE DEPTH OF THE DENT AS SHOWN IN FIGURE 4.	
AS···.AS (conj)	Construction used to show comparison or relation. For "as long as", refer to "long (as long as)".	MOVE THE CONTROL AS QUICKLY AS POSSIBLE.	
ascertain (v)	MAKE SURE (v)	MAKE SURE THAT THE LIGHT IS OFF.	Ascertain that the light is off.
ask (v)	TELL (v)	TELL PERSON B TO MAKE SURE THAT THE SWITCH IS OFF.	Ask Person B to make sure that the switch is off.
	SPEAK (v)	SPEAK TO THE LOCAL AIR TRAFFIC CONTROLLER	Ask the local air traffic controller.
ASSEMBLE (v), ASSEMBLES, ASSEMBLED, ASSEMBLED	To attach, connect, or put together the parts of something	ASSEMBLE THE VALVE AS FOLLOWS:	

ASD STE 100

Word (part of speech)	Approved meaning / ALTERNATIVES	APPROVED EXAMPLE	Not approved example
ASSEMBLY (n)	Items that are connected for a specified function	REMOVE THE WHEEL BRAKE ASSEMBLY FROM THE AXLE.	
assess (v)	CALCULATE (v)	CALCULATE THE QUANTITY OF FUEL THAT IS NECESSARY.	Assess the quantity of fuel that is necessary.
	ESTIMATE (n)	MAKE AN ESTIMATE OF THE DAMAGE.	Assess the damage.
assessment (n)	ESTIMATE (n)	MAKE AN ESTIMATE OF THE DAMAGE.	Carry out an assessment of the damage.
	CALCULATE (v)	CALCULATE THE NUMBER OF SHIMS THAT ARE NECESSARY.	Do an assessment of the number of shims that are necessary.
assign (v)	GIVE (v)	GIVE A CODE TO EACH CONNECTOR.	Assign a code to each connector.
assist (v)	HELP (v)	KEEP THE DATA TO HELP YOU WITH SUBSEQUENT PROCEDURES.	Keep the data to assist subsequent procedures.
assistance (n)	AID (n)	YOU MUST HAVE THE AID OF ONE MORE PERSON FOR THE STEP THAT FOLLOWS.	You must have the assistance of one more person for the step that follows.
associated (adj)	CORRECT (adj)	INSTALL THE DUMP VALVE AND THE CORRECT GASKET.	Install the dump valve with the associated gasket.
	RELATED (adj)	REMOVE THE PANELS FROM THE RELATED DOORS.	Remove the panels from the associated doors.
	ITS, THEIR (pron)	REMOVE THE BOLT AND ITS WASHER	Remove the bolt and the associated washer.
		REMOVE THE EIGHT BOLTS AND THEIR WASHERS.	Remove the eight bolts and the associated washers.
assume (v)	THINK (v)	IF YOU THINK THAT YOU CAN REPAIR THE DAMAGE, REFER TO THE REPAIR SECTION.	If damage is assumed to be repairable, refer to the repair section.

Word (part of speech)	Approved meaning / ALTERNATIVES	APPROVED EXAMPLE	Not approved example
assure (v)	MAKE SURE (v)	USE FERRULES TO MAKE SURE THAT THE LOCATION IS CORRECT.	Ferrules must be used to assure correct location.
as to (prep)	ABOUT (prep)	REFER TO TABLE 7001 FOR INFORMATION ABOUT HOW THE PIVOT ASSEMBLY IS MADE.	Refer to Table 7001 for information as to the construction of the pivot assembly.
asymmetric (adj)	NOT SYMMETRICAL	IF THE RESULT THAT YOU GET IS NOT SYMMETRICAL, DO A RIGGING TEST.	If you get an asymmetric result, do a rigging test.
AT (prep)	Function word that shows the location, position, direction, or time that something occurs	DISCONNECT THE HOSE AT THE PITOT HEAD. AT APPROXIMATELY 300 KNOTS, THE LIGHT COMES ON. WITH THE NOSEWHEEL AT 30 DEG. TO THE CENTER LINE, SET THE LEVER TO "UP".	
at least (adv)	MINIMUM (adj)	THE MINIMUM TIME BETWEEN CHECKS IS TWO MINUTES.	Allow at least two minutes between checks.
	MINIMUM (n)	DO STEPS 13 THRU 16 A MINIMUM OF THREE TIMES.	Do steps 13 thru 16 at least three times.
ATTACH (v), ATTACHES, ATTACHED, ATTACHED	To stay together or to cause different items to stay together	MAKE SURE THAT THE LABEL FULLY ATTACHES TO THE SURFACE AND THAT THERE ARE NO BUBBLES. TEMPORARILY ATTACH THE CABLE TO THE ADJACENT STRUCTURE.	

ASD STE 100

Word (part of speech)	Approved meaning / ALTERNATIVES	APPROVED EXAMPLE	Not approved example
attachment (n)	ATTACH (v)	MAKE SURE THAT THE DUCT IS CORRECTLY ATTACHED TO THE FILTER.	Make sure that the attachment of the duct to the filter is correct.
attain (v)	SHOW (v)	WHEN THE VOLTMETER SHOWS 28 VOLTS DC, THE RELAY CLOSES.	When 28 volts DC is attained, the relay closes.
	BE (v)	WHEN THE VOLTAGE IS 28 VOLTS DC, THE RELAY CLOSES.	When 28 volts DC is attained, the relay closes.
	GET (v)	WHEN YOU GET 28 VOLTS DC, THE RELAY CLOSES.	When 28 volts DC is attained, the relay closes.
attempt (n)	TRY (v)	TRY TO LIFT THE COVER MANUALLY.	Make an attempt to lift the cover manually.
attempt (v)	TRY (v)	TRY TO FIND THE DEFECT.	Attempt to find the defect.
attention (n)	AID (n)	IF YOU GET THE SPRAY IN YOUR EYES, GET MEDICAL AID.	If you get the spray in your eyes, get medical attention.
	CAREFUL (adj)	BE CAREFUL WHEN YOU REMOVE THE CONTROL UNIT.	Pay attention when you remove the control unit.
	MONITOR (v)	MONITOR THE RESULTS.	Pay attention to the results.

Word (part of speech)	Approved meaning / ALTERNATIVES	APPROVED EXAMPLE	Not approved example
audible (adj)	HEAR (v)	IF YOU CANNOT HEAR THE ALARM, ADJUST THE VOLUME CONTROL.	If the alarm is not audible, adjust the volume control.
	LISTEN (v)	LISTEN FOR AIR FROM THE LINES.	Check the lines for audible leaks of air.
augment (v)	INCREASE (v)	A MIXTURE OF WATER AND METHANOL INCREASES THE POWER OF THE ENGINE.	A mixture of water and methanol augments the power of the engine.
aurally (adv)	LISTEN (v)	LISTEN TO MAKE SURE THAT THE FLUID FLOWS.	Check aurally to ensure fluid flow.
	HEAR (v)	YOU CAN HEAR THE WARNING IN THE COCKPIT.	The warning is given aurally in the cockpit.
authentic (adj)	ACCURATE (adj)	IF THE ADJUSTMENT OF THE STOPS IS NOT CORRECT, THE RESULTS OF THE TEST WILL NOT BE ACCURATE.	If the adjustment of the stops is not correct, the results of the test will not be authentic.
AUTHORITY (n)	An official organization that gives approval to something	GET THE APPROVAL OF THE DESIGN AUTHORITY BEFORE YOU CHANGE THE PROCEDURE.	
authorized (adj)	APPROVED (adj)	ONLY APPROVED PERSONS ARE PERMITTED TO STAY IN THIS AREA.	Only authorized persons are permitted to stay in this area.
AUTOMATIC (adj)	That operates without other input	USE THE AUTOMATIC SYSTEM TO OPEN THE DOORS.	
AUTOMATICALLY (adv)	That operates without other input	THE FUEL FLOW STOPS AUTOMATICALLY.	

129

Word (part of speech)	Approved meaning / ALTERNATIVES	APPROVED EXAMPLE	Not approved example
AUXILIARY (adj)	1. That operates in a secondary function	LUBRICANTS FOR THE ENGINE AND THE AUXILIARY EQUIPMENT ARE THE SAME	
	2. That gives help	USE AUXILIARY SCREWS TO ASSEMBLE THE UNIT TEMPORARILY.	
AVAILABLE (adj)	Prepared or supplied for you to use	IF ELECTRICAL POWER IS AVAILABLE, DO A CONTINUITY CHECK.	
avert (v)	PREVENT (v)	IF THE MICROSWITCH BECOMES UNSERVICEABLE, DO THE DEACTIVATION PROCEDURE OF THE ACTUATOR TO PREVENT DAMAGE TO THE VALVE.	If the microswitch becomes unserviceable, do the deactivation procedure of the actuator to avert damage to the valve.
avoid (v)	PREVENT (v)	TURN THE CONTROLS SLOWLY TO PREVENT DAMAGE	Turn the controls slowly to avoid damage.
	DO NOT	DO NOT PUSH ON THE SEALS.	Avoid pushing on the seals.
aware (adj)	KNOW (v)	ALL PERSONNEL MUST KNOW THE EFFECT.	All personnel must be aware of the effect.
		TELL ALL PERSONNEL ABOUT THE EFFECT.	All personnel must be aware of the effect.
AWAY FROM (prep)	In or to a different position or direction	DO THE WORK IN AN AREA AWAY FROM EQUIPMENT OR METAL FRAME BUILDINGS.	
AXIAL (adj)	Related to an axis	DO STEPS 1 THRU 4 TO MAKE SURE THAT NO AXIAL LOAD IS APPLIED ON THE ROD.	
AXIALLY (adv)	Related to an axis	APPLY THE LOAD AXIALLY.	

Word (part of speech)	Approved meaning / ALTERNATIVES	APPROVED EXAMPLE	Not approved example
back (adj)	REAR (adj)	DISCONNECT THE CABLE FROM THE REAR SIDE OF THE INSTRUMENT.	Disconnect the cable from the back side of the instrument.
BACK (adv)	To an initial condition	MOVE THE ENGINE THROTTLE BACK TO 60% RPM.	
back (n)	REAR (n)	THE CONTROL UNIT IS AT THE REAR.	The control unit is at the back.
back and forth (adv)	DIRECTION (n)	MOVE THE SLEEVE IN THE PISTON TO ONE DIRECTION AND THEN BACK AGAIN.	Move the sleeve back and forth in the piston.
back off (v)	LOOSEN (v)	DO NOT LOOSEN THE NUT TO ALIGN IT.	Do not back off the nut to obtain alignment.
backup (n)	EMERGENCY (n)	IN AN EMERGENCY, THE ONE-SHOT BATTERY SUPPLIES DC POWER.	The one-shot battery is a backup for the DC electrical supply.
	AUXILIARY (adj)	USE AUXILIARY SCREWS TO ASSEMBLE THE UNIT TEMPORARILY.	Use some screws as a backup to assemble the unit temporarily.
backward (adv)	REARWARD (adv)	MOVE THE LEVER REARWARD.	Move the lever backward
BAD (adj) (WORSE, WORST)	Not satisfactory. Do not use this word if a more specific word is available.	REFER TO CHAPTER 6 FOR INSTRUCTIONS ABOUT HOW TO PARK IN BAD WEATHER CONDITIONS.	

Word (part of speech)	Approved meaning / ALTERNATIVES	APPROVED EXAMPLE	Not approved example
badly (adv)	INCORRECTLY (adv)	IF THE SLEEVE IS INCORRECTLY ATTACHED, ADJUST IT.	If the sleeve is badly attached, adjust it.
	UNSATISFACTORILY (adv)	DISCARD ALL SEALS WHICH ARE UNSATISFACTORILY BONDED.	Discard all seals which are badly bonded.
	DECREASE (v)	FUEL LEAKS CAN DECREASE ENGINE PERFORMANCE.	A fuel leak can cause the engine to operate badly.
BALANCE (v), BALANCES, BALANCED, BALANCED	To make equal	BALANCE THE ELECTRICAL LOADS ON EACH GENERATOR.	
bank (v)	BANK (TN)	THE V-BARS GIVE THE INDICATION FOR A BANK.	The V-BARS indicate the command to bank.
BARE (adj)	Without a surface layer or protection	BARE METAL SURFACES ARE USUALLY SATISFACTORY FOR AN ELECTRICAL BOND.	
bared (adj)	BARE (adj)	GIVE TEMPORARY PROTECTION TO AREAS OF BARE METAL.	Give temporary protection to areas of bared metal
base (n)	BOTTOM (n)	MAKE SURE THAT THE TWO SPIGOTS AT THE BOTTOM OF THE UNIT ENGAGE.	Make sure that the two spigots at the base of the unit engage.
base (v)	USE (v)	USE THE TORQUE VALUES GIVEN IN CHAPTER 10.	Base the torque values on those given in Chapter 10.
BASIC (adj)	Approved minimum	THIS MODIFICATION CHANGES THE BASIC CONFIGURATION OF THE SYSTEM	

Word (part of speech)	Approved meaning / ALTERNATIVES	APPROVED EXAMPLE	Not approved example
BE (v), IS, WAS, (also ARE, WERE) No other forms of this verb.	1. To occur, exist	IF THERE IS CORROSION ON THE PUMP VANES, REPLACE THE PUMP.	
	2. To have a property, to be equal to	ACID SOLUTIONS ARE DANGEROUS.	
bear down (v)	APPLY (v)	APPLY WEIGHT ON THE SURFACE OF THE PATCH TO MAKE SURE THAT THE PARTS BOND CORRECTLY.	Bear down on the surface of the patch to make sure that the parts bond correctly.
		APPLY A LOAD TO THE PANEL UNTIL IT MOVES INTO POSITION WITH A CLICK.	Bear down on the panel until it moves into place with a click.
BECAUSE (conj)		BECAUSE THE FLUID LEVEL IS INCORRECT, THE SYSTEM WILL NOT OPERATE	
BECAUSE OF (prep)	As a result of	IF YOU CANNOT REMOVE A BOLT BECAUSE OF CORROSION, APPLY PENETRATING OIL	
BECOME (v), BECOMES, BECAME	To come to be	THE SCREEN BECOMES AVAILABLE.	
BEFORE (conj)	That precedes a specified time, sequence, or operation	BLEED THE SYSTEM BEFORE YOU DISCONNECT THE COMPONENTS.	
BEFORE (prep)	That precedes a specified time, sequence, or operation	THE BAR MOVES DOWN BEFORE 20 SECONDS.	
begin (v)	START (v)	INCREASE THE PRESSURE UNTIL THE FLOW STARTS AGAIN.	Increase pressure until the flow begins again.

Word (part of speech)	Approved meaning / ALTERNATIVES	APPROVED EXAMPLE	Not approved example
beginning (n)	START (n)	YOU CAN GET SLOW MOVEMENT AT THE START.	You can get slow movement at the beginning.
	SOURCE (n)	FIND THE SOURCE OF THE FUEL LEAKAGE.	Find the beginning of the fuel leak.
	START (v)	WHEN THE LEVER STARTS TO MOVE, THE MICROSWITCH OPERATES.	At the beginning of the lever movement, the microswitch will operate.
BEHIND (prep)	In a position at the rear of INSTALLED BEHIND	THE PUMP IS THE HYDRAULIC MOTOR.	
BELOW (prep)	In (or to) a position farther down than something	THE DATE IS WRITTEN BELOW THE CYLINDER NECK.	
	For other meanings, use: LESS THAN	MAKE SURE THAT THE DIAMETER OF THE HOLE IS LESS THAN THE SPECIFIED VALUE.	Make sure that the diameter of the hole is below the specified value.
BEND (n)	The area where something is bent	EXAMINE THE BENDS FOR CRACKS.	
BEND (v), BENDS, BENT, BENT	To change or cause to change from straight to curved	BEND THE PIPE CAREFULLY.	
		THESE PARTS CAN EASILY BEND, BREAK OR BECOME INCORRECTLY ALIGNED.	
beneath (prep)	BELOW (prep)	PUT THE JACK BELOW THE AXLE.	Put the jack beneath the axle.
beside (prep)	ADJACENT TO	THE FUEL PUMP IS ADJACENT TO THE SPAR.	The fuel pump is beside the spar.

Word (part of speech)	Approved meaning / ALTERNATIVES	APPROVED EXAMPLE	Not approved example
BETWEEN (prep)	Related to something before and after in time or position	MAKE SURE THAT THE STOPWATCH INDICATION IS BETWEEN 2 AND 4 MINUTES.	
beware (v)	CAREFUL (adj)	BE CAREFUL OF DANGEROUS VOLTAGES	Beware of dangerous voltages.
beyond (prep)	MORE THAN	REPLACE ALL COMPONENTS THAT ARE WORN MORE THAN THE MAXIMUM LIMITS.	Replace all components that are worn beyond their maximum limits.
big (adj)	LARGE (adj)	INSTALL THE LARGER BOLTS.	Install the bigger bolts.
bind (v)	FREELY (adv)	MAKE SURE THAT THE VALVES MOVE FREELY.	Check that valves do not bind.
	WIND AROUND	WIND TWO LAYERS OF TAPE AROUND THE PIPE JOINTS.	Bind the pipe joints with two layers of tape.
blank (v)	CAP (TN)	PUT A CAP ON THE CONNECTOR.	Blank the connector.
	COVER (TN)	PUT A COVER ON THE OUTLET PORT	Blank the outlet port.
blank off (v)	SEAL (v)	SEAL THE HOSES.	Blank off the hoses.
blank out (v)	CANCEL (v)	CANCEL THE DISPLAY.	Blank out the display.
BLEED (v), BLEEDS, BLED, BLED	To let a gas out of	BLEED THE SPEEDBRAKE HYDRAULIC SYSTEM.	
blend (v)	MIX (v)	MIX THE ADHESIVE WITH THE HARDENER.	Blend the adhesive with the hardener.
block (v)	CAUSE A BLOCKAGE	MAKE SURE THAT THE SEALANT DOES NOT CAUSE A BLOCKAGE OF THE DRAIN.	Check that the sealant does not block the drain.

ASD STE 100

Word (part of speech)	Approved meaning / ALTERNATIVES	APPROVED EXAMPLE	Not approved example
BLOCKAGE (n)	That which prevents correct operation	MAKE SURE THAT THERE IS NO BLOCKAGE OF THE PITOT PIPE.	
BLOCKED (adj)	That prevents correct operation	A BLOCKED OIL JET CAN CAUSE INCORRECT OPERATION.	
blot (v)	DRY (v)	DRY THE SURFACE WITH A TOWEL.	Blot the surface with a towel.
BLOW (v), BLOWS, BLEW, BLOWN	To cause gas to move	BLOW DRY AIR THROUGH THE FEED AND SPRAY TUBES.	
BLUNT (adj)	Not sharp	REMOVE THE SEALANT WITH A BLUNT SCRAPER.	
blunted (adj)	BLUNT (adj)	EXAMINE THE STATIC DISCHARGERS FOR BENT AND BLUNT PINS.	Inspect the static dischargers for bent and blunted pins
bolt (v)	ATTACH (v) (WITH A BOLT [TN] OR BOLTS [TN])	ATTACH THE TRACK TO THE CHANNELS WITH THE BOLTS.	Bolt the track to the channels
BOND (n)	1. A connection between structural components for electrical continuity	DO A RESISTANCE CHECK OF THE PRIMARY BONDS.	
	2. A firm connection with another material	MAKE SURE THAT THE BOND BETWEEN THE HONEYCOMB CORE AND THE SKIN IS CORRECT.	

Word (part of speech)	Approved meaning / ALTERNATIVES	APPROVED EXAMPLE	Not approved example
BOND (v), BONDS, BONDED, BONDED	1. To make an electrical bond	THE STATIC DISCHARGER IS ELECTRICALLY BONDED TO THE FRAME.	
	2. To attach firmly or become firmly attached with another material	IF THE FILLER BONDS TO THE TOOL, MAKE THE TOOL MOIST WITH COLD WATER.	
		WHEN YOU BOND THE MATERIALS, APPLY A THIRD LAYER OF ADHESIVE.	
both (adj)	THE TWO (TN)	ATTACH THE TWO ENDS OF THE HOSE.	Attach both ends of the hose.
BOTTOM (adj)	That is lowermost	REMOVE THE BOTTOM BOLT.	
BOTTOM (n)	The lowermost position	THE DRAIN PLUG IS AT THE BOTTOM OF THE UNIT.	
bottom (v)	TOUCH (v)	OPEN THE DOOR UNTIL IT TOUCHES THE FLOOR.	Open the door until it bottoms on the floor.
bounds (n)	LIMIT (n)	MAKE SURE THAT THE CLEARANCE IS IN THE LIMITS.	Make sure that the clearance is in bounds.
brace (v)	HOLD (v)	SUPPORT STRUTS HOLD THE FLOOR STRUCTURE IN POSITION.	Support struts brace the floor structure.
	STRONG (adj)	REINFORCEMENT PLATES MAKE THE LAP JOINTS STRONGER.	Reinforcement plates brace the lap joints.
branch (v)	DIVIDE (v)	THE PRESSURE LINES DIVIDE IN DIFFERENT DIRECTIONS.	The pressure lines branch in different directions.
breadth (n)	WIDTH (n)	THE WIDTH OF THE MATERIAL MUST BE LARGER THAN 10 mm.	The breadth of the material must be larger than 10 mm.

ASD STE 100

Word (part of speech)	Approved meaning / ALTERNATIVES	APPROVED EXAMPLE	Not approved example
break (n)	STOP (v)	IF THE TRANSMISSION STOPS, CANCEL THE TEST.	If there is a break in the transmission, cancel the test.
BREAK (v), BREAKS, BROKE, BROKEN	To cause to separate or become separated into parts by force	BREAK THE BOND OF THE SEALANT	
		IF THE SHEAR PIN BREAKS, DO AN INSPECTION OF THE TOWBAR.	
breakdown (n)	STOP (v)	IF THE PRESSURE SUPPLY STOPS, CANCEL THE TEST.	If there is a breakdown in the pressure supply, cancel the test.
BREATHE (v), BREATHES, BREATHED, BREATHED	To get gas into or out of the lungs	DO NOT BREATHE THE SOLVENT FUMES.	
		BREATHE INTO THE OXYGEN MASK.	
BRIGHT (adj) (BRIGHTER, BRIGHTEST)	That gives much light	THE NAVIGATION LIGHTS CHANGE FROM DIM TO BRIGHT.	
BRIGHTLY (adv)	In a bright manner	THE LIGHTS COME ON BRIGHTLY.	
brightness (n)	INTENSITY (n)	OPERATE THE DIMMER SWITCH AND MAKE SURE THAT THE INTENSITY OF THE LIGHT CHANGES.	Operate the dimmer switch and check that the brightness of the light changes.
	BRIGHT (adj)	TURN THE ADJUSTER CLOCKWISE TO MAKE THE DISPLAY BRIGHTER.	The display brightness is increased by turning the adjuster clockwise.
brilliance (n)	INTENSITY (n)	SET THE INTENSITY TO THE MINIMUM.	Set the brilliance to the minimum.
	BRIGHT (adj)	TURN THE BRT CONTROL CLOCKWISE TO MAKE CONTROL THE DISPLAY BRIGHTER.	To increase the display brilliance, turn the BRT clockwise.

Word (part of speech)	Approved meaning / ALTERNATIVES	APPROVED EXAMPLE	Not approved example
bring (v)	MOVE (v)	MOVE THE PANEL INTO POSITION.	Bring the panel into place.
	PUT (v)	PUT THE PANEL INTO POSITION.	Bring the panel into place.
briskly (adv)	QUICKLY (adv)	RUB THE SURFACE QUICKLY WITH A SOFT, DRY CLOTH.	Rub the surface briskly with a soft, dry cloth.
broadcast (v)	TRANSMIT (v)	TRANSMIT THE DATA ON THE TWO CHANNELS.	Broadcast the data on both channels.
brush (v)	BRUSH (TN)	USE A BRUSH TO CLEAN THE FILTER ELEMENT.	Brush the filter element to clean it.
		CLEAN THE FILTER ELEMENT WITH A BRUSH.	Brush the filter element to clean it.
brush on (v)	BRUSH (TN)	APPLY THE PAINT WITH A BRUSH.	Brush the paint on.
BUBBLE (n)	A small quantity of gas in a liquid or a solid	ADJUST THE CLINOMETER UNTIL THE BUBBLE IS IN THE CENTER.	
build (n)	STRUCTURE (n)	THE WING STRUCTURE GIVES MAXIMUM FUEL CAPACITY.	The build of the wing allows maximum fuel storage.
build (v)	ASSEMBLE (v)	ASSEMBLE THE UNIT.	Build the unit.
bump (v)	HIT (v)	THE FUELING HOSE MUST NOT HIT THE EDGE OF THE TANK.	The fueling hose must not bump the edge of the tank.
BURN (v), BURNS, BURNED, BURNED	1. To cause or undergo combustion FUEL	THE TURBINE BURNS THE SEALANT BURNS AT 109 DEG. F.	
	2. To cause injury or damage through heat	HOT SURFACES CAN BURN YOU.	

ASD STE 100

Word (part of speech)	Approved meaning / ALTERNATIVES	APPROVED EXAMPLE	Not approved example
burst (v)	BREAK (v)	IF THE DISK BREAKS, STOP THE SUPPLY.	If the disk bursts, switch off the supply.
BUT (conj)	On the contrary	TIGHTEN THE NUTS BUT DO NOT TORQUE THEM AT THIS TIME.	
butt (v)	TOUCH (v)	THE WIRE MUST TOUCH THE REAR OF THE CONTACT.	The wire must butt against the rear of the contact.
BY (prep)	Mathematical function word Use as a function word to show agency when a passive construction is necessary in descriptive writing.	DIVIDE THE VALUE BY TWO. INCREASE THE TEMPERATURE BY 10 DEGREES.	
by means of (prep)	WITH (prep)	PRESSURIZE THE SYSTEM TO 150 BAR WITH THE HAND PUMP.	By means of the hand pump, pressurize the system to 150 bar.
BYPASS (v), BYPASSES, BYPASSED, BYPASSED	To change a circuit so that it goes past something instead of through it	IN THIS CONFIGURATION, THE HYDRAULIC PRESSURE BYPASSES THE VALVE.	

Word (part of speech)	Approved meaning / ALTERNATIVES	APPROVED EXAMPLE	Not approved example
CALCULATE (v), CALCULATES, CALCULATED, CALCULATED	To find a result by mathematics	CALCULATE THE PERCENTAGE WITH THE APPLICABLE FORMULA.	
calculation (n)	CALCULATE (v)	IN THIS EXAMPLE, WE CALCULATED THE DATA APPLICABLE ONLY TO A TYPE B UNIT.	The data that we got from the calculations in this example apply only to a Type B unit.
CALIBRATE (v), CALIBRATES, CALIBRATED, CALIBRATED	To measure and adjust the precision of something	CALIBRATE THE THERMOMETER TO THE CELSIUS SCALE.	
CALIBRATION (n)	The procedure that calibrates	WRITE THE RESULTS OF THE CALIBRATION ON THE CORRECTION CHART.	
call (v)	TELL (v)	TELL PERSON A TO REMOVE THE CHOCKS	Call Person A to remove the chocks.
CAN (v), CAN, COULD	Helping verb that means to be possible, to be able to, or to be permitted to	A MIXTURE OF FUEL AND OXYGEN CAN CAUSE AN EXPLOSION. YOU CAN CLEAN THE DRAIN HOLES WITH THE CLEANING TOOL. OU CAN OPERATE THE VEHICLE AFTER THE INSPECTION IS COMPLETED.	
CANCEL (v), CANCELS, CANCELED, CANCELED	1. To do the necessary steps to stop a process	ACCIDENTALLY PUSH THE SWITCH, CANCEL THE START SEQUENCE.	
	2. To remove the validity of something	A NEW REVISION IS AVAILABLE, THE STATUS OF THE LAST REVISION CHANGES TO "CANCELED".	

Word (part of speech)	Approved meaning / ALTERNATIVES	APPROVED EXAMPLE	Not approved example
CANNOT (v)	Helping verb that means to not be able to	THE WHEEL CANNOT MOVE WHEN THE LOCK IS ENGAGED	
cap (v)	SEAL (v)	SEAL ALL THE HOSES.	Cap all the hoses.
	CAP (TN)	PUT CAPS ON THE CONNECTORS.	Cap the connectors.
	COVER (TN)	PUT A COVER ON THE INLET PORT.	Cap the inlet port.
capability (n)	FUNCTION (n)	THESE FUNCTIONS OPEN THE APPLICABLE GRAPHIC DEVICE.	These capabilities open the applicable graphic device.
	CAN (v)	THE COMPUTER CAN CALCULATE THE RESULT AUTOMATICALLY.	The computer has the capability to calculate the result automatically
capable (adj)	APPROVED (adj)	AN APPROVED PERSON MUST DO THE IMPORTANT CHECKS.	Vital checks are to be carried out by a capable person.
	CAN (v)	THE POWER UNIT CAN SUPPLY 28 VDC.	The power unit is capable of producing 28 VDC.
CAPACITY (n)	The maximum quantity that something can hold or make	THE CAPACITY OF THE TANK IS 564 LITERS.	
care (n)	PRECAUTION (n)	OBEY THE SAFETY PRECAUTIONS WHEN YOU DO WORK WITH HIGH VOLTAGES.	You must take care when you work with high voltages.
	CAREFUL (adj)	BE CAREFUL WHEN YOU INSTALL THE NUTS.	Take care when installing the nuts.
	CAREFULLY (adv)	REMOVE THE GEARBOX CAREFULLY.	Remove the gearbox with great care.
CAREFUL (adj)	With precaution	BE CAREFUL WHEN YOU REMOVE THE COVER.	
CAREFULLY (adv)	In a careful manner	CAREFULLY APPLY A BEAD OF SEALING COMPOUND	

Dictionary

Word (part of speech)	Approved meaning / ALTERNATIVES	APPROVED EXAMPLE	Not approved example
carry (v)	TRANSMIT (v)	THE CABLE TRANSMITS THE ELECTRICAL ENERGY FROM THE IGNITION EXCITER TO THE IGNITER.	The cable carries the electrical energy from the ignition exciter to the igniter.
	TRANSPORT (TN)	THIS VEHICLE IS FOR THE TRANSPORT OF 5 PASSENGERS.	This vehicle is meant to carry 5 passengers.
carry out (v)	DO (v)	DO THE LEAK TEST.	Carry out the leak test.
	💡 You can use a more specific command verb. MEASURE (v)	MEASURE THE CLEARANCE OF THE IMPELLER.	Carry out the clearance measurement of the impeller.
case (n)	CONDITION (n)	FIGURE 1 SHOWS THE DATA FOR ALL OPERATIONAL CONDITIONS.	The data for all operational cases are in shown in Figure 1.
case (in case of) (conj)	IF (conj)	IF THERE IS A FIRE, OPERATE THE CRASH SWITCHES.	In case of a fire, operate the crash switches.
CATCH (v), CATCHES, CAUGHT, CAUGHT	To stop or prevent the movement of something	THE LUG ON THE PANEL OPENING CATCHES THE BOTTOM OF THE DRAWER.	
		DO NOT LET THE TOOL CATCH ON THE PANEL.	
	💡 For other meanings, use: COLLECT (v)	COLLECT THE LEAKAGE IN A GRADUATED BEAKER.	Catch the leakage in a graduated beaker.
categorize (v)	CATEGORY (TN)	THE TESTING EQUIPMENT DIVIDES THE FAULTS INTO CATEGORIES.	The testing equipment categorizes the faults.

143   ASD STE 100

Word (part of speech)	Approved meaning / ALTERNATIVES	APPROVED EXAMPLE	Not approved example
CAUSE (n)	Something that brings about a result	DO THE TROUBLESHOOTING PROCEDURE TO FIND THE CAUSE OF THE MALFUNCTION.	
CAUSE (v), CAUSES, CAUSED, CAUSED	To be the cause of	METAL OBJECTS CAN CAUSE MAGNETIC INTERFERENCE.	
caution (v)	TELL (v)	TELL ALL PERSONNEL NOT TO SMOKE NEAR FUEL TANKS.	Caution all personnel not to smoke near fuel tanks.
cautiously (adv)	CAREFULLY (adv)	CAREFULLY FEEL THE HEATER WITH YOUR HANDS TO MAKE SURE THAT IT OPERATES.	Cautiously feel the heater with your hands to make sure that it operates.
cavity (n)	HOLE (n)	FILL THE HOLE WITH RESIN.	Fill the cavity with resin.
	SPACE (n)	FILL THE SPACE BETWEEN THE PATCH AND THE ADJACENT STRUCTURE WITH SEALANT.	Fill the cavity between the patch and the adjacent structure with sealant.
cease (v)	STOP (v)	THE WARNING STOPS AT 17 DEG.	The warning ceases at 17 deg.
center (v)	CENTER (TN)	ALIGN THE PISTON WITH THE CENTER OF THE SLEEVE.	Center the piston in the sleeve.
centralize (v)	CENTER (TN)	SET THE CONTROLS TO THE CENTER POSITION.	Centralize the controls.
	NEUTRAL (TN)	SET THE CONTROLS TO THE NEUTRAL POSITION.	Centralize the controls.
certain (adj)	SURE (adj)	IF YOU ARE NOT SURE THAT THE RESULTS ARE CORRECT, DO THE TEST AGAIN.	If you are not certain that the results are correct, do the test again.
	SOME (adj)	SOME FUNCTIONS ARE NOT AVAILABLE.	Certain functions are not available.
	SPECIFIED (adj)	THE SPECIFIED FUNCTIONS ARE NOT AVAILABLE.	Certain functions are not available.

Word (part of speech)	Approved meaning / ALTERNATIVES	APPROVED EXAMPLE	Not approved example
certify (v)	WRITE (v)	WRITE THE CHANGE IN THE LOGBOOK	Certify the change in the logbook.
	APPROVAL (n)	GET APPROVAL FROM YOUR SUPERVISOR FOR THE REPAIR.	Get the supervisor to certify the repair.
chafe (v)	RUB (v)	DO NOT LET THE WIRES RUB.	Do not let the wires chafe.
chafed (adj)	WORN (adj)	EXAMINE THE TUBING FOR WORN AREAS.	Examine the tubing for chafed areas.
chance (by chance) (n)	RISK (n)	IF THERE IS A RISK OF LEAKAGE, PUT A CONTAINER BELOW THE UNIT.	If there is a chance of leakage, put a container below the unit.
	ACCIDENTALLY (adv)	IF THE LEVER MOVED ACCIDENTALLY, DO THE TEST AGAIN.	If, by chance, the lever moved, do the test again.
CHANGE (n)	That which occurs when something changes	THE COLOR CHANGE SHOWS THAT THE TEMPERATURE IS TOO HIGH.	
CHANGE (v), CHANGES, CHANGED, CHANGED	To become or to cause to become different	IF THE HUMIDITY CHANGES FREQUENTLY, PUT A COVER ON THE UNIT.	
	For other meanings, use: REPLACE (v)	CHANGE THE COLOR OF THE DISPLAY.	
		REPLACE THE DAMAGED VALVE.	Change the damaged valve.
channel (v)	CHANNEL (TN)	INSTALL THE WIRES IN THE CHANNEL ALONG THE HOUSING.	Channel the wires along the housing.
characteristic (n)	PROPERTY (n)	THE PROPERTIES OF THESE SEALANTS PREVENT CORROSION.	The characteristics of these sealants prevent corrosion.
	QUALITY (n)	DO NOT USE THIS MATERIAL, BECAUSE IT DOES NOT HAVE THE NECESSARY QUALITIES.	Do not use this material, because it doesn't have the necessary characteristics.

Word (part of speech)	Approved meaning / ALTERNATIVES	APPROVED EXAMPLE	Not approved example
CHARGE (v), CHARGES, CHARGED, CHARGED	To accumulate or add electrical energy	CHARGE THE BATTERY.	
	For other meanings, use: FILL (v)	MAKE SURE THAT THE BATTERY CHARGES.	
		FILL THE TANK WITH 10 LITERS OF METHANOL.	Charge the tank with 10 liters of methanol.
	PRESSURIZE (v)	PRESSURIZE THE ACCUMULATOR WITH NITROGEN.	Charge the accumulator with nitrogen.
CHECK (n)	The procedure you do to make sure that something operates correctly or has no defects	DO A CHECK OF THE HYDRAULIC SYSTEM.	
		DO A CHECK FOR LOOSE FASTENERS.	
check (v)	MAKE SURE (v)	MAKE SURE THAT IT IS SAFE TO SUPPLY ELECTRICAL POWER.	Check that it is safe to supply electrical power.
	MEASURE (v)	MEASURE THE DISTANCE BETWEEN THE FACES.	Check the distance between the faces.
	EXAMINE (v)	EXAMINE THE CASTING FOR CORROSION.	Check the casting for corrosion.
	CHECK (n)	DO A LEAKAGE CHECK	Check the valve for leakage.
CHEMICAL (adj)	Related to a chemical	REMOVE THE CORROSION WITH THE CHEMICAL COMPOUND THAT IS SPECIFIED IN TABLE 6001.	
CHEMICALLY (adv)	Related to a chemical	REMOVE CORROSION CHEMICALLY.	

Word (part of speech)	Approved meaning / ALTERNATIVES	APPROVED EXAMPLE	Not approved example
chip (n)	PARTICLE (n)	EXAMINE THE FILTER ELEMENT FOR METAL PARTICLES.	Examine the filter element for metal chips.
chip (v)	DAMAGED (adj)	IF THE ENAMEL IS DAMAGED, REPLACE THE UNIT.	If the enamel is chipped, replace the unit.
chock (v)	CHOCK (TN)	PUT THE CHOCKS AGAINST THE WHEELS.	Chock the wheels.
choice (n)	SELECTION (n)	MAKE A SELECTION FROM THE AVAILABLE SHIMS TO GET THE CORRECT THICKNESS.	Make a choice from the available shims to get the correct thickness.
	ALTERNATIVE (adj)	TABLE 1 GIVES ALTERNATIVE ADHESIVES WHICH YOU CAN USE.	In Table 1, there is a choice of adhesives which you are allowed to use.
choose (v)	SELECT (v)	SELECT THE HYDRAULIC SYSTEM THAT YOU WILL PRESSURIZE.	Choose the hydraulic system that you will pressurize.
circa (prep)	APPROXIMATELY (adv)	PUT A CONTAINER (APPROXIMATELY 5 LITERS) BELOW THE WASTE WATER OUTLET.	Put a container (circa 5 liters) under the waste water outlet.
circle (v)	AROUND (prep)	THE POINTER MOVES AROUND THE DIAL.	The pointer circles the dial.
CIRCULAR (adj)	That has the shape of a circle	POLISH THE WINDOW WITH A CIRCULAR MOVEMENT.	
circulate (v)	SUPPLY (v)	SUPPLY AIR AT 24 °C TO THE AREA.	Circulate air at 24 °C in the area.
clamp (v)	ATTACH (v) (WITH A CLAMP [TN] OR CLAMPS [TN])	ATTACH THE ADJACENT CABLES WITH CLAMPS.	Clamp the adjoining cables together.
	PUT (v)	PUT CLAMPS ON THE CABLE TO HOLD IT IN POSITION.	Clamp the cable in position.

ASD STE 100

Word (part of speech)	Approved meaning / ALTERNATIVES	APPROVED EXAMPLE	Not approved example
classification (n)	CLASS (TN)	THERE ARE FOUR GENERAL CLASSES OF FASTENERS.	Fasteners can be separated into four general classifications.
	CATEGORY (TN)	YOU CAN DIVIDE THE FASTENERS INTO FOUR GENERAL CATEGORIES.	Fasteners can be separated into four general classifications.
CLEAN (adj)	That does not include dirt or unwanted material	MAKE SURE THAT THE AREA IS CLEAN.	
CLEAN (v), CLEANS, CLEANED, CLEANED	To remove dirt or unwanted materials	CLEAN THE GASKET CONTACT SURFACE	
cleanliness (n)	CLEAN (adj)	CONDITIONS FOR A SATISFACTORY BOND ARE: - A CLEAN SURFACE - A CORRECT TEMPERATURE - A CORRECT PRESSURE.	A satisfactory bond depends on the cleanliness of the surface, the temperature, and the pressure.
CLEAR (adj)	Without blockage or interference	MAKE SURE THAT THE PITOT AIR INLET IS CLEAR.	
	💡 For other meanings, use: TRANSPARENT (adj)	PUT THE UNIT IN A TRANSPARENT PLASTIC BAG.	Put the unit in a clear plastic bag.
clear (v)	CLEAN (v)	CLEAN THE DRAIN HOLE.	Clear the drain hole.
	💡 You can also use a different construction.	LIFT THE SEAT UNTIL IT IS AWAY FROM THE TRACK LOCKS.	Lift the seat so that it clears the track locks.
CLEARANCE (n)	The space between two objects that must be clear to make sure that they do not touch	MAKE SURE THAT THERE IS CLEARANCE BETWEEN THE LEVER AND THE ROLLER.	
CLEARLY (adv)	In a clear manner	MAKE SURE THAT YOU HEAR THE SIGNALS CLEARLY AT ALL STATIONS.	

Word (part of speech)	Approved meaning / ALTERNATIVES	APPROVED EXAMPLE	Not approved example
CLICK (n)	A short, sharp sound	TURN THE ADJUSTER FIVE CLICKS CLOCKWISE.	
click (v)	CLICK (n)	WHEN THE SOLENOID MAKES A CLICK, THE VALVE IS OPEN.	When the solenoid clicks, the valve is open.
	You can use this word as a technical verb for computer processes and applications.	CLICK "NEXT" TO CONTINUE.	
clip (v)	CUT (v)	CUT THE WIRE TO THE CORRECT LENGTH.	Clip the wire to the correct length.
	ATTACH (v) (WITH A CLIP [TN] OR CLIPS [TN])	ATTACH THE CONDUIT TO THE STRUCTURE WITH CLIPS.	The conduit should be clipped to the structure.
CLOCKWISE (adv)	In the direction in which the hands of a clock turn when seen from the front	TURN THE NOZZLE 40 DEG. CLOCKWISE.	
CLOGGED (adj)	Blocked with unwanted material.	IF THE FILTER IS CLOGGED, REPLACE IT.	
close (adj)	NEAR (prep)	DO NOT USE METHYL ETHYL KETONE NEAR FLAMES OR SPARKS.	Do not use methyl ethyl ketone in close contact with flames or sparks.
CLOSE (v), CLOSES, CLOSED, CLOSED	1. To move together, or to move to a position that stops or prevents materials from going in or out	CLOSE THE INSTRUMENT PANEL. MAKE SURE THAT THE DOORS CLOSE FULLY.	
	2. To operate a circuit breaker to make an electrical circuit	MAKE SURE THAT THE CIRCUIT BREAKER IS CLOSED. MAKE SURE THAT THE CIRCUIT BREAKER CLOSES.	

Word (part of speech)	Approved meaning / ALTERNATIVES	APPROVED EXAMPLE	Not approved example
closely (adv)	CAREFULLY (adv)	CAREFULLY MONITOR THE OPERATION OF THE SYSTEM.	Closely monitor the operation of the system.
close to (adv)	NEAR (prep)	PUT THE CLINOMETER NEAR THE FUSELAGE CENTERLINE.	Put the clinometer close to the fuselage centerline.
coat (n)	LAYER (n)	APPLY A LAYER OF SEALANT PR 1440 B2 ON THE SURFACE.	Spread a coat of sealant PR 1440 B2 on the surface.
coat (v)	LAYER (n)	APPLY A LAYER OF GREASE TO THE BATTERY CABLES.	Coat the battery cables with grease.
coating (n)	LAYER (n)	THE METAL HAS A LAYER OF PLASTIC ON IT TO PREVENT CORROSION.	The metal has a coating of plastic on it to prevent corrosion.
cock (v)	SET (v)	SET THE RACK HOOKS.	Cock the rack hooks.
CODE (n)	A sequence of symbols, letters, and/or numbers used for identification	EACH ELECTRICAL SYSTEM HAS A CODE TO IDENTIFY IT.	
code (v)	IDENTIFY (v)	IDENTIFY THE CABLES WITH A CODE.	Code the cables.
	CODE (n)	PUT A CODE ON THE CABLES.	Code the cables.
COIL (n)	A sequence of loops	MAKE SURE THAT THE COILS OF THE OXYGEN HOSE DO NOT RUB TOGETHER.	
coil (v)	WIND (v)	WIND THE CABLES CAREFULLY.	Coil the cables carefully.
coincide (v)	ALIGN (v)	THE FASTENERS MUST ALIGN WITH THE HOLES IN THE TRACK.	The fasteners must coincide with the holes in the track.
coincident (adj)	SYNCHRONIZED (adj)	MAKE SURE THAT THE MOVEMENT OF THE TWO SURFACES IS SYNCHRONIZED	Make sure that the movement of the two surfaces is coincident.
COLD (adj) (COLDER, COLDEST)	At low temperature	MAKE SURE THAT COLD AIR COMES OUT OF THE OUTLETS.	

Word (part of speech)	Approved meaning / ALTERNATIVES	APPROVED EXAMPLE	Not approved example
collapse (v)	CLOSE (v)	CLOSE THE BOX.	Collapse the box.
	FALL (v)	THE BOARDING BRIDGE FELL.	The boarding bridge collapsed.
COLLECT (v), COLLECTS, COLLECTED, COLLECTED	To come, or cause to come, together in one location	FLUID COLLECTS IN THE BOTTOM OF THE COWLING.	
		COLLECT ALL LOOSE ITEMS AND PUT THEM IN THE CONTAINER.	
COLOR (n)	A property of light	THE COLOR CHANGES FROM BLUE TO RED.	
color code (v)	IDENTIFY (v)	IDENTIFY THE ASSEMBLY WITH THE CORRECT COLOR.	The assembly must be color coded.
	CODE (n)	PUT A COLOR CODE ON EACH OF THE ASSEMBLIES.	Color code the assemblies.
colored (adj)	COLOR (n)	THE SCALE HAS TWO AREAS OF DIFFERENT COLOR.	The scale is divided into two colored areas.
combine (v)	MIX (v)	MIX THE WATER AND THE GLYCOL.	Combine water and glycol.
	PUT TOGETHER	DO NOT PUT DIFFERENT HPT SEGMENTS TOGETHER.	Do not combine different HPT segments.
combustible (adj)	FLAMMABLE (adj)	KEEP FLAMMABLE MATERIALS AT A MINIMUM DISTANCE OF 50 FEET FROM THE WORK AREA.	Keep combustible materials at a minimum distance of 50 feet from the work area.
COME (v), COMES, CAME	To move to your location	FUMES MUST NOT COME INTO THE CABIN.	
COME ON (v), COMES ON, CAME ON	To become bright with light when an internal power source is energized	THE LIGHTS MUST COME ON.	

Word (part of speech)	Approved meaning / ALTERNATIVES	APPROVED EXAMPLE	Not approved example
commence (v)	START (v)	THE WARNING STARTS AND THE INDICATORS FLASH.	The warning commences and the indicators flash.
commencement (n)	START (v)	AFTER THE TEST STARTS, MONITOR THE RESULTS ON THE SCREEN.	After the test commencement, monitor the results on the screen.
common (adj)	SAME (adv)	THE REMOVAL PROCEDURE IS THE SAME FOR THE TWO ITEMS.	The removal procedure is common to both items.
communicate (v)	TELL (v)	TELL PERSON B TO SET THE SWITCH TO "OFF".	Communicate with Person B to set the switch to OFF.
	SPEAK (v)	USE A TELEPHONE TO SPEAK WITH PERSON B.	Use a telephone to communicate with Person B.
communication (n)	SPEAK (v)	MAKE SURE THAT PERSON A CAN SPEAK TO PERSON C.	Make sure that there is communication between Person A and Person C.
	HEAR (v)	MAKE SURE THAT AIR TRAFFIC CONTROL CAN HEAR YOU.	Make sure that you are in communication with ATC.
COMPARE (v), COMPARES, COMPARED, COMPARED	To examine for differences	COMPARE THE TWO VALUES.	
comparison (n)	COMPARE (v)	COMPARE THE TWO INDICATIONS.	Make a comparison of the two readings.
COMPATIBLE (adj)	That can operate together satisfactorily or be used together safely	THIS SOFTWARE IS COMPATIBLE ONLY WITH THE SPECIFIED OPERATING SYSTEM.	
		THE COOLANT IS COMPATIBLE WITH ALL AEROSPACE ALLOYS.	

Word (part of speech)	Approved meaning / ALTERNATIVES	APPROVED EXAMPLE	Not approved example
compile (v)	MAKE A LIST	MAKE A LIST OF THE NECESSARY TOOLS.	Compile a list of the required tools.
	RECORD (v)	RECORD THE AILERON MOVEMENTS ON FORM B.	Compile the aileron movements on Form B.
	COLLECT (v)	COLLECT ALL LOG RECORDS FOR THE COMPONENT.	Compile all log records for the component.
complete (adj)	FULL (adj)	EXTEND AND RETRACT THE ACTUATOR THROUGH THREE FULL CYCLES.	Extend and retract the actuator through three complete cycles.
	ALL (adj)	SEND ALL THE TEST RESULTS TO THE MANUFACTURER.	The complete test results must be sent to themanufacturer.
	COMPLETED (adj)	THE GREEN INDICATION SHOWS THAT SERVICING IS COMPLETED.	The green indication shows that servicing is complete.
COMPLETE (v), COMPLETES, COMPLETED, COMPLETED	To bring to an end	COMPLETE THE FUNCTIONAL TEST.	
COMPLETED (adj)	Successfully brought to an end	SEND THE COMPLETED REPORT TO THE SUPERVISOR FOR APPROVAL.	
completely (adv)	FULLY (adv)	LET THE FIRST LAYER OF PAINT DRY FULLY BEFORE YOU APPLY THE SECOND LAYER.	Allow the first layer of paint to dry completely before applying the second layer.
completion (n)	END (n)	AT THE END OF THIS PROCEDURE, REFER TO 72-00, TEST 001.	See 72-00, Testing 001 upon completion of this procedure.
	COMPLETE (v)	TWO HOURS ARE NECESSARY TO COMPLETE THIS TASK.	Completion of the task will require two hours.
complicated (adj)	NOT EASY	THIS TEST PROCEDURE IS NOT EASY WITHOUT THE CORRECT EQUIPMENT.	This test procedure is complicated without the right equipment.

ASD STE 100

Word (part of speech)	Approved meaning / ALTERNATIVES	APPROVED EXAMPLE	Not approved example
comply (v)	OBEY (v)	OBEY THESE INSTRUCTIONS.	You must comply with these instructions.
	Used in regulatory language. Refer to Rule 1.12.	THE SHIP CERTIFICATE MUST COMPLY WITH ALL THE REQUIREMENTS OF THE AUTHORITIES.	
COMPONENT (n)	A part, subassembly, or unit that has a specified function	DO NOT CLEAN THESE COMPONENTS WITH TRICHLORO-ETHYLENE.	
comprehensive (adj)	FULL (adj)	DO A FULL INSPECTION OF THE FAIRING.	Do a comprehensive inspection of the fairing.
COMPRESS (v), COMPRESSES, COMPRESSED, COMPRESSED	To decrease or cause to decrease in dimension or volume	COMPRESS THE SPRING AND CAREFULLY INSTALL THE COVER	
		WHEN THE SPRING COMPRESSES, THE VALVE OPENS.	
comprise (v)	HAVE (v)	THE VALVE ASSEMBLY HAS THESE PARTS :	The valve assembly comprises these parts :
	CONTAIN (v)	EACH SURVIVAL KIT CONTAINS THESE ITEMS.	Each survival kit comprises these items.
compulsory (adj)	MANDATORY (adj)	BEFORE YOU PUT NEW OIL IN THE SYSTEM, IT IS MANDATORY TO REPLACE THE FILTER.	Before you put new oil in the system, it is compulsory to replace the filter.
compute (v)	CALCULATE (v)	CALCULATE THE VOLTAGE IN THE CIRCUIT.	Compute the voltage in the circuit.
concentrate (v)	ALL (adj)	ALL THE WEIGHT MUST BE ON THE SPAR TIP.	The weight must be concentrated on the spar tip.
CONCENTRATION (n)	The strength of something contained in a mixture	IN A HIGH CONCENTRATION, THIS MATERIAL IS POISONOUS.	

Word (part of speech)	Approved meaning / ALTERNATIVES	APPROVED EXAMPLE	Not approved example
CONCENTRIC (adj)	That has a common center	THE EXTERNAL DIAMETER MUST BE CONCENTRIC TO THE INTERNAL DIAMETER.	
concern (v)	APPLICABLE (adj)	THIS PROCEDURE IS APPLICABLE ONLY TO A TYPE B UNIT.	This procedure only concerns a Type B unit.
conclusion (n)	END (n)	AT THE END OF THE TEST, SET THE SWITCH TO "NORMAL".	At the conclusion of the test, you must switch to "NORMAL".
	RESULT (n)	IF THE RESULTS OF THE TEST ARE UNSATISFACTORY, REPLACE THE UNIT.	If the conclusions of the test are unsatisfactory, replace the unit.
concurrently (adj)	AT THE SAME TIME	DO THESE TWO PROCEDURES AT THE SAME TIME.	These two procedures must be applied concurrently.
CONDENSATION (n)	The result when a gas changes into a liquid	SET THE SWITCH TO THE "ON" POSITION TO REMOVE THE CONDENSATION	
CONDITION (n)	Something that is necessary for what occurs	THESE INITIAL CONDITIONS ARE NECESSARY TO GET CORRECT RESULTS.	
	The state of an item	DO A CHECK OF THE UNIT CONDITION.	
	💡 Use IF (conj) for "on the condition that."	IF THERE IS NO WIND, DO THE TEST OUTDOORS.	On the condition that there is no wind, do the test outdoors.
conduct (v)	DO (v)	DO THE LEAK TEST.	Conduct the leak test.
confine to (v)	ONLY (adv)	IF THE DAMAGE IS ONLY TO THE MIDDLE TREADS, THE TIRE IS SERVICEABLE.	If the damage is confined to the middle treads, the tire is serviceable.
confirm (v)	MAKE SURE (v)	IF POSSIBLE, DO AN ENGINE GROUND RUN TO MAKE SURE THAT YOU GET THE SAME INDICATIONS.	If possible, ground run the engine to confirm the indications.

Word (part of speech)	Approved meaning / ALTERNATIVES	APPROVED EXAMPLE	Not approved example
conflict (n)	DIFFERENT (adj)	IF THE TWO INDICATIONS ARE DIFFERENT, DO THE TEST AGAIN	If there is a conflict between the two indicators, repeat the test.
	AGREE (v)	IF THE TWO INDICATIONS DO NOT AGREE, DO THE TEST AGAIN.	If there is a conflict between the two indicators, repeat the test.
conform (v)	AGREE (v)	IF THE FLAP EXTENSION DOES NOT AGREE WITH THE POSITION OF THE FLAP CONTROL LEVER, DO THE RIGGING PROCEDURE AGAIN.	If the flap extension does not conform to the setting of the flap control lever, do the rigging procedure again.
conformance (n)	AGREE (v)	THE INDICATIONS MUST AGREE WITH THOSE IN TABLE 2.	The indications must be in conformance with those in Table 2.
conformity (n)	AGREE (v)	THE PRECISION OF THE GAUGES MUST AGREE WITH THE APPLICABLE QUALITY STANDARD.	The accuracy of the gauges must be in conformity with the applicable quality standard.
CONNECT (v), CONNECTS, CONNECTED, CONNECTED	To come together or cause to come together to make one unit or system	CONNECT THE ELECTRICAL CONNECTORS TO THE INSTRUMENT.	
		PLUG "A" CONNECTS TO SOCKET "B".	
CONNECTION (n)	That which connects or is connected	MAKE SURE THAT ALL THE FUEL AND AIR CONNECTIONS ARE INSTALLED.	
consecutive (adj)	ONE (TN) AFTER THE OTHER	DO NOT DO MORE THAN THREE STARTS, ONE AFTER THE OTHER.	Do not do more than three consecutive starts.
consecutively (adv)	ONE (TN) AFTER THE OTHER	DO THESE STEPS ONE AFTER THE OTHER.	These actions must be done consecutively.
consequence (n)	BECAUSE OF (prep)	BECAUSE OF THIS PROBLEM, THE UNIT WILL NOT OPERATE.	As a consequence of this problem, the unit will not operate.

Word (part of speech)	Approved meaning / ALTERNATIVES	APPROVED EXAMPLE	Not approved example
consider (v)	THINK (v)	IF YOU THINK THAT THE INDICATION IS NOT CORRECT, DO THE TEST AGAIN.	If you consider that the indication is not correct, do the test again.
considerable (adj)	LARGE (adj)	CLEAN YOUR SKIN WITH A LARGE QUANTITY OF WATER.	Clean your skin with a considerable quantity of water.
	IMPORTANT (adj)	CONTAMINATION OF CABIN AIR CAN BE AN IMPORTANT PROBLEM.	Contamination of cabin air can be a considerable problem.
	DANGEROUS (adj)	HYDRAULIC FLUID IS DANGEROUS FOR YOUR EYES.	Hydraulic fluid can cause considerable eye injury.
consist of (v)	HAVE (v)	EACH ANTENNA HAS THREE PARTS.	Each antenna consists of three parts.
consistent (adj)	AGREE (v)	MAKE SURE THAT THE INDICATIONS AGREE WITH THE POSITION OF THE FLAPS.	Check that the indications are consistent with the position of the flaps.
CONSTANT (adj)	That continues to be the same, without change	MAKE SURE THAT THE CABIN PRESSURE STAYS CONSTANT.	
CONSTANTLY (adv)	Incessantly	THE INSTRUMENT WILL CONSTANTLY SHOW THIS VALUE.	
construct (v)	ASSEMBLE (v)	ASSEMBLE THE UNIT.	Construct the unit.
consult (v)	REFER (v)	FOR MORE INFORMATION, REFER TO THE USER'S MANUAL.	For more information, consult the User's Manual.
contact (v)	TOUCH (v)	THE TOOL MUST NOT TOUCH THE CABLE.	The tool must not contact the cable.
	SPEAK (v)	SPEAK TO THE CREW CHIEF ON THE INTERPHONE.	Contact the crew chief on the interphone.
	WRITE (v)	FOR MORE INFORMATION ABOUT SPARE PARTS, WRITE TO THE SALES DEPARTMENT.	For more information about spare parts, contact the sales department.

ASD STE 100

Word (part of speech)	Approved meaning / ALTERNATIVES	APPROVED EXAMPLE	Not approved example
CONTAIN (v), CONTAINS, CONTAINED, CONTAINED	To have in something or hold in something	EACH SURVIVAL KIT CONTAINS THESE ITEMS:	
CONTAINER (n)	Something that holds fluids, materials, or objects	PUT THE CONTAINER BELOW THE DRAIN PLUG.	
contaminant (n)	CONTAMINATION (n)	THIS FILTER REMOVES ALL CONTAMINATION FROM THE AIR SUPPLY.	This filter removes all contaminants from the air supply.
contaminated (adj)	DIRTY (adj)	REPLACE THE DIRTY OIL.	Contaminated oil must be replaced.
	CONTAMINATION (n)	REMOVE ALL CONTAMINATION FROM THE HYDRAULIC FLUID WITH A CLASS 5 FILTER.	Filter the contaminated hydraulic fluid through a Class 5 filter.
CONTAMINATION (n)	Unwanted change of the original condition of a material because of chemical or physical agents or a material that causes such a change	DUST CAN CAUSE CONTAMINATION ON ALL FILTERS.	
CONTENTS (n)	Something that is in a container	EXAMINE THE CONTENTS OF THE BOX FOR MISSING ITEMS.	
contiguous (adj)	ADJACENT (adj)	REMOVE THE SENSOR TO GET ACCESS TO THE ADJACENT STRUCTURE.	Remove the sensor to get access to the contiguous structure.
CONTINUE (v), CONTINUES, CONTINUED, CONTINUED	To stay or keep in current condition or operation	CONTINUE THE TEST. IF THE LOW PRESSURE CONDITION CONTINUES, REPLACE THE UNIT.	

Word (part of speech)	Approved meaning / ALTERNATIVES	APPROVED EXAMPLE	Not approved example
CONTINUOUS (adj)	That continues	MAKE SURE THAT THERE IS CONTINUOUS MOVEMENT OF THE PROBE.	
CONTINUOUSLY (adv)	In a continuous manner	APPLY PRESSURE CONTINUOUSLY.	
CONTOUR (n)	The outer line of something	CUT ALONG THE CONTOUR TO REMOVE THE DAMAGED SKIN.	
CONTROL (n)	Something that controls	IN AN EMERGENCY, USE THE MANUAL CONTROL.	
CONTROL (v), CONTROLS, CONTROLLED, CONTROLLED	To give or send signals that adjust, operate, or keep something to a limit, or that cause something to operate	RADIO MASTER SWITCH 1 CONTROLS THE BUS BAR.	
conventional (adj)	STANDARD (adj)	PULL THE VEHICLE TO A SAFE AREA WHERE YOU CAN USE THE STANDARD PROCEDURES.	Pull the vehicle to a safe location where more conventional procedures can be applied.
converse (adj)	OPPOSITE (adj)	THE RESET DEVICE OPERATES IN THE OPPOSITE DIRECTION.	The reset device operates in the converse direction.
convert (v)	CHANGE (v)	CHANGE THE UNITS FOR THE FUEL LOAD TO U.S. GALLONS.	Convert the fuel load to U.S. gallons.
convey (v)	MOVE (v)	MOVE THE EQUIPMENT TO A SAFE AREA.	Convey the equipment to a safe area.
	TELL (v)	TELL THE INFORMATION TO YOUR MANAGER.	Convey the information to your manager.
COOL (adj)	Moderately cold	WHEN THE AREA IS SUFFICIENTLY COOL, POLISH THE SURFACE.	

Word (part of speech)	Approved meaning / ALTERNATIVES	APPROVED EXAMPLE	Not approved example
cool (v)	DECREASE (v)	LET THE TEMPERATURE OF THE COMPONENT DECREASE UNTIL IT IS THE SAME AS THE AMBIENT TEMPERATURE.	Let the temperature of the component cool to ambient.
	COOL (adj)	OPERATE THE PARKING BRAKE WHEN THE BRAKES ARE COOL.	Apply the parking brake when the brakes have cooled.
coordinate (v)	SYNCHRONIZED (adj)	MAKE SURE THAT COMPASS SYSTEM 1 AND COMPASS SYSTEM 2 ARE SYNCHRONIZED.	Coordinate compass system 1 and compass system 2.
COPY (n)	An object made the same as another object	SEND FIVE COPIES OF THE DEFECT REPORT TO THE ENGINEERING AUTHORITY.	
copy (v)	WRITE (v)	WRITE THE TAIL NUMBER ON THE RECORD FORM.	Copy the tail number on the record form.
	COPY (n)	MAKE A COPY OF THE DATA THAT IS ON THE IDENTIFICATION PLATE.	Copy the data on the identification plate.
	RECORD (v)	RECORD THE DATA THAT IS ON THE IDENTIFICATION PLATE.	Copy the data on the identification plate.
CORNER (n)	The point or the angle made when lines, sides, or edges touch	EXAMINE THE OPENING FOR CRACKS THAT START AT ITS CORNERS.	
CORRECT (adj)	That agrees with all that is necessary to the maximum	MAKE SURE THAT THE POLARITIES ARE CORRECT.	
CORRECT (v), CORRECTS, CORRECTED, CORRECTED	To make correct	CORRECT THE TENSION.	

Word (part of speech)	Approved meaning / ALTERNATIVES	APPROVED EXAMPLE	Not approved example
CORRECTION (n)	A change to make something correct	DO NOT MAKE THE CORRECTION AT THIS HEADING.	
CORRECTLY (adv)	In a correct manner	MAKE SURE THAT THE CIRCLIP IS CORRECTLY INSTALLED.	
correctness (n)	CORRECT (adj)	THIS ADJUSTMENT MUST BE CORRECT.	The correctness of this adjustment is important.
	CORRECTLY (adv)	IT IS IMPORTANT TO DO THIS ADJUSTMENT CORRECTLY.	The correctness of this adjustment is important.
correspond (v)	AGREE (v)	MAKE SURE THAT THE POSITION OF THE CLAMP AGREES WITH THE POSITION THAT YOU RECORDED DURING THE REMOVAL PROCEDURE.	Make sure that the position of the clamp corresponds to the position recorded during the removal procedure.
	SAME (adj)	CLOSE THE VALVE WHEN THE TWO GAUGES SHOW THE SAME INDICATION.	Close the valve when the indications on the two gauges correspond.
	DIFFERENT (adj)	IF THE TWO INDICATIONS ARE DIFFERENT, DO THE TEST AGAIN.	If the two indications do not correspond, repeat the test.
corresponding (adj)	RELATED (adj)	THE RELATED CAUTION LIGHT MUST GO OFF AFTER 30 SECONDS.	The corresponding caution light shall go off after 30 seconds.
corrode (v)	CORROSION (TN)	THIS MATERIAL CAUSES CORROSION OF SURFACES WITH NO PROTECTION.	This material corrodes unprotected surfaces.
corrosive (adj)	CORROSION (TN)	HYDRAULIC FLUID CAN CAUSE CORROSION.	Hydraulic fluid is corrosive.

ASD STE 100

Word (part of speech)	Approved meaning / ALTERNATIVES	APPROVED EXAMPLE	Not approved example
COUNT (v), COUNTS, COUNTED, COUNTED	To add the number of objects or occurrences to get a total	COUNT THE NUMBER OF TREADS ON THE TIRE.	
COUNTER- CLOCKWISE (adv)	In the opposite direction to clockwise	MAKE SURE THAT YOU TURN THE CONTROL KNOB COUNTERCLOCKWISE.	
couple (v)	CONNECT (v)	CONNECT THE FUELING NOZZLE TO THE AIRCRAFT.	Couple the fueling nozzle to the aircraft.
	ATTACH (v)	ATTACH THE FUELING NOZZLE TO THE IRCRAFT.	Couple the fueling nozzle to the aircraft.
cover (v)	INCLUDE (v)	THIS PROCEDURE INCLUDES THE INSTRUCTIONS TO REMOVE THE CONSTANT SPEED DRIVE (CSD).	This procedure covers the removal of the Constant Speed Drive (CSD).
	HAVE (v)	THE BOTTOM EDGE OF THE PANEL HAS CARPET ON IT.	The bottom edge of the panel is covered with carpet.
	COVER (TN)	PUT THE COVER ON THE CONTAINER.	Cover the container.
crack (v)	OPEN (v)	WHEN THE RELIEF VALVE OPENS, THE PRESSURE DECREASES.	When the relief valve cracks open, the pressure decreases.
	CRACK (TN)	IF THERE ARE CRACKS IN THE CENTER PLY, REPLACE THE WINDSHIELD PANEL.	If a center ply is cracked, replace the windshield panel.
create (v)	MAKE (v)	CUT THE BRACKET TO MAKE A CLEARANCE.	Cut the bracket to create a clearance.
	CAUSE (v)	VIBRATION CAN CAUSE CRACKS.	Vibration can create cracks.

Word (part of speech)	Approved meaning / ALTERNATIVES	APPROVED EXAMPLE	Not approved example
critical (adj)	VERY IMPORTANT	THE CONDITION OF THE RADOME IS VERY IMPORTANT FOR ITS PERFORMANCE	The condition of the radome is critical to its performance.
	CAREFUL (adj)	MAKE A CAREFUL ESTIMATE OF THE DAMAGED AREA.	Make a critical estimate of the damaged area.
cross (v)	ACROSS (adv)	DO NOT GO ACROSS THE SAFETY LINE.	Do not cross the safety line.
	CORRECTLY (adv)	CONNECT THE WIRES CORRECTLY	Do not cross the wires.
curvature (n)	BEND (n)	THE BEND IN THE PIPE MUST HAVE A 30 mm RADIUS.	The curvature of the pipe must have a 30 mm radius.
	CURVE (n)	THE RADIUS OF THE CURVE MUST BE A MINIMUM OF 8 mm.	The radius of the curvature must be a minimum of 8 mm.
	RADIUS (TN)	BEND THE PIPE TO THE CORRECT RADIUS.	Bend the pipe to the correct curvature.
CURVE (n)	The shape of something which is bent but which has no angles	THE RADIUS OF THE CURVE MUST BE A MINIMUM OF 8 mm.	
curve (v)	MAKE A CURVE	BEND THE STRIP OF METAL TO MAKE A CURVE.	Curve the strip of metal.
CUT (v), CUTS, CUT, CUT	1. To divide into parts	CUT THE CABLE INTO THREE EQUAL LENGTHS.	
	2. To remove with a sharp tool	CUT AND DISCARD THE LOCKWIRE.	
CYCLE (n)	One complete sequence of operation	SET THE SWITCH TO THREE CYCLES A MINUTE.	
cycle (v)	OPERATE (v)	OPERATE THE ACTUATOR THROUGH THREE CYCLES.	Cycle the actuator three times.

Word (part of speech)	Approved meaning / ALTERNATIVES	APPROVED EXAMPLE	Not approved example
DAMAGE (n)	The result of an occurrence that causes deterioration of the condition of something	LOOK FOR DAMAGE.	
damage (v)	DAMAGE (n)	DISCONNECT THE SPRING TO PREVENT DAMAGE TO THE ROD.	Disconnect the spring so as not to damage the rod.
DAMAGED (adj)	That has or can be affected by damage	REPLACE THE DAMAGED PARTS.	
damp (adj)	MOIST (adj)	REMOVE ALL LOOSE DIRT FROM THE SEAT WITH A MOIST CLOTH.	Remove all loose dirt from the seat with a damp cloth.
dampen (v)	DECREASE (v)	THE MOUNTING PADS DECREASE VIBRATION.	The mounting pads dampen vibration.
	MAKE MOIST	MAKE THE CLOTH MOIST WITH SOLVENT.	Dampen the cloth with solvent.
danger (n)	RISK (n)	THERE IS A RISK OF FIRE.	There is a danger of fire.
	DANGEROUS (adj) ⚫ This word is a technical name when it identifies a safety instruction	HYDRAULIC FLUID IS DANGEROUS FOR YOUR HEALTH.	Hydraulic fluid is a danger to your health.
DANGEROUS (adj)	That can cause injury, damage to health or can kill	IT IS DANGEROUS TO USE AIR IN THIS SYSTEM.	
dangerously (adv)	DANGEROUS (adj)	DO NOT OPEN THE CARGO DOOR IN STRONG WINDS. STRONG WINDS ARE DANGEROUS.	Do not open the cargo door if the wind-speed is dangerously high.

Word (part of speech)	Approved meaning / ALTERNATIVES	APPROVED EXAMPLE	Not approved example
DATA (n)	1. Known facts	MAKE SURE THAT YOU GET ALL THE DATA ABOUT THE PROBLEM.	
	2. Numbers and symbols used by computers	DO A TEST TO FIND IF THE MANAGEMENT UNIT TRANSMITS THESE DATA.	
	💡 You can also use the singular.	DO A TEST TO FIND IF THE MANAGEMENT UNIT TRANSMITS THIS DATA	
DATE (n)	The time at which an event occurs	ON THE LABEL, READ THE DATE OF THE LAST INSPECTION.	
deactivate (v)	STOP (v)	THE WARNING BELL AND THE HORN WILL OPERATE AND THEN STOP.	The warning bell and the horn will be activated and then deactivated.
	DISCONNECT (v)	MAKE SURE THAT THE MICROSWITCHES ARE DISCONNECTED.	Make sure that the microswitches are deactivated.
	ISOLATE (v)	OPEN THE CIRCUIT BREAKER TO ISOLATE THE LANDING GEAR SYSTEM.	Open the circuit breaker to deactivate the landing gear system.
deadly (adj)	KILL (v)	HIGH VOLTAGES CAN KILL YOU.	High voltages are deadly.
deaerate (v)	BLEED (v)	BLEED THE No. 1 HYDRAULIC SYSTEM.	Deaerate the No. 1 hydraulic system.
	AIR (TN)	THE VACUUM EQUIPMENT REMOVES THE AIR FROM THE COMPOUND.	The vacuum equipment deaerates the compound.
dearm (v)	DISARM (v)	DISARM THE ESCAPE SLIDE.	Dearm the escape slide.
	REMOVE (v)	REMOVE THE CARTRIDGES FROM THE FIRE BOTTLES.	Dearm the fire bottles.

ASD STE 100

Word (part of speech)	Approved meaning / ALTERNATIVES	APPROVED EXAMPLE	Not approved example
decay (v)	DECREASE (v)	WHEN THE ENGINE SPEED DECREASES TO 500 RPM, STOP THE ENGINE.	When the engine speed decays to 500 rpm, stop the engine.
decelerate (v)	DECREASE (v)	MAKE SURE THAT THE ENGINE SPEED DECREASES TO 500 RPM.	Make sure that the engine decelerates to 500 rpm.
	SLOWER (adj)	TO MAKE THE CURING PROCESS SLOWER, DECREASE THE HEAT THAT YOU APPLY TO THE COMPOUND.	The curing process of the compound can be decelerated by decreasing the heat applied.
decide (v)	SELECT (v)	SELECT THE HYDRAULIC SYSTEM THAT YOU WILL PRESSURIZE.	Decide which hydraulic system you will pressurize.
	DECISION (n)	IF YOUR DECISION IS NOT TO REPLACE THE UNIT, MONITOR ITS TEMPERATURE FOR A MINIMUM OF 15 CYCLES.	If you decide not to replace the existing unit, watch its temperature for at least 15 cycles.
DECISION (n)	The result after you think about a problem	MAKE A DECISION ABOUT WHICH PROCEDURE YOU WILL USE.	
decontamination (n)	REMOVE CONTAMINATION	REMOVE THE CONTAMINATION FROM THE INSTRUMENTS AND MEDICAL EQUIPMENT.	Do the decontamination of the instruments and medical equipment.
	CLEAN (v)	CLEAN THE AIRCRAFT IN AN APPROVED AREA.	The decontamination of the aircraft shall be done in an authorized area.
decrease (n)	DECREASE (v)	THE PRESSURE MUST DECREASE BY MORE THAN 2 BAR.	There must be a decrease in pressure of more than 2 bar.

Word (part of speech)	Approved meaning / ALTERNATIVES	APPROVED EXAMPLE	Not approved example
DECREASE (v), DECREASES, DECREASED, DECREASED	To make or become smaller or lower	DECREASE THE HEADING INDICATIONS.	
decrement (n)	INCREMENT (n)	TURN THE ADJUSTER COUNTERCLOCKWISE IN INCREMENTS OF 60 DEG.	Turn the adjuster anticlockwise in decrements of 60 deg.
DEDICATED (adj)	That is used only for one purpose	A DEDICATED TOOL IS NECESSARY FOR THE INSTALLATION OF THE UNIT.	
DE-ENERGIZE (v), DE-ENERGIZES, DE-ENERGIZED, DE-ENERGIZED	To remove electrical power from	DE-ENERGIZE THE AC AND DC BUSBARS.	
deep (adj)	DEPTH (n)	MEASURE THE DEPTH OF THE DENT WITH A STRAIGHTEDGE AND FEELER GAUGES.	Measure how deep the dent is with a straightedge and feeler gauges.
DEFECTIVE (adj)	Unserviceable for operation	REPLACE THE DEFECTIVE BOOSTER PUMP.	
define (v)	CALCULATE (v)	CALCULATE THE QUANTITY OF FUEL THAT IS NECESSARY FOR THE FLIGHT.	Define the amount of fuel required for the flight.
	GIVE (v)	THE BRAKE INDICATOR GIVES THE WEAR ON THE BRAKE SHOE.	The brake indicator defines the wear on the brake shoe.
	SPECIFIED (adj)	THE FLAP ANGLES ARE SPECIFIED IN TABLE 1.	Table 1 defines the flap angles.

Word (part of speech)	Approved meaning / ALTERNATIVES	APPROVED EXAMPLE	Not approved example
DEFLATE (v), DEFLATES, DEFLATED, DEFLATED	To make or become smaller as a result of depressurization	DEFLATE THE TIRE TO A PRESSURE OF 2 BAR (29 PSI).	
		IF THE WHEEL TEMPERATURE INCREASES TO MORE THAN 177 DEG, THE CORE OF THE FUSIBLE PLUG MELTS AND THE TIRE DEFLATES.	
deflect (v)	MOVE (v)	THE BARS MOVE TO THE RIGHT SIDE.	Bars deflect to the right.
deflection (n)	MOVEMENT (n)	REMOVE ALL THE RIGGING PINS AND EQUIPMENT THAT PREVENT FREE MOVEMENT OF THE CONTROL SURFACES.	Remove all rigging pins and equipment preventing free deflection of control surfaces.
	POSITION (n)	MAKE SURE THAT THE POSITION IS 23 DEG.	Ensure that deflection is 23 deg.
	TRAVEL (n)	MAKE SURE THAT THE TRAVEL IS 23 DEG.	Ensure that deflection is 23 deg.
deformed (adj)	DAMAGED (adj)	THE COVER ON THE GUN CAMERA IS DAMAGED.	The cover on the gun camera is deformed.
	DEFORMATION (TN)	MAKE SURE THAT THE TUBES HAVE NO DEFORMATION.	Make sure that the tubes are not deformed.
DEFUEL (v), DEFUELS, DEFUELED, DEFUELED	To remove fuel	DEFUEL THE TANK.	
defueling (n)	DEFUEL (v)	DEFUEL ONLY IN AN OPEN AREA THAT HAS A GOOD AIRFLOW.	Only do the defueling in an open area that is well-ventilated.
degrease (v)	GREASE (TN)	REMOVE ALL GREASE FROM THE FAYING SURFACE WITH SOLVENT.	Degrease the faying surface with solvent.
de-ice (v)	ICE (TN)	REMOVE THE ICE FROM THE AIRCRAFT.	De-ice the aircraft.

Word (part of speech)	Approved meaning / ALTERNATIVES	APPROVED EXAMPLE	Not approved example
delay (n)	INTERVAL (n)	AN INTERVAL OF 5 MINUTES IS NECESSARY BEFORE YOU CONTINUE THE TEST.	A delay of 5 minutes is necessary before continuing with the test.
	IMMEDIATELY (adv)	THE JAWS OF THE UPLOCK UNIT MUST OPEN IMMEDIATELY.	The jaws of the uplock unit must open with no delay.
delay (v)	AFTER (prep)	ONLY USE THE STARTER AFTER A PERIOD OF 20 MINUTES.	Use of the starter must be delayed for 20 minutes.
delete (v)	ERASE (v)	ERASE THE FLIGHT DATA FROM THE TAPE.	Delete the flight data from the tape.
	REMOVE (v)	REMOVE THE PENCIL MARKS WITH AN ERASER.	Delete the pencil marks with an eraser.
	You can use this word as a technical verb for computer processes and applications.	DELETE THE FILE.	
delicate (adj)	EASILY DAMAGED	BE CAREFUL WITH EASILY DAMAGED PARTS.	Be careful with delicate parts.
deliver (v)	SUPPLY (v)	SET THE RIG TO SUPPLY A PRESSURE OF 800 kPa.	Set the rig so that it delivers a pressure of 800 kPa.
delivery (n)	SUPPLY (v)	A CENTRIFUGAL PUMP SUPPLIES HYDRAULIC FLUID TO THE UNIT.	Hydraulic fluid delivery to the unit is ensured by a centrifugal pump.
demand (v)	MANDATORY (adj)	IN THIS CONFIGURATION, A DIFFERENT TEST PROCEDURE IS MANDATORY.	This configuration demands a different test procedure.
denote (v)	SHOW (v)	FIGURE 2 SHOWS THAT YOU CAN INSTALL AN ALTERNATIVE RELAY.	Figure 2 denotes that an alternative relay may be installed.

Word (part of speech)	Approved meaning / ALTERNATIVES	APPROVED EXAMPLE	Not approved example
dent (v)	DENT (TN)	DO NOT MAKE DENTS IN THE BELLOWS.	Do not dent the bellows.
depend (v)	IF (conj)	THE TENSION IN THE CABLES DECREASES IF THE TEMPERATURE INCREASES.	Cable tension changes depending on the temperature.
deplete (v)	DECREASE (v)	DO NOT OPERATE THE BRAKES TO DECREASE THE PRESSURE IN THE ACCUMULATORS.	Do not deplete accumulators by operating the brakes.
DEPLOY (v), DEPLOYS, DEPLOYED, DEPLOYED	To move or cause to move from a specified position of storage and into operation	KEEP PERSONNEL AWAY FROM THE AIRCRAFT WHEN THE THRUST REVERSER DEPLOYS.	
		DEPLOY THE SLIDE RAFT.	
deposit (n)	PARTICLE (n)	IF THERE ARE METAL PARTICLES IN THE OIL FILTER, EXAMINE THE FILTER ELEMENT FOR WEAR.	If there are metal deposits in the oil filter, check the filter element for wear.
	CONTAMINATION (n)	FLUSH THE PIPES TO REMOVE CONTAMINATION.	Flush the pipes to remove deposits.
depress (v)	PUSH (v)	PUSH THE BUTTON AND THEN RELEASE IT.	Depress and release th button.
depressurize (v)	PRESSURE (TN)	RELEASE THE PRESSURE FROM THE HYDRAULIC SYSTEM.	Depressurize the hydraulic system.
DEPTH (n)	The distance from the top down, from the surface down, from the front surface to the rear surface	MEASURE THE DEPTH OF THE DENT AS SHOWN IN FIGURE 4.	
describe (v)	GIVE (v)	THIS SECTION GIVES THE PROCEDURES FOR THE LEAK TEST OF THE SYSTEM.	This section describes the procedures for testing the system for leaks.
deselect (v)	CANCEL (v)	PUSH THE BUTTON TO CANCEL THE FREEZE MODE.	Press the button to deselect the freeze mode.

Word (part of speech)	Approved meaning / ALTERNATIVES	APPROVED EXAMPLE	Not approved example
design (v)	HAVE (v)	THE MAIN LANDING GEAR DOORS HAVE STEPS FOR ACCESS TO THE LANDING GEAR BAY.	The main landing gear doors are designed with steps for access to landing gear bay.
desired (adj)	NECESSARY (adj)	ADD THE NECESSARY QUANTITY OF OIL.	Add the desired quantity of oil.
	CORRECT (adj)	TIGHTEN THE TURNBUCKLE UNTIL THE TENSION IN THE CABLE IS CORRECT.	Tighten the turnbuckle until you have the desired tension in the cable.
destroy (v)	UNSERVICEABLE (adj)	MAKE THE CONTAINER UNSERVICEABLE TO MAKE SURE THAT YOU CANNOT USE IT AGAIN.	To prevent further use, destroy the container.
detach (v)	DISCONNECT (v)	DISCONNECT THE PIPELINE FROM THE UNION.	Detach the pipeline from the union.
	DISENGAGE (v)	BEFORE YOU MOVE THE CONTROLS, DISENGAGE THE LOCKS.	Before moving the controls, detach the locks.
	REMOVE (v)	DO NOT REMOVE THE PROTECTIVE LAYER.	Do not detach the protective film.
detail (n)	INSTRUCTION (n)	THIS PROCEDURE GIVES THE INSTRUCTIONS TO ATTACH THE PYLON.	This procedure gives details on how to attach the pylon.
detail (v)	GIVE (v)	THIS SECTION GIVES THE REMOVAL / INSTALLATION INSTRUCTIONS.	This section details the Removal / Installation instructions.
	REFER (v)	DO THE LEAK TEST (REFER TO PARAGRAPH 4.0).	Do the leak test as detailed in paragraph 4.0.
	SPECIFIED (adj)	DO THE LEAK TEST AS SPECIFIED IN PARAGRAPH 4.0.	Do the leak test as detailed in paragraph 4.0.

ASD STE 100

Word (part of speech)	Approved meaning / ALTERNATIVES	APPROVED EXAMPLE	Not approved example
detect (v)	FIND (v)	TO FIND DAMAGE ON WIRES, RUB A CLOTH ALONG THEM.	To detect damage to wires, rub a cloth along them.
	SENSE (v)	THE COMPUTER SENSES THE DIFFERENCES BETWEEN THE SIGNALS.	The computer detects discrepancies between the signals.
DETERIORATION (n)	A worse condition	THIS CONDITION WILL CAUSE DETERIORATION OF THE SURFACE.	
determine (v)	FIND (v)	FIND THE DEFECTS IN THE SYSTEM.	Determine the defects in the system.
	GIVE (v)	DIMENSIONS 1 AND 2 GIVE THE CORRECT POSITION.	The correct position is determined by dimensions 1 and 2.
	SELECT (v)	SELECT THE HYDRAULIC SYSTEM THAT YOU WILL PRESSURIZE.	Determine which hydraulic system you will pressurize.
	CALCULATE (v)	CALCULATE THE DIMENSION OF THE SHIM WITH THIS FORMULA :	Determine the dimension of the shim with this formula :
detrimental (adj)	DANGEROUS (adj)	HYDRAULIC FLUID IS DANGEROUS FOR YOUR HEALTH.	Hydraulic fluid is detrimental to health.
	DAMAGE (n)	SMALL QUANTITIES OF SURFACE BLOOMING, WHICH CAN OCCUR ON ITEMS IN STORAGE, DO NOT CAUSE DAMAGE TO THE COMPONENT.	Light surface blooming, which can occur on items in storage, is not detrimental to the component.

Word (part of speech)	Approved meaning / ALTERNATIVES	APPROVED EXAMPLE	Not approved example
develop (v)	START (v)	IF A FIRE STARTS, OPERATE THE FIRE SHUTOFF VALVE.	If a fire develops, operate the fire shutoff valve.
	CAUSE (v)	DO NOT LET HYDRAULIC FLUID STAY ON YOUR SKIN. HYDRAULIC FLUID CAN CAUSE DERMATITIS.	Do not leave hydraulic fluid on your skin, as dermatitis could develop.
deviate (v)	OBEY (v)	PERSONNEL MUST OBEY THIS PROCEDURE.	Personnel must not deviate from this procedure.
DEVICE (n)	Something used to do a task	INSTALL THE SAFETY DEVICES.	
devise (v)	MAKE (v)	IF THE HOLDING FIXTURE IS NOT AVAILABLE, MAKE A SUPPORT FROM THE SHIPPING CONTAINER.	If the holding fixture is not available, devise one from the shipping container.
	FIND (v)	FIND NEW TROUBLESHOOTING PROCEDURES.	Devise new troubleshooting procedures.
diagnose (v)	FIND (v)	FIND THE CAUSE OF THE MALFUNCTION.	Diagnose the cause of the malfunction.
DIAGONALLY (adv)	In a diagonal direction	APPLY THE FIRST LAYER OF TAPE ACROSS THE CUTOUT AND THE SECOND AND THIRD LAYERS DIAGONALLY.	
diametrically (adv)	OPPOSITE (adj)	MAKE SURE THAT THE TWO OPPOSITE V-GROOVES ALIGN WITH THE RAILS.	Ensure the two diametrically opposed V-grooves are in line with the rails
differ (v)	DIFFERENT (adj)	IF THE VALUES ARE DIFFERENT, DO THIS TEST.	If the values differ, do the following test.
DIFFERENCE (n)	That which is different between two quantities, numbers, or functions	THE DIFFERENCE BETWEEN THE TWO DIMENSIONS MUST NOT BE MORE THAN 0.10 mm	

173

Word (part of speech)	Approved meaning / ALTERNATIVES	APPROVED EXAMPLE	Not approved example
DIFFERENT (adj)	Not the same	IF THE INDICATIONS ARE DIFFERENT, DO THESE STEPS.	
DIFFERENTLY (adv)	In a different manner	THE TWO EXTRACTORS OPERATE DIFFERENTLY.	
differentiate (v)	IDENTIFY (v)	LETTERS IDENTIFY THE WIRE SEGMENTS.	Letters are used to differentiate between the wire segments.
difficult (adj)	NOT EASY	IF IT IS NOT EASY TO INSTALL THE RIGGING PIN, ADJUST THE LENGTH OF THE ROD.	If the rigging pin is difficult to install, adjust the length of the rod.
	NOT EASILY	IF YOU CANNOT INSTALL THE RIGGING PIN EASILY, ADJUST THE LENGTH OF THE ROD.	If the rigging pin is difficult to install, adjust the length of the rod.
difficulty (n)	NOT EASY	IF IT IS NOT EASY TO REMOVE THE BOLT, APPLY PENETRANT OIL	If there is difficulty in removing the bolt, apply penetrant oil.
	NOT EASILY	IF YOU CANNOT REMOVE THE BOLT EASILY, APPLY PENETRANT OIL.	If there is difficulty in removing the bolt, apply penetrant oil.
DIGITAL (adj)	Related to digits	CONNECT THE PRODS OF THE DIGITAL VOLTMETER.	
DIGITALLY (adv)	Given by digits	THE VALUE IS SHOWN DIGITALLY ON THE DISPLAY.	
dilute (v)	MIX (v)	MIX THE PRIMER WITH SOLVENT.	Dilute the primer with solvent.
	ADD (v)	DO NOT ADD MORE THAN AN EQUAL PART OF WATER TO THE ANTIFREEZE.	Do not dilute the antifreeze with more than an equal part of water.

Word (part of speech)	Approved meaning / ALTERNATIVES	APPROVED EXAMPLE	Not approved example
dim (v)	DECREASE (v)	MAKE SURE THAT THE INTENSITY OF THE RETICLE LIGHT GRADUALLY DECREASES TO ZERO.	Check that the reticle brightness dims gradually until it disappears.
DIM (adj) (DIMMER, DIMMEST)	Not bright	DURING NIGHT OPERATION, MAKE SURE THAT THE PANEL LIGHTS ARE DIM.	
DIMENSION (n)	The result when something is measured in one direction	DIMENSION "A" MUST NOT BE MORE THAN 50 PER CENT OF DIMENSION "D".	
diminish (v)	DECREASE (v)	IF THE HYDRAULIC PRESSURE DECREASES, CLOSE THE VALVE.	If the hydraulic pressure diminishes, close the valve.
DIMLY (adv)	Not bright	MAKE SURE THAT THE LIGHT COMES ON DIMLY.	
dip (v)	MOMENTARILY (adv)	PUT THE ELEMENT INTO THE SOLVENT MOMENTARILY.	Dip the element in solvent.
direct (v)	POINT (v)	POINT THE OPEN END OF THE DRAIN HOSE AWAY FROM THE STRUCTURE.	Direct the open end of the drain hose away from the structure.
DIRECTION (n)	The line on which something moves or is pointed	THE ARROW ON THE VALVE BODY SHOWS THE DIRECTION OF THE FLOW.	
DIRECTLY (adv)	In a direct procedure or by direct effect	DO NOT FILL THE SYSTEM DIRECTLY FROM A HIGH-PRESSURE STORAGE-CYLINDER.	
DIRTY (adj) (DIRTIER, DIRTIEST)	Not clean	A DIRTY CONTACT IN THE CONNECTION UNITS WILL CAUSE THEM TO OPERATE INCORRECTLY.	

ASD STE 100

Word (part of speech)	Approved meaning / ALTERNATIVES	APPROVED EXAMPLE	Not approved example
disappear (v)	VIEW (n)	THE HORIZONTAL BAR GOES OUT OF VIEW	The horizontal bar disappears from the window.
DISARM (v), DISARMS,	To remove armaments	DISARM THE AIRCRAFT.	
DISARMED, DISARMED	To prevent automatic operation	DISARM THE LIFT DUMPER.	
DISASSEMBLE (v), DISASSEMBLES, DISASSEMBLED, DISASSEMBLED	To take an assembly apart	DISASSEMBLE THE VALVE ASSEMBLY.	
DISCARD (v), DISCARDS, DISCARDED, DISCARDED	To not use again	REMOVE THE O-RINGS AND DISCARD THEM.	
discharge (v)	RELEASE (v)	RELEASE PRESSURE FROM THE TANKS.	Discharge pressure from the tanks.
		THE UNWANTED AIR GOES OVERBOARD	The unwanted air discharges overboard.
DISCONNECT (v), DISCONNECTS, DISCONNECTED, DISCONNECTED	To separate something from the thing that it is connected to, or to become separated	DISCONNECT THE POWER SUPPLY.	
		WHEN YOU TOUCH THIS ICON, THE COMPUTER DISCONNECTS FROM THE INTERNET.	
discontinue (v)	STOP (v)	STOP THE TEST PROCEDURE.	Discontinue the test procedure.
discover (v)	FIND (v)	IF YOU FIND CORROSION DURING THE INSPECTION, REMOVE IT.	If you discover corrosion during the inspection, remove it.
discrepancy (n)	DIFFERENCE (n)	IF THERE IS A DIFFERENCE OF MORE THAN 5 mm, MAKE SURE THAT THE ADJUSTMENT IS CORRECT.	If the discrepancy is greater than 5 mm, check the adjustment.

Word (part of speech)	Approved meaning / ALTERNATIVES	APPROVED EXAMPLE	Not approved example
DISENGAGE (v), DISENGAGES, DISENGAGED, DISENGAGED	To release or become released from that engages	DISENGAGE THE CLUTCH BEFORE YOU START THE ENGINE IF THERE IS A MALFUNCTION, THE GEARS WILL AUTOMATICALLY DISENGAGE.	
disinfect (v)	DISINFECTANT (TN)	USE DISINFECTANT TO CLEAN THE MASK ASSEMBLIES.	Disinfect the mask assemblies.
dismantle (v)	DISASSEMBLE (v)	DISASSEMBLE THE BRAKE UNIT IN THE WORKSHOP.	Dismantle the brake unit in the workshop.
dispatch (v)	SEND (v)	SEND A REPORT TO THE INSPECTION DEPARTMENT.	Dispatch a report to the Inspection Department.
disperse (v)	REMOVE (v)	BLOW THROUGH THE TUBES TO REMOVE THE REMAINING FLUID.	Blow through the tubes to disperse the residual fluid.
displace (v)	MOVE (v)	THE PISTON MOVES THE FLUID.	Fluid is displaced by the piston.
DISPLAY (n)	A visual indication	A NUMBER IN THE TOP LEFT CORNER OF THE DISPLAY REFERS TO THE RELATED PAGE.	
display (v)	SHOW (v)	THE COMPASS INDICATORS SHOW THE HEADINGS.	The headings are displayed on the compass indicators.
dispose of (v)	DISCARD (v)	DISCARD THE USED SOLVENT AS SPECIFIED IN THE APPLICABLE PROCEDURE.	Dispose of the used solvent according to the applicable procedure.

Word (part of speech)	Approved meaning / ALTERNATIVES	APPROVED EXAMPLE	Not approved example
disposition (n)	LOCATION (n)	MAKE SURE THAT THE FIRE EXTINGUISHERS ARE IN THEIR CORRECT LOCATIONS BEFORE YOU START THE ENGINE.	Check the disposition of the fire extinguishers before you start the engine.
	POSITION (n)	MAKE SURE THAT THE POSITION OF THE SWITCHES IS CORRECT.	Ensure that the switch disposition is correct.
disregard (v)	IGNORE (v)	DO THE GENERATOR DRIVE TEST, BUT IGNORE STEPS 16 THRU 20.	Perform the generator drive test, but disregard steps 16 thru 20.
DISTANCE (n)	The dimension between two points or objects	MEASURE THE DISTANCE BETWEEN POINTS "A" AND "B".	
distinct (adj)	CLEAR (adj)	MAKE SURE THAT THE SOUND IS CLEAR	Ensure the sound is distinct.
distinctly (adv)	CLEARLY (adv)	YOU MUST HEAR THE SOUND CLEARLY.	You must hear the sound distinctly.
distort (v)	TWIST (v)	DO NOT TWIST THE PIPE WHEN YOU TURN THE CONNECTORS	Do not distort the pipe when turning the connectors.
distribute (v)	APPLY (v)	APPLY THE LOAD EQUALLY ON THE AREA.	Distribute the load evenly over the area.
	SUPPLY (v)	THE SYSTEM SUPPLIES HYDRAULIC POWER.	The system distributes hydraulic power.
distribution (n)	SUPPLY (n)	THE FUEL SUPPLY IS FROM THE COLLECTOR TANKS.	The fuel distribution is from the collector tanks.
disturb (v)	MOVE (v)	DO NOT MOVE THE TIMING WHEN YOU INSTALL THE DISTRIBUTOR.	Do not disturb the timing during the distributor installation.
	CHANGE (v)	DO NOT CHANGE THE SEQUENCE OF THE WORK STEPS IN THE TEST.	Do not disturb the sequence of the work steps in the test.

Word (part of speech)	Approved meaning / ALTERNATIVES	APPROVED EXAMPLE	Not approved example
DIVIDE (v), DIVIDES, DIVIDED, DIVIDED	1. To separate into parts or groups	YOU CAN DIVIDE THE DRAINS INTO THREE GROUPS.	
		THE PRESSURE LINES DIVIDE AND GO IN DIFFERENT DIRECTIONS.	
	2. To do mathematical division	TO FIND THE MIDDLE POINT, DIVIDE THE MEASURED CLEARANCE BY TWO.	
DO (v), DOES, DID, DONE	1. To complete a procedure, task, or step	DO A FUNCTIONAL TEST.	
	2. As a helping verb a. As part of a negative command or statement	DO NOT BREATHE THE SOLVENT FUMES.	
	b. As part of a question	DOES THE LIGHT COME ON?	
don (v)	USE (v)	USE PROTECTIVE GOGGLES WHEN YOU DO WORK ON FIRE EXTINGUISHERS.	You must don protective goggles when working on fire extinguishers.
	PUT ON (v)	PUT THE MASK ON AND BREATHE THROUGH IT TO MAKE SURE THAT THE OXYGEN SUPPLY IS CORRECT.	Don the mask and breathe through it to check the oxygen supply.
double (adj)	TWO (TN)	YOU MUST SEE TWO MARKS ON THE STAND.	Double marks must appear on the stand.
doubt (n)	NOT SURE	IF YOU ARE NOT SURE THAT THE UNIT IS SERVICEABLE . DISCARD IT.	If there are doubts about the serviceability of the unit, discard it.
	THINK (v)	IF YOU THINK THAT THE RESULTS ARE INCORRECT, DO THE TEST AGAIN.	If you are in doubt about the results, repeat the test.

ASD STE 100

Word (part of speech)	Approved meaning / ALTERNATIVES	APPROVED EXAMPLE	Not approved example
DOWN (adj)	In a position below	MAKE SURE THAT THE ANCHOR IS DOWN.	
DOWN (adv)	To a position below	THE POINTER MOVES DOWN.	
DOWN (prep)	To a position below	LET THE SLEEVE MOVE DOWN THE GUIDE TUBE.	
DOWNSTREAM (adj)	In the direction of the flow	DISCONNECT THE DOWNSTREAM CONNECTION.	
DOWNSTREAM (adv)	In the direction of the flow	MOVE THE PROBE DOWNSTREAM AND MONITOR THE TEMPERATURE AGAIN.	
DOWNSTREAM OF (prep)	In the direction of the flow	DISCONNECT THE CONNECTION WHICH IS DOWNSTREAM OF THE VALVE.	
downward (adv)	DOWN (adv)	MAKE SURE THAT THE AIR OUTLET POINTS DOWN.	Make sure that the air outlet is positioned downward.
drag (v)	PULL (v)	PULL THE WIRES THROUGH THE CONDUIT.	Drag the wires through the conduit.
	You can use this word as a technical verb for computer processes and applications	DRAG THE ICON TO A NEW POSITION.	
DRAIN (v), DRAINS, DRAINED, DRAINED	To remove liquid	DRAIN THE SYSTEM FULLY.	
draw (v)	MAKE (v)	MAKE A LINE ON THE BLADE.	Draw a line on the blade.
	PULL (v)	PULL THE WIRE OUT OF THE CONDUIT.	Draw the wire out of the conduit.

Word (part of speech)	Approved meaning / ALTERNATIVES	APPROVED EXAMPLE	Not approved example
dress (v)	USE (v)	USE PROTECTIVE CLOTHING BEFORE YOU GO INTO THE FUEL TANK.	Dress suitably before entering the fuel tank.
	PUT ON (v)	PUT ON PROTECTIVE CLOTHING BEFORE YOU GO INTO THE FUEL TANK.	Dress suitably before entering the fuel tank.
drift (v)	MOVE (v)	THE HORIZON BAR CAN MOVE A SMALL DISTANCE.	The horizon bar may drift slightly.
	REMOVE (v) (WITH A DRIFT [TN])	REMOVE THE PIN FROM ITS HOLE. USE A DRIFT.	Drift the pin from its hole.
DRINK (v), DRINKS, DRANK, DRUNK	To consume liquid	DO NOT DRINK IN THE WORK AREA.	
	For safety instructions, use: SWALLOW (v)	DO NOT SWALLOW THE SOLVENT	Do not drink the solvent.
drive (v)	MOVE (v)	THE ACTUATOR MOVES TO ZERO.	The actuator is driven to zero.
	REMOVE (v)	REMOVE THE LOCKBOLT FROM THE HOLE.	Drive the lockbolt out of the hole.
	OPERATE (v)	A HYDRAULIC MOTOR OPERATES THE PUMP.	A hydraulic motor drives the pump.
droop (v)	MOVE (v)	IF YOU DO NOT INSTALL THE RIGGING PIN, THE ELEVATORS WILL MOVE DOWN WHEN THERE IS NO PRESSURE IN THE SYSTEM.	If you do not install the rigging pin, the elevators will droop when there is no pressure in the system.
DROP (n)	A small quantity of liquid in a spherical shape	MAKE SURE THAT NO DROPS OF ADHESIVE FALL ONTO THE MATERIAL.	

Word (part of speech)	Approved meaning / ALTERNATIVES	APPROVED EXAMPLE	Not approved example
drop (v)	FALL (v)	PARTICLES THAT FALL INTO THE INTAKE CAN CAUSE DAMAGE.	Particles that drop into the intake may cause damage.
	DECREASE (v)	THE PRESSURE DECREASES WHILE THE TIRES BECOME COOL.	The pressure drops as the tires cool.
DRY (adj) (DRIER, DRIEST)	Without liquid or moisture	MAKE SURE THAT THE SURFACE IS DRY.	
DRY (v), DRIES, DRIED, DRIED	To remove liquid or moisture, or to become dry	DRY THE FILTER IN AN OVEN	
		LET THE PAINT DRY AT AMBIENT TEMPERATURE.	
due to (prep)	BECAUSE OF (prep)	BECAUSE OF THE SMALL DIAMETER OF THE HOLE, THE FLOW IS LOW.	Due to the small diameter of the hole, the flow is low.
	BECAUSE (conj)	THE SHAFT MOVED BECAUSE THE ACTUATOR OPERATED.	The shaft moved due to the actuator action.
dull (adj)	DIM (adj)	THE LAMP COMES ON WITH A DIM LIGHT.	The lamp comes on with a dull light.
	MATT (adj)	THE LETTERS WILL BE MATT BLACK ON WHITE.	The letters will be dull black on a white background.
duration (n)	DURING (prep)	DO NOT MAKE ADJUSTMENTS DURING THIS TEST.	Do not make adjustments for the duration of this test.
DURING (prep)	In or for a specified time	MONITOR THE INDICATIONS DURING THE RETRACTION TEST.	
dust (v)	APPLY (v)	APPLY TALCUM POWDER TO THE AREA.	Dust the area with talcum powder.

Word (part of speech)	Approved meaning / ALTERNATIVES	APPROVED EXAMPLE	Not approved example
EACH (adj)	Every one of two or more objects or persons, seen together as a group but identified separately	MAKE SURE THAT THE SWITCH IN EACH PANEL IS SET TO "OFF".	
EACH (pron)	Every one of two or more objects or persons, seen together as a group but identified separately	INSTALL TWO SPACERS, EACH WITH A THICKNESS OF 3.5 mm.	
EACH OTHER (pron)	Each of two or more in reciprocal action or relation	WHEN YOU REMOVE THE PROBES, DO NOT LET THEM TOUCH EACH OTHER.	
early (adj)	SHORT (adj)	IF THE FILTERS BECOME CLOGGED AFTER AN UNUSUALLY SHORT TIME, SEND THEM TO THE LABORATORY FOR ANALYSIS OF THE CONTAMINATION.	If the filters clog at an unusually early stage, send them to the laboratory for analysis of the contamination.
earth (n)	GROUND (n)	MAKE SURE THAT THE ELECTRICAL SUPPLY GOES TO GROUND.	Make sure the electric supply goes to earth.
earth (v)	GROUND (v)	MAKE SURE THAT THE FUEL TANKS ARE CORRECTLY GROUNDED.	Make sure the fuel tanks are correctly earthed.
ease (n)	EASILY (adv)	MAKE SURE THAT YOU CAN MOVE THE HANDLE EASILY.	The handle must move with ease.
	EASY (adj)	MAKE SURE THAT IT IS EASY TO MOVE THE HANDLE.	The handle must move with ease.
ease (v)	CAREFULLY REMOVE	CAREFULLY REMOVE THE TRIM COVER FROM THE ADHESIVE TAPE.	Ease the trim cover from the adhesive tape.
	CAREFULLY MOVE	CAREFULLY MOVE THE PIPE INTO THE CORRECT POSITION.	Ease the pipe into the right position

Word (part of speech)	Approved meaning / ALTERNATIVES	APPROVED EXAMPLE	Not approved example
EASILY (adv)	Without difficulty	OXIDATION OCCURS VERY EASILY	
EASY (adj) (EASIER, EASIEST)	Without difficulty	USE THE LEFT OPENING FOR EASY ACCESS.	
EAT (v), EATS,	To consume food	DO NOT EAT IN THE WORK AREA.	
ATE, EATEN	For safety instructions, use : SWALLOW (v)	DO NOT SWALLOW THE POTTING COMPOUND.	Do not eat the potting compound.
EDGE (n)	A line that is the intersection of two surfaces of a solid object	THE DISTANCE BETWEEN THE EDGE OF THE PANEL AND THE PARTITION MUST NOT BE MORE THAN 0.05 mm.	
EFFECT (n)	The result of a cause	WHEN DUST MIXES WITH OIL, IT HAS AN ABRASIVE EFFECT.	
effect (v)	DO (v)	DO THE TIGHTENING PROCEDURE.	Effect the tightening procedure.
effective (adj)	GOOD (adj)	THIS MATERIAL GIVES GOOD PROTECTION FROM CORROSION.	This material provides effective protection from corrosion.
efficacious (adj)	GOOD (adj)	THIS IS A GOOD PROCEDURE TO REMOVE PAINT.	This is an efficacious way to remove paint.
efficient (adj)	SATISFACTORY (adj)	THE TRANSMISSION CONTROL PROTOCOL IS NOT SATISFACTORY FOR THE TRANSMISSION OF INTERACTIVE TRAFFIC.	The Transmission Control Protocol is not efficient for the transmission of interactive traffic.

Word (part of speech)	Approved meaning / ALTERNATIVES	APPROVED EXAMPLE	Not approved example
efficiently (adv)	SATISFACTORILY (adv)	MAKE SURE THAT THE UNIT OPERATES SATISFACTORILY.	Make sure the unit operates efficiently.
efflux (n)	EXHAUST (n)	MAKE SURE THAT THERE ARE SAFETY BARRIERS AROUND THE ENGINE EXHAUST AREA.	Ensure that there are safety barriers around the engine efflux area.
effort (n)	FORCE (TN)	DO NOT TIGHTEN THE BOLTS WITH TOO MUCH FORCE.	Do not use too much effort to tighten the bolts.
	TRY (v)	FIRST, TRY TO TURN THE SHAFT WITH YOUR HANDS.	First, make an effort to turn the shaft with your hands.
either (adj)	ONE (TN) OF THE TWO(TN)	IF THERE IS MERCURY CONTAMINATION IN ONE OF THE TWO COMPARTMENTS, CLEAN THE AREA IMMEDIATELY.	If there is mercury spillage in either compartment, clean the area immediately.
either (conj)	ONE (TN) OF THE TWO(TN)	YOU CAN USE A RED PEN OR A GREEN PEN.	You can use either a red pen or a green pen.
either (pron)	ONE (TN) OF THE TWO(TN)	APPLY ELECTRICAL POWER TO ONE OF THE TWO SOLENOIDS	Apply electrical power to either of the solenoids.
EJECT (v), EJECTS, EJECTED, EJECTED	To move or to cause a person or item to move from an aircraft or equipment with force	IF YOU PULL THE EJECTION SEAT HANDLE, THE SEAT WILL EJECT.	
ejection (n)	EJECT (v)	PUSH THE APPLICABLE BUTTON TO EJECT THE DISK DRIVE.	Push the applicable button for disk drive ejection.
elapse (v)	TIME (n)	MAKE SURE THAT THE TIME BETWEEN STARTS IS A MINIMUM OF 30 SECONDS.	Check that 30 seconds have elapsed between starts.
	AFTER (prep)	AFTER 30 SECONDS, DO THE TEST AGAIN	When 30 seconds have elapsed, do the test again.
	INTERVAL (n)	AT INTERVALS OF SIX MONTHS, DO THE CHECK OF THE OIL LEVEL	When six months have elapsed, do the check of the oil level.

ASD STE 100

Word (part of speech)	Approved meaning / ALTERNATIVES	APPROVED EXAMPLE	Not approved example
ELECTRIC (adj)	Operated by electricity	IF THE HYDRAULIC PUMP DOES NOT SUPPLY A PRESSURE OF 3000 PSI, USE THE ELECTRIC PUMP.	
ELECTRICAL (adj)	Related to electricity	SUPPLY ELECTRICAL POWER TO THE SYSTEM.	
ELECTRICALLY (adv)	Related to or operated by electricity	THE SYSTEM IS HYDRAULICALLY OPERATED AND ELECTRICALLY CONTROLLED.	
ELECTRO-MAGNETIC (adj)	Related to electromagnetism	THE ELECTRO-MAGNETIC TEST PROCEDURE USES ELECTROMAGNETIC FORCE.	
ELECTRO-MAGNETICALLY (adv)	Related to electromagnetism	THE SYSTEM HOLDS THE POSITION ELECTRO-MAGNETICALLY.	
ELECTRONIC (adj)	Related to or operated by electronics	THIS BAY CONTAINS SOME OF THE ELECTRONIC EQUIPMENT.	
ELECTRONICALLY (adv)	Related to or operated by electronics	THIS UNIT IS ELECTRONICALLY CONTROLLED.	
eliminate (v)	REMOVE (v)	REMOVE ALL SHARP EDGES.	Eliminate all sharp edges.
	STOP (v)	PUT A BAG OF DESICCANT IN THE PACKAGE TO STOP CONDENSATION.	Put a bag of desiccant in the package to eliminate condensation.
	PREVENT (v)	PUT A BAG OF DESICCANT IN THE PACKAGE TO PREVENT CONDENSATION.	Put a bag of desiccant in the package to eliminate condensation.

Word (part of speech)	Approved meaning / ALTERNATIVES	APPROVED EXAMPLE	Not approved example
EMERGENCY (n)	A condition that occurs suddenly and is dangerous	IN AN EMERGENCY, BREAK THE GLASS.	
emit (v)	FROM (prep)	THE VAPORS FROM THIS MATERIAL ARE DANGEROUS TO THE SKIN.	The vapors that this material emits are dangerous to the skin.
employ (v)	USE (v)	TYPE B USES A LOOSE COLLAR.	Type B employs a loose collar.
EMPTY (adj)	Without contents	MAKE SURE THAT THE RESERVOIR IS EMPTY.	
empty (v)	REMOVE (v)	REMOVE ALL FUEL FROM THE FUEL TANKS.	Empty the fuel tanks.
enable (v)	LET (v)	THE DISASSEMBLY FIXTURE LETS YOU DISASSEMBLE THE MODULE.	The disassembly fixture enables you to disassemble the module.
encircle (v)	AROUND (prep)	PUT SEALANT AROUND EACH SCREW HOLE.	Encircle each screw hole with sealant.
enclosed (adj)	CLOSED (adj)	IF YOU USE SOLVENT IN A CLOSED SPACE, MAKE SURE THAT THERE IS GOOD AIRFLOW IN THE WORK AREA.	The work area must be well-ventilated if solvent is used in an enclosed space.
encounter (v)	BE (v)	IF THERE ARE ROUGH AREAS, REMOVE THEM WITH EMERY CLOTH.	If rough spots are encountered, remove them with emery cloth.
	FIND (v)	IF YOU FIND ROUGH AREAS, REMOVE THEM WITH EMERY CLOTH.	If rough spots are encountered, remove them with emery cloth.
END (n)	Where time, distance, or sequence are completed	EXAMINE THE SHACKLE AT THE END OF THE SLING	

ASD STE 100

Word (part of speech)	Approved meaning / ALTERNATIVES	APPROVED EXAMPLE	Not approved example
end (v)	STOP (v)	STOP THE TEST.	End the test.
	COMPLETE (v)	WHEN YOU COMPLETED THE TEST, REMOVE THE SENSOR.	When the test has ended, remove the sensor.
		WHEN THE TEST IS COMPLETED, REMOVE THE SENSOR.	When the test has ended, remove the sensor.
ENERGIZE (v), ENERGIZES, ENERGIZED, ENERGIZED	To supply electrical power to	ENERGIZE THE AC AND DC BUSBARS.	
enforce (v)	OBEY (v)	ALL PERSONNEL MUST OBEY THE SAFETY PRECAUTIONS.	Safety precautions must be enforced.
ENGAGE (v), ENGAGES, ENGAGED, ENGAGED	To correctly align and come together	ENGAGE THE CLUTCH.	
		MAKE SURE THAT THE CLUTCH ENGAGES.	
engagement (n)	ENGAGE (v)	MAKE SURE THAT THE SPLINES ENGAGE FULLY.	Make sure there is full engagement of the splines.
enlarge (v)	INCREASE (v)	INCREASE THE DIAMETER OF THE RIVET HOLE.	Enlarge the rivet hole diameter.
	LARGE (adj)	MAKE THE HOLES LARGER.	Enlarge the holes.
enough (adj)	SUFFICIENT (adj)	MAKE SURE THAT THERE IS SUFFICIENT PRESSURE IN THE ACCUMULATOR.	Make sure that there is enough pressure in the accumulator.
ensue (v)	CAUSE (v)	INCORRECT INSTALLATION WILL CAUSE DAMAGE.	Damage will ensue from incorrect installation.
ensure (v)	MAKE SURE (v)	MAKE SURE THAT THE CORRECT SEALS ARE INSTALLED.	Ensure that the correct seals are installed.

Word (part of speech)	Approved meaning / ALTERNATIVES	APPROVED EXAMPLE	Not approved example
entail (v)	MUST (v)	FOR THIS PROCEDURE, YOU MUST USE SPECIAL TOOLS.	This procedure entails the use of special tools.
enter (v)	GO INTO	DO NOT GO INTO THE ENGINE TEST AREA WITHOUT APPROVAL.	Do not enter the engine test area without approval.
	RECORD (v)	RECORD THE DATA IN THE LOGBOOK.	Enter the data in the logbook.
	ENTRY (n)	MAKE AN ENTRY IN THE LOGBOOK TO SHOW THAT YOU DID THE DEACTIVATION PROCEDURE.	Enter in the logbook that you did the deactivation procedure.
	You can use this word as a technical verb for computer processes and applications.	ENTER YOUR PASSWORD.	
entire (adj)	FULL (adj)	MAKE A SCAN OF THE FULL RANGE OF FREQUENCIES AVAILABLE.	Scan the entire range of frequencies available.
	ALL (adj)	EXAMINE ALL OF THE SYSTEM TO FIND THE CAUSE OF THE INTERFERENCE.	Check the entire system to determine the cause of interference.
entirely (adv)	FULLY (adv)	THE SYSTEM IS FULLY AUTOMATIC.	The system is entirely automatic.
ENTRANCE (n)	An opening to go into a space	PUT SAFETY BARRIERS AT THE ENTRANCE TO THE WORK AREA.	
ENTRY (n)	A record of an occurrence	MAKE AN ENTRY IN THE LOG CARD.	
EQUAL (adj)	The same dimension, quality, quantity, or number	MAKE SURE THAT THERE IS AN EQUAL DISTANCE BETWEEN THE HOLES.	

Word (part of speech)	Approved meaning / ALTERNATIVES	APPROVED EXAMPLE	Not approved example
equal (v)	SAME (adj)	DIMENSION "X" MUST BE THE SAME AS DIMENSION "Z".	Dimension X must equal dimension Z.
	EQUAL (adj)	DIMENSION "X" MUST BE EQUAL TO DIMENSION "Y".	Dimension X must equal dimension Y.
EQUALLY (adv)	The same dimension, quality, quantity, or number	ADJUST THE TURNBUCKLES EQUALLY.	
equip (v)	INSTALL (v)	INSTALL THE SHUTOFF VALVES ON EACH HP MANIFOLD.	Equip each HP manifold with shutoff valves.
EQUIPMENT (n)	The objects or tools used for operation and maintenance	REMOVE ALL THE EQUIPMENT FROM THE WORK AREA.	
equipped (adj)	HAVE (v)	BE CAREFUL WHEN YOU MOVE JET PIPES OR EXHAUST CONES THAT HAVE INSULATING BLANKETS.	Be careful when handling jet pipes or exhaust cones equipped with insulating blankets.
EQUIVALENT (adj)	Has the same properties, functions, or values	MATERIALS (REF. No. 2) AND (REF. No. 18) ARE EQUIVALENT.	
EQUIVALENT (n)	Something that has the same properties, functions, or values	USE CLEANING COMPOUND ARDROX 6025, OR AN EQUIVALENT.	
ERASE (v), ERASES, ERASED, ERASED	To remove data from a medium	ERASE THE TAPE.	
erect (v)	ASSEMBLE (v)	ASSEMBLE THE MOVABLE HOIST BEFORE YOU LIFT THE GEARBOX.	Erect the movable hoist before lifting the gearbox.
	BECOME STABLE	LET THE VERTICAL GYRO BECOME STABLE.	Give the vertical gyro time to erect.
erratic (adj)	IRREGULAR (adj)	THE OPERATION OF THE COMPASS IS IRREGULAR	The compass is erratic.

Word (part of speech)	Approved meaning / ALTERNATIVES	APPROVED EXAMPLE	Not approved example
ERROR (n)	The difference from that which is correct or accurate	IF THE ERROR IS MORE THAN 3 DEG., CALIBRATE THE COMPASS.	
escape (v)	DEFLATE (v)	DEFLATE THE TIRE.	Let the air escape from the tire.
	RELEASE (v)	RELEASE ALL THE NITROGEN.	Allow all the nitrogen to escape.
essential (adj)	NECESSARY (adj)	HYDRAULIC POWER IS NOT NECESSARY.	Use of hydraulic power is not essential.
	MUST (v)	YOU MUST COMPLETE THE TEST.	It is essential to complete the test.
establish (v)	MAKE SURE (v)	IN THIS STEP, YOU WILL MAKE SURE THAT THE FUEL PUMP OPERATES CORRECTLY.	The following step establishes the correct functioning of the fuel pump.
ESTIMATE (n)	A calculated, approximate result	MAKE AN ESTIMATE OF THE NECESSARY QUANTITY.	
estimate (v)	ESTIMATE (n)	MAKE AN ESTIMATE OF THE QUANTITY OF CLEANING FLUID THAT IS NECESSARY.	Estimate the amount of cleaning fluid that is necessary.
evaluate (v)	EXAMINE (v)	EXAMINE THE DAMAGE AFTER AN ACCIDENT.	Evaluate the damage after an accident.
	ANALYSIS (TN)	MAKE AN ANALYSIS OF THE TEST RESULTS.	Evaluate the test results.
evaluation (n)	EXAMINE (v)	EXAMINE THE DAMAGE.	Do an evaluation of the damage.
	ANALYSIS (TN)	MAKE AN ANALYSIS OF THE TEST RESULTS.	Do an evaluation of the test results.
evaporate (v)	DRY (v)	LET THE COMPOUND DRY.	Allow the solvent to evaporate from the compound.

ASD STE 100

Word (part of speech)	Approved meaning / ALTERNATIVES	APPROVED EXAMPLE	Not approved example
even (adj)	SMOOTH (adj)	A GUIDE ROD IS ATTACHED TO THE METAL BELLOWS DISC FOR A SMOOTH MOVEMENT OF THE BELLOWS.	A guide rod is attached to the metal bellows disc for an even movement of the bellows.
	SAME (adj)	APPLY THE SAME LOAD ON THE TWO BRAKES.	Braking must be even on the two brakes.
	FLAT (adj)	MAKE SURE THAT THE SURFACE IS FLAT.	Ensure the surface is even.
	FLUSH (adj)	MAKE SURE THAT THE FASTENER HEADS ARE FLUSH WITH THE SKIN.	Make sure that the fastener heads are even with the skin.
	LEVEL (adj)	MAKE SURE THAT THE MARK ON THE BOLT IS LEVEL WITH THE MARK ON THE HANDLE.	Make sure that the mark on the bolt is even with the mark on the handle.
evenly (adv)	GRADUALLY (adv)	INCREASE THE TEMPERATURE GRADUALLY.	Increase the temperature evenly.
	EQUALLY (adv)	APPLY THE LOAD EQUALLY ON THE AREA.	Apply the load evenly on the area.
event (n)	IF (conj)	IF THE PRESSURE DECREASES SUDDENLY, CLOSE THE VALVE.	In the event of a sudden dropping of pressure, close the valve.
eventually (adv)	SOME TIME	IF THE CABLE RUBS, IT WILL BREAK AFTER SOME TIME.	If the cable chafes, it will eventually break.
every (adj)	ALL (adj)	REMOVE ALL SAFETY PINS BEFORE FLIGHT.	Every safety pin must be removed before flight.
	EACH (adj)	SET THE BTRY SWITCH TO "ON" EACH TIME.	It is necessary to set the BTRY switch to ON every time.
	INTERVAL (n)	DO AN INSPECTION AT INTERVALS OF 20,000 FLIGHT HOURS.	Do an inspection every 20,000 flight hours.

Word (part of speech)	Approved meaning / ALTERNATIVES	APPROVED EXAMPLE	Not approved example
evidence (n)	INDICATION (n)	IF THERE IS AN INDICATION OF A LEAK, REPLACE THE VALVE.	If there is evidence of a leak, replace the valve.
	SIGN (n)	ONE SIGN OF A LEAK OF HOT AIR FROM A JOINT IS THAT THE TEMPERATURE INDICATION DECREASES.	Evidence of a leak of hot air from a joint is that the temperature reading drops.
	SHOW (v)	REPLACE THE INSULATION BLANKETS THAT SHOW CHAFING.	Replace the insulation blankets with evidence of chafing.
evidence (v)	SHOW (v)	IF THE TEST SHOWS NO FAULT, CONTINUE THE PROCEDURE.	If no fault is evidenced by the test, continue the procedure.
	FIND (v)	IF YOU DO NOT FIND DAMAGE DURING THE INSPECTION PROCEDURE, ASSEMBLE THE UNIT.	If the inspection does not evidence any damage, assemble the unit.
evident (adj)	FIND (v)	IF YOU DO NOT FIND DAMAGE, CONTINUE THE INSPECTION.	If no damage is evident, continue the inspection.
exact (adj)	ACCURATE (adj)	IF THE INDICATION IS NOT ACCURATE, DO THE TEST AGAIN.	If the indication is not exact, do the test again.
	CORRECT (adj)	IF THE INDICATION IS NOT CORRECT, DO THE TEST AGAIN.	If the indication is not exact, do the test again.
exactly (adv)	ACCURATELY (adv)	PUT THE REPAIR SHEET ACCURATELY ON THE DAMAGED AREA.	Put the repair sheet exactly on the damaged area.
	FULLY (adv)	FIND THE BOLT HOLE THAT ALIGNS FULLY WITH ONE OF THE OUTER SLOTS.	Find the bolt hole that aligns exactly with one of the outer slots.
	CORRECT (adj)	THE SEAL MUST BE OF THE CORRECT DIMENSION FOR THE GROOVE.	The seal must fit the groove exactly.

Word (part of speech)	Approved meaning / ALTERNATIVES	APPROVED EXAMPLE	Not approved example
examination (n)	EXAMINE (v)	EXAMINE THE BLADE FOR CRACKS.	Do an examination of the blades for cracks.
	FIND (v)	IF YOU FIND CORROSION, REMOVE IT WITH THE SPECIFIED MATERIAL.	If the examination reveals corrosion, it must be removed with the specified material.
EXAMINE (v), EXAMINES, EXAMINED, EXAMINED	To look carefully at	EXAMINE THE COMPUTER FOR DAMAGE.	
EXAMPLE (n)	Something from a group which has the same qualities as the group	FIGURE 2 IS AN EXAMPLE OF A REPAIR PROCEDURE FOR A DAMAGED WEB.	
exceed (v)	MORE THAN	MAKE SURE THAT THE INDICATION IS NOT MORE THAN 400 KNOTS.	Ensure that the indication does not exceed 400 knots.
except (prep)	To replace this word, use a different construction. Be specific.	KEEP ALL THE PARTS THAT ARE SERVICEABLE AND DISCARD THOSE THAT ARE BROKEN.	Keep all parts except those that are broken.
		REMOVE ALL SCREWS, BUT NOT THE ONE ON THE LEFT SIDE OF THE FLANGE.	Remove all screws except the one on the left side of the flange.
exception (n)	To replace this word, use a different construction. Be specific.	KEEP ALL THE PARTS THAT ARE SERVICEABLE AND DISCARD THOSE THAT ARE BROKEN.	Keep all parts with the exception of those that are broken.
		REMOVE ALL SCREWS, BUT NOT THE ONE ON THE LEFT SIDE OF THE FLANGE.	Remove all screws with the exception of the one on the left side of the flange.
exceptional (adj)	UNUSUAL (adj)	IF YOU MUST APPLY UNUSUAL FORCE TO OPEN THE UNIT, EXAMINE THE CONTROL LINKAGE.	If exceptional force is needed to open the unit, examine the control linkage.

Word (part of speech)	Approved meaning / ALTERNATIVES	APPROVED EXAMPLE	Not approved example
exceptionally (adv)	UNUSUALLY (adv)	IF THE TIRE PRESSURE IS UNUSUALLY HIGH, OPEN THE VALVE.	If the tire pressure is exceptionally high, open the valve.
excess (adj)	TOO MUCH	DO NOT APPLY TOO MUCH ADHESIVE ON THE GASKET.	Do not apply excess adhesive on the gasket.
	MORE THAN	DO NOT PUT MORE THAN THE PERMITTED WEIGHT ON THE TROLLEY.	Do not put excess weight on the trolley.
	UNWANTED (adj)	REMOVE UNWANTED COMPOUND FROM THE GASKET.	Wipe excess ompound from the gasket.
	NOT NECESSARY	REMOVE ALL REMAINING SEALANT THAT IS NOT NECESSARY.	Remove all the excess sealant.
excess (n)	TOO MUCH	IF YOU USE TOO MUCH PAINT, THE FINISH WILL BE UNSATISFACTORY.	An excess of paint will give a poor finish.
	MORE THAN	THE HYDRAULIC PRESSURE MUST NOT BE MORE THAN 200 BARS.	The hydraulic pressure must not be in excess of 200 bars.
excessive (adj)	TOO MUCH	TOO MUCH FORCE CAN CAUSE DAMAGE TO THE SEAL.	Excessive force can damage the seal.
	MORE THAN	IF THE PRESSURE IS MORE THAN 1000 kPa, STOP THE TEST.	If the pressure is excessive, stop the test.
excessively (adv)	TOO MUCH	BE CAREFUL THAT YOU DO NOT TURN THE INNER RACES TOO MUCH.	Be careful not to excessively rotate the inner races.
	MORE THAN	IF THE OIL LEAKAGE IS MORE THAN FIVE DROPS A MINUTE, EXAMINE THE SEALANT.	If oil leaks excessively, check the sealant.

ASD STE 100

Word (part of speech)	Approved meaning / ALTERNATIVES	APPROVED EXAMPLE	Not approved example
exchange (v)	INTERCHANGE (v)	INTERCHANGE THE No. 1 AND No. 2 COMPUTERS. THEN DO THE TEST AGAIN.	Exchange the No. 1 and No. 2 computers. Then do the test again.
	REPLACE (v)	REPLACE THE O-RINGS.	Exchange the O-rings.
exclude (v)	NOT INCLUDE	THIS PROCEDURE DOES NOT INCLUDE THE REMOVAL OF THE PISTON.	This procedure excludes the removal of the piston.
	NOT USE	DO NOT USE OXYGEN.	Exclude the use of oxygen.
excluding (prep)	WITHOUT (prep)	THE WEIGHT OF THE UNIT, WITHOUT THE PUMP, IS 10 kg.	The weight of the unit, excluding the pump, is 10 kg.
execute (v)	DO (v)	DO THESE STEPS.	Execute the following operations.
exempt (adj)	NO (adj)	MAKE SURE THAT THERE ARE NO METAL PARTICLES IN THE OIL.	Ensure the oil is exempt from metal particles.
	NOT SHOW	MAKE SURE THAT THE SEALS DO NOT SHOW SIGNS OF DETERIORATION.	Ensure the seals are exempt from signs of deterioration.
exercise (v)	MAKE SURE (v)	MAKE SURE THAT YOU DO NOT GET ACID ON YOUR SKIN.	Exercise caution not to allow acid to contact skin.
	CAREFUL (adj)	BE CAREFUL THAT YOU DO NOT GET ACID ON YOUR SKIN.	Exercise caution not to allow acid to contact skin.
exert (v)	APPLY (v)	DO NOT APPLY PRESSURE TO THE AFT FLANGE.	Do not exert pressure on the aft flange.
exhale (v)	BREATHE (v)	BREATHE INTO THE OXYGEN MASK.	Exhale into the oxygen mask.
EXHAUST (n)	The gas from an engine	THE EXHAUST FROM THE APU IS DANGEROUS.	

Word (part of speech)	Approved meaning / ALTERNATIVES	APPROVED EXAMPLE	Not approved example
exhaust (v)	REMOVE (v)	USE A FAN TO REMOVE THE GASES.	Exhaust the gases using a fan.
	DECREASE (v)	DECREASE THE NITROGEN PRESSURE TO 120 PSI.	Exhaust the nitrogen pressure to 120 psi.
	RELEASE (v)	RELEASE THE HYDRAULIC PRESSURE IN THE ACCUMULATOR.	Exhaust all the hydraulic pressure in the accumulator.
exhaustive (adj)	ALL (adj)	ALL THE TEST CONDITIONS ARE GIVEN IN PARAGRAPH 2.0.	An exhaustive list of test conditions is given at paragraph 2.0.
	FULL (adj)	THIS IS NOT A FULL LIST.	The list is not exhaustive.
exist (v)	BE (v)	THERE ARE TWO DIFFERENT PROCEDURES FOR THIS REPAIR.	Two different procedures exist for this repair.
EXIT (n)	An opening to go out of a space	MAKE SURE THAT ALL THE EMERGENCY EXITS ARE CLEAR OF UNWANTED OBJECTS.	
EXPAND (v), EXPANDS, EXPANDED, EXPANDED	To increase in dimension, volume, or time	THE BELLOWS MUST EXPAND. HEAT EXPANDS THE GAS IN THE CONTAINER.	
expect (v)	POSSIBLE (adj)	IF IT IS POSSIBLE THAT THE TEMPERATURE WILL DECREASE TO -20 DEGREES C, REMOVE THE BATTERIES.	If temperature is expected to drop to -20 degrees C, remove the batteries.

Word (part of speech)	Approved meaning / ALTERNATIVES	APPROVED EXAMPLE	Not approved example
expel (v)	REMOVE (v)	REMOVE THE AIR BUBBLES FROM THE COMPOUND WITH A SPATULA.	Expel the air bubbles from the compound with a spatula.
	BLEED (v)	BLEED ALL NITROGEN FROM THE SYSTEM.	Expel all nitrogen from the system.
	RELEASE (v)	RELEASE ALL NITROGEN.	Expel all nitrogen.
EXPIRED (adj)	More than the permitted life	MAKE SURE THAT THE SHELF LIFE IS NOT EXPIRED.	
explain (v)	TELL (v)	TELL THE GROUND CREW THAT YOU WILL OPERATE THE SYSTEM.	Explain to the ground crew that you will operate the system.
EXPLOSION (n)	The effect when an explosive material quickly releases its energy	THIS CONDITION CAN CAUSE AN EXPLOSION.	
EXPLOSIVE (adj)	That can cause an explosion	THE SAFETY PRECAUTIONS THAT FOLLOW ARE APPLICABLE TO EXPLOSIVE ITEMS.	
expose (v)	GET (v)	REMOVE THE COVER ASSEMBLY TO GET ACCESS TO THE LAMP ASSEMBLY.	Remove cover assembly to expose lamp assembly.
EXTEND (v), EXTENDS, EXTENDED, EXTENDED	To increase, or cause something to increase, in dimension or range	FULLY EXTEND THE JACK RAM.	
		MAKE SURE THAT THE RODS EXTEND AND RETRACT.	
EXTENSION (n)	1. The action when something extends	MAKE SURE THAT THE EXTENSION OF THE ACTUATOR IS SMOOTH.	
	2. The result when something extends	THE TOTAL EXTENSION OF THE PISTON IS 125 mm.	

Word (part of speech)	Approved meaning / ALTERNATIVES	APPROVED EXAMPLE	Not approved example
extent (n)	DEPTH (n)	MEASURE THE DEPTH OF THE CRACK.	Measure the extent of the crack.
	LENGTH (n)	MEASURE THE LENGTH OF THE CRACK.	Measure the extent of the crack.
	WIDTH (n)	MEASURE THE WIDTH OF THE CRACK.	Measure the extent of the crack.
exterior (n)	EXTERNAL (adj)	EXAMINE THE EXTERNAL SURFACE OF THE CONTAINER.	EXAMINE THE EXTERNAL SURFACE OF THE CONTAINER.
EXTERNAL (adj)	Of, or on, the outer side	CONNECT THE EXTERNAL POWER SUPPLY.	
EXTERNALLY (adv)	Of, or on, the outer side	THE BOX IS INSTALLED EXTERNALLY.	
EXTINGUISH (v), EXTINGUISHES, EXTINGUISHED, EXTINGUISHED	To stop burning	TO EXTINGUISH A FIRE IN THE ENGINE, PULL THE "FIRE" HANDLE.	
	For lights or lamps, use	WHEN THE FLAME EXTINGUISHES, STOP THE ENGINE TEST	
	GO OFF	THE AUTO BRK PUSHBUTTON LIGHT GOES OFF.	THE AUTO BRK PUSHBUTTON LIGHT GOES OFF.
	BE OFF	MAKE SURE THAT THE GREEN LIGHT ON THE PANEL IS OFF.	Make sure that the green light on the panel extinguishes
extra (adj)	MORE (adj)	THIS MATERIAL GIVES MORE PROTECTION.	This material provides extra protection
extract (v)	REMOVE (v)	REMOVE THE BOLT	Extract the bolt.

Word (part of speech)	Approved meaning / ALTERNATIVES	APPROVED EXAMPLE	Not approved example
extreme (adj)	VERY HIGH (adj)	DO NOT APPLY VERY HIGH LOADS.	Do not apply extreme loads.
	VERY BAD (adj)	WHEN THE WEATHER IS VERY BAD, KEEP THESE PARTS IN A DRY AREA.	In extreme weather conditions, keep these parts in a dry area.
	VERY COLD (adj)	MAKE SURE THAT YOU KNOW THE RISKS RELATED TO VERY COLD TEMPERATURES.	Make sure that you know the risks related to extreme cold temperatures.
	VERY HOT (adj)	MAKE SURE THAT YOU KNOW THE RISKS RELATED TO VERY HOT TEMPERATURES.	Make sure that you know the risks related to extreme hot temperatures.
extremely (adv)	VERY (adv)	IT IS VERY IMPORTANT TO OBEY THE FUEL SAFETY PRECAUTIONS.	It is extremely important to observe the fuel safety precautions.
exude (v)	OUT OF (prep)	MAKE SURE THAT NEW GREASE COMES OUT OF THE JOINT.	Make sure fresh grease exudes from the joint.

Word (part of speech)	Approved meaning / ALTERNATIVES	APPROVED EXAMPLE	Not approved example
fabricate (v)	MAKE (v)	USE COPPER TO MAKE THE CHILL BLOCK.	Use copper to fabricate the chill block.
FACE (n)	The front surface of an object	CLEAN THE FACE OF THE INDICATOR.	
	💡 This word is a technical name when it is referred to a part of the body.	WHEN YOU DO MAINTENANCE ON THE WASTE WATER SYSTEM, DO NOT TOUCH YOUR FACE WITH YOUR GLOVES.	
face (v)	POINT (v)	WHEN YOU INSTALL THE PITOT HEAD, MAKE SURE THAT THE OPENING POINTS FORWARD.	When installing the pitot head, make sure that the opening is facing forward.
		TURN YOUR FACE AWAY FROM THE DRAIN VALVE BEFORE YOU PUSH THE VALVE STEM DOWN.	Face away from the drain valve when pushing the valve stem down.
facilitate (v)	HELP (v)	IDENTIFY THE COMPONENT WITH A CODE TO HELP YOU TO CORRECTLY INSTALL IT AGAIN.	Mark the component with a code that will facilitate its correct reinstallation.
	MAKE ⋯ EASIER	THIS MAKES FAULT ISOLATION EASIER.	This facilitates fault isolation.
facility (n)	💡 Be specific. Use the name of the facility as a technical name.	WEIGH THE AIRCRAFT ON A WEIGHBRIDGE	You need a special facility to weigh the aircraft.
FACT (n)	Something that occurred or is correct.	GET ALL THE FACTS ABOUT THE INCIDENT FROM THE PILOT.	
factor (n)	CAUSE (n)	THERE CAN BE MANY CAUSES FOR CORROSION.	Corrosion can be caused by several factors.

Word (part of speech)	Approved meaning / ALTERNATIVES	APPROVED EXAMPLE	Not approved example
fail (v)	IF ⋯ NOT	IF YOU DO NOT OBEY THESE INSTRUCTIONS, THERE IS A RISK OF INJURY.	If you fail to comply with these instructions, there is a risk of injury.
	FAILURE (TN)	IF YOU DO NOT OBEY THE PROCEDURE CORRECTLY, FAILURE OF THE EMERGENCY FLOTATION GEAR CAN OCCUR.	If you do not follow the procedure correctly, the emergency flotation gear can fail.
	UNSATISFACTORY (adj)	IF THE TEST RESULTS UNSATISFACTORY, DO THE FAULT ISOLATION PROCEDURE	If the test fails, do the fault isolation procedure.
failed (adj)	DEFECTIVE (adj)	REPLACE THE DEFECTIVE PUMP	Replace the failed pump.
	UNSERVICEABLE (adj)	REPLACE THE UNSERVICEABLE VALVE.	Replace the failed valve.
failure (n)	IF ⋯ NOT	IF YOU DO NOT OBEY THESE INSTRUCTIONS, THERE IS A RISK OF INJURY.	Failure to comply with these instructions, will result in a risk of injury.
	💡 This word when it means a performance error or loss of serviceability is a technical name	CONTAMINATION CAN CAUSE A FAILURE OF THE PUMP.	
faint (adj)	DIM (adj)	IF THE LIGHT IS TOO DIM, REPLACE THE BATTERY.	If the light is faint, replace the battery.
	INTENSITY (n) 💡 Refer also to BRIGHT (adj).	TURN THE KNOB COUNTERCLOCKWISE TO DECREASE THE INTENSITY OF THE LIGHT.	Turn the knob anticlockwise to make the light fainter.

Word (part of speech)	Approved meaning / ALTERNATIVES	APPROVED EXAMPLE	Not approved example
fall (n)	DECREASE (v)	WHEN THE PRESSURE DECREASES, THE INDICATOR SHOWS THAT THERE IS A LEAK.	When there is a fall in pressure, the indicator shows a leak.
FALL (v), FALLS, FELL, FALLEN	To move down by the force of gravity	MAKE SURE THAT THE TOOLS DO NOT FALL INTO THE ENGINE.	
false (adj)	INCORRECT (adj)	MAKE SURE THAT THERE ARE NO INCORRECT INDICATIONS ON THE INSTRUMENTS.	Make sure there are no false indications on the instruments.
falter (v)	SMOOTHLY (adv)	MAKE SURE THAT THE GENERATOR OPERATES SMOOTHLY.	Make sure that the generator does not falter.
	CONSTANT (adj)	MAKE SURE THAT THE PRESSURE STAYS CONSTANT.	Make sure that the pressure does not falter.
familiar (adj)	KNOW (v)	ALL PERSONNEL MUST FULLY KNOW THE SAFETY PRECAUTIONS.	All personnel must be thoroughly familiar with the safety precautions.
FAR (adj) (FARTHER, FARTHEST)	At or to a relatively large distance	REMOVE THE BOLT THAT IS FARTHEST FROM THE CENTER.	
fashion (n)	PROCEDURE (n)	USE THIS PROCEDURE TO DO THE TASK.	Carry out the task in this fashion.
FAST (adj) (FASTER, FASTEST)	At high speed	A FAST MOVEMENT OF THE THROTTLE WILL CAUSE A SURGE.	
fast (adv)	QUICKLY (adv)	DO NOT LET THE CABIN ALTITUDE CHANGE TOO QUICKLY.	Do not let the cabin altitude change too fast.

ASD STE 100

Word (part of speech)	Approved meaning / ALTERNATIVES	APPROVED EXAMPLE	Not approved example
fasten (v)	ATTACH (v)	ATTACH THE TWO STRINGERS TOGETHER WITH RIVETS.	Fasten the two stringers together with rivets.
	CONNECT (v)	CONNECT THE HOSE TO THE TEST EQUIPMENT.	Fasten the hose to the test equipment.
fatal (adj)	KILL (v)	HIGH VOLTAGE IN THE ELECTRONIC SYSTEM CAN KILL YOU.	High voltage in the electronic system can be fatal.
faulty (adj)	DEFECTIVE (adj)	REPLACE ALL DEFECTIVE ELECTRONIC COMPONENTS.	All faulty electronic components must be replaced.
	INCORRECT (adj)	AN INCORRECT ADJUSTMENT OF THE PRESSURE REGULATOR CAN BE DANGEROUS.	Faulty adjustment of the pressure regulator can be dangerous.
	UNSERVICEABLE (adj)	REPLACE THE UNSERVICEABLE CONTROL UNIT.	Replace the faulty control unit.
	UNSATISFACTORY (adj)	UNSATISFACTORY OPERATION OF THE SYSTEM CAN CAUSE DAMAGE.	Faulty operation of the system can
fear (v)	THINK (v)	DO A TEST OF THE UNIT IF YOU THINK THAT THERE IS A PROBLEM WITH ITS OPERATION.	Test the unit if you fear that there is a problem with its operation.
	MAKE SURE (v)	DO A TEST OF THE UNIT TO MAKE SURE THAT THERE IS NO PROBLEM WITH ITS OPERATION.	Test the unit if you fear that there is a problem with its operation.
feasible (adj)	POSSIBLE (adj)	DO THE PROCEDURE MANUALLY IF IT IS NOT POSSIBLE TO USE THE AUTOMATIC CONTROL.	Do the manual procedure if it is not feasible to use the automatic control.
	CAN (CANNOT) (v)	IF YOU CANNOT REMOVE THE BOLT, YOU MUST CUT IT.	If it is not feasible to remove the bolt, you must cut it.

Word (part of speech)	Approved meaning / ALTERNATIVES	APPROVED EXAMPLE	Not approved example
FEATHER (v), FEATHERS, FEATHERED, FEATHERED	To put a propeller to a position of minimum drag	PUT THE CONDITION LEVER IN THE FTR POSITION TO FEATHER THE PROPELLER.	
feature (v)	HAVE (v)	THESE NUTS HAVE A FLAT FLANGE.	These nuts feature a flat flange
feed (v)	PUT (v)	PUT THE WIRE THROUGH THE CONDUIT.	Feed the wire through the conduit.
	SUPPLY (v)	SUPPLY COOL AIR TO THE CABIN.	Feed cool air to the cabin.
FEEL (v), FEELS, FELT, FELT	To touch to find	CAREFULLY LIFT THE MAGNETIC LEVEL INDICATOR UNTIL YOU FEEL THE MAGNETS.	
few (adj)	SMALL NUMBER 💡 If possible, give a specific number	THIS PROCEDURE IS ONLY FOR REPAIRS THAT INCLUDE VERY SMALL NUMBER OF RIVETS	This procedure is only for repairs that include very few rivets.
few (a few) (adj)	SOME (adj)	LET THE ENGINE OPERATE FOR SOME MINUTES.	Let the engine run for a few minutes.
	💡 If this alternative is not sufficient, give the range, number, or quantity.	AFTER APPROXIMATELY 5 SECONDS, THE LIGHT COMES ON AGAIN.	After a few seconds, the light comes on again.
file (v)	REMOVE (v) (WITH A FILE (TN)	DO NOT REMOVE TOO MUCH MATERIAL WITH THE FILE.	Take care not to file too deeply.
filing (n)	PARTICLE (n)	REMOVE ALL THE METAL PARTICLES.	Remove all the metal filings.
FILL (v), FILLS, FILLED, FILLED	To put into a container or a space to the maximum level or, if specified, to a given level, pressure, or quantity	FILL THE TANK WITH METHANOL. MAKE SURE THAT THE RESERVOIR FILLS WITH WATER.	

ASD STE 100

Word (part of speech)	Approved meaning / ALTERNATIVES	APPROVED EXAMPLE	Not approved example
film (n)	LAYER (n)	APPLY A LAYER OF COMPOUND ON THE SURFACE OF THE DISC.	Spread a film of compound on the surface of the disc.
filter (v)	FILTER (TN)	PUT THE OIL THROUGH A FILTER.	Filter the oil.
FILTERED (adj)	That has gone through a filter	DRY THE UNIT WITH LOW-PRESSURE FILTERED AIR.	
final (adj)	LAST (adj)	THE LAST STEP WILL OPEN THE VALVE.	The final action will open the valve.
FIND (v), FINDS, FOUND, FOUND	To discover, to examine something so that you know	YOU CAN FIND THE NUMBERS ON THE SWITCH.	
finding (n)	RESULT (n)	TELL THE QUALITY DEPARTMENT ABOUT THE RESULTS OF THE ANALYSIS.	Report the findings of the analysis to the quality department.
fine (adj)	SMALL (adj)	ONLY PARTICLES SMALLER THAN 5 MICRONS CAN GO THROUGH THE FILTER.	Only particles finer than 5 microns can go through the filter.
finger-tighten (v)	TIGHTEN … WITH YOUR FINGERS	TIGHTEN THE NUT WITH YOUR FINGERS.	Finger-tighten the nut.
FINISH (n)	The result of a finishing procedure	DO NOT CAUSE DAMAGE TO THE SURFACE FINISH OF THE HOUSING.	
finish (v)	COMPLETE (v)	COMPLETE THE TEST.	Finish the test.
FIRE (n)	The light and/or heat from a material when it burns	IF THERE IS A FIRE IN THE ENGINE COMPARTMENT, YOU WILL HEAR THE GONG.	

Word (part of speech)	Approved meaning / ALTERNATIVES	APPROVED EXAMPLE	Not approved example
FIRE (v), FIRES, FIRED, FIRED	To ignite, or to operate items that contain an explosive material	FIRE THE CARTRIDGES.	
		WHEN YOU PUSH THE AGENT PUSHBUTTON, THE FIRE EXTINGUISHER CARTRIDGE FIRES.	
firmly (adv)	TIGHTLY (adv)	HOLD THE CYLINDER TIGHTLY.	Hold the cylinder firmly.
FIRST (adv)	Before other persons or things	FILL THE INNER TANKS FIRST.	
FIT (n)	The relation between two related parts, a limit of tolerance	YOU WILL FIND DATA ABOUT FITS AND CLEARANCES IN SECTION 9001.	
fit (v)	INSTALL (v)	INSTALL THE DUCT.	Fit the duct.
	ATTACH (v)	ATTACH THE PANEL TO THE STRUCTURE WITH THE BOLTS.	Fit the panel to the structure with the bolts.
	CORRECT (adj)	MAKE SURE THAT THE REPAIR PLUG HAS THE CORRECT DIMENSIONS.	Ensure the repair plug fits.
fix (v)	ATTACH (v)	ATTACH THE TRIM WITH DOUBLE-SIDED ADHESIVE TAPE.	Fix the trim with doublesided adhesive tape.
	SET (v)	SET THE LENGTH OF THE CONTROL ROD AS NECESSARY.	Fix the length of the control rod as required.
	REPAIR (v)	REPAIR ALL LOOSE OR DAMAGED UPHOLSTERY.	Fix any loose or torn upholstery.
	INSTALL (v)	INSTALL THE RETAINER BOLTS ON THE RETAINER.	Fix the retainer bolts to the retainer.
FLAME (n)	Burning gas	IF YOU SEE FLAMES FROM THE EXHAUST PIPE, STOP THE ENGINE.	

ASD STE 100

Word (part of speech)	Approved meaning / ALTERNATIVES	APPROVED EXAMPLE	Not approved example
FLAMMABLE (adj)	That burns easily	THE SOLVENT IS FLAMMABLE.	
FLANGE (n)	An end surface at an angle	MAKE SURE THAT THE FLANGE IS NOT DAMAGED.	
FLASH (v), FLASHES, FLASHED, FLASHED	To come on and go off frequently	THE RED LIGHTS FLASH IN HALF-SECOND INTERVALS	
FLAT (adj) (FLATTER, FLATTEST)	That has a continuous surface in the same plane	LUBRICATE ONE SIDE OF THE FLAT WASHERS.	
flatness (n)	FLAT (adj)	THE SURFACE MUST BE FLAT TO GET A CORRECT BOND.	A correct bond depends on the surface flatness.
flatten (v)	FLAT (adj)	MAKE SURE THAT YOU DO NOT CAUSE THE TUBES TO BECOME FLAT.	Make sure that you do not flatten the tubes.
flaw (n)	DAMAGE (n)	MAKE SURE THAT THERE IS NO DAMAGE TO THE SURFACE FINISH.	Make sure that there are no flaws in the surface finish.
	DEFECTIVE (adj) 💡 Be specific if possible.	MAKE SURE THAT THE SURFACE FINISH IS NOT DEFECTIVE.	Make sure that there are no flaws in the surface.
flex (v)	BEND (v)	THE WING CAN BEND UP AND DOWN DURING FLIGHT	The wing can flex up and down during flight.
FLEXIBLE (adj)	That can easily bend again and again	CONNECT THE FLEXIBLE HOSES TO THE PUMP.	
FLIGHT (n)	The time an aircraft is in the air	AFTER EACH FLIGHT, READ THE COUNTER UNIT INDICATIONS.	
flood (v)	USE TOO MUCH	DO NOT USE TOO MUCH SOLVENT ON THE AREA.	Do not flood the area with solvent.

Word (part of speech)	Approved meaning / ALTERNATIVES	APPROVED EXAMPLE	Not approved example
FLOW (n)	A continuous movement of fluid	AN ARROW ON THE VALVE SHOWS THE DIRECTION OF FUEL FLOW.	
FLOW (v), FLOWS, FLOWED, FLOWED	To move as a fluid moves	THE OIL MUST FLOW OUT OF THE VALVE.	
fluctuate (v)	CONSTANT (adj)	MAKE SURE THAT THE PRESSURE STAYS CONSTANT.	Make sure that the pressure does not fluctuate.
FLUID (n)	Liquid or gas	THESE FLUIDS CAN CAUSE CORROSION.	
FLUSH (adj)	Of a surface that is level or continuous with another surface	MAKE SURE THAT THE DOOR IS FLUSH WITH THE FUSELAGE SKIN.	
FLUSH (v), FLUSHES, FLUSHED, FLUSHED	To remove something or to operate with a flow of liquid	FLUSH THE TUBES WITH PRESSURIZED FUEL.	
		MAKE SURE THAT THE TOILET ASSEMBLY FLUSHES CORRECTLY.	
focus (v)	FOCUS (TN)	PUT THE OPTICAL FIXTURE INTO FOCUS	Focus the optical fixture.
fold (n)	FOLD (v)	FOLD THE MATERIAL.	Make a fold in the material.
FOLD (v), FOLDS, FOLDED, FOLDED	To double over or to cause to double over on itself	DISENGAGE THE UPPER AND LOWER GUIDE ARMS AND FOLD THEM BACK.	
		FOLD THE ROTOR BLADES.	

Word (part of speech)	Approved meaning / ALTERNATIVES	APPROVED EXAMPLE	Not approved example
FOLLOW (v), FOLLOWS, FOLLOWED, FOLLOWED	To come after, to go after	THIS TEST FOLLOWS THE INSTALLATION OF THE HP PUMP.	
		DO THE PROCEDURE THAT FOLLOWS.	
	For other meanings, use: OBEY (v)	FOLLOW THE GREEN LIGHTS TO THE NEAREST STAIRCASE.	
		WHEN YOU USE THIS MATERIAL, OBEY THE MANUFACTURER'S INSTRUCTIONS.	When you use this material, follow the manufacturer's instructions.
following (adj)	THESE (adj)	MAKE SURE THAT THESE CIRCUIT BREAKERS ARE CLOSED.	Make sure that the following circuit breakers are closed.
	FOLLOW (v)	OBEY THE PRECAUTIONS THAT FOLLOW.	Obey the following precautions.
FOR (prep)	Function word that shows purpose, intent, time, result, or the object of an action	LET THE POTTING COMPOUND DRY FOR ONE HOUR.	
		OBEY THE REMOVAL PROCEDURES FOR THE COMPONENTS.	
FOR EXAMPLE	Used to introduce something chosen as a typical case	WHEN YOU REMOVE THE STUD, USE APPLICABLE TOOLS. FOR EXAMPLE, USE A PLASTIC MALLET AND A PUNCH.	
forbidden (adj)	NOT PERMITTED	IT IS NOT PERMITTED TO INSTALL MORE THAN TWO WASHERS FOR EACH BOLT.	It is forbidden to install more than two washers for each bolt.

Word (part of speech)	Approved meaning / ALTERNATIVES	APPROVED EXAMPLE	Not approved example
force (v)	PUSH (v)	PUSH THE CLIP OUT TO REMOVE IT.	Clip may be removed by forcing it out.
	FORCE (TN)	DO NOT USE FORCE TO PUT THE COVER INTO POSITION.	Do not attempt to force the cover into position.
forecast (v)	POSSIBLE (adj)	IF BAD WEATHER IS POSSIBLE, MOOR THE AIRCRAFT SAFELY.	If unfavorable weather conditions are forecast, moor the aircraft securely.
foreign (adj)	UNWANTED (adj)	THIS COVER WILL KEEP DIRT, PARTICLES, OR OTHER UNWANTED MATERIAL OUT OF THE SYSTEM.	This cover will prevent dirt, particles, or other foreign material from entering the system.
form (n)	SHAPE (n)	THE SEAL HAS THE SHAPE OF AN ELLIPSE.	The seal is in the form of an ellipse.
form (v)	BE (v)	IF THERE IS CONTAMINATION IN THE FUEL TANKS, REMOVE IT IMMEDIATELY.	If contamination has formed in the fuel tanks, remove it immediately.
fortify (v)	STRONG (adj)	CARBON-FIBER STRUTS MAKE THE FLOOR STRUCTURE STRONGER.	Carbon-fiber struts fortify the floor structure.
FORWARD (adj)	Nearer to the front	THE CONTROL UNIT IS INSTALLED IN THE FORWARD PART OF THE CARGO COMPARTMENT.	
FORWARD (adv)	In the direction of the front	MOVE THE LEVERS FORWARD	
FORWARD OF (prep)	At a position nearer to the front	THE TENSION REGULATOR IS INSTALLED FORWARD OF THE PRESSURE BULKHEAD.	

ASD STE 100

Word (part of speech)	Approved meaning / ALTERNATIVES	APPROVED EXAMPLE	Not approved example
foul (v)	CATCH (v)	MAKE SURE THAT THE RODS CANNOT CATCH ON THE FLAPS	Make sure that the rods cannot foul the flaps.
	HIT (v)	IF YOU INSTALL THE UPPER DRAG STRUT INCORRECTLY, IT WILL HIT THE LOWER DRAG STRUT DURING RETRACTION.	Do not install the upper drag strut so that it fouls the gear retraction.
	TOUCH (v)	IF THE BRACKET TOUCHES THE CAM, ADD A SHIM WASHER.	Should the bracket foul the cam, add a shim washer.
	CLEARANCE (n)	MAKE SURE THAT THE RODS HAVE SUFFICIENT CLEARANCE.	Check that the rods do not foul each other.
fouled (adj)	DIRTY (adj)	REMOVE ALL DIRTY IGNITER PLUGS.	Remove all fouled igniter plugs.
	CLOGGED (adj)	REMOVE ALL CLOGGED FILTER ELEMENTS.	Remove all fouled filter elements.
	CATCH (v)	MAKE SURE THAT THE CABLES DO NOT CATCH ON THE LEVERS.	Make sure that the levers are not fouled by the cables.
fragile (adj)	EASILY DAMAGED	THE WATER QUANTITY TRANSMITTER IS EASILY DAMAGED.	The water quantity transmitter is fragile.
FREE (adj)	That can move easily	MAKE SURE THAT THE NUTS ARE FREE TO TURN ON THE SLEEVES.	
	💡 Do not use compound adjectives with free, for example, lintfree, dustfree, unless they are technical names.	MAKE SURE THAT THERE IS NO DUST ON THE SURFACE.	Make sure that the surface is dust free.
free from (adj)	NO (adj)	MAKE SURE THAT THERE IS NO DUST ON THE SURFACE.	Make sure that the surface is free from dust.

Word (part of speech)	Approved meaning / ALTERNATIVES	APPROVED EXAMPLE	Not approved example
free (v)	RELEASE (v)	REMOVE THE SLEEVE TO RELEASE THE SLIDING TUBE.	Remove the sleeve to free the sliding tube.
FREELY (adv)	That can move easily	OXYGEN MUST FLOW FREELY FROM THE END OF THE HOSE.	
FREEZE (v), FREEZES, FROZE, FROZEN	To go or cause to go to a temperature below the freezing point of a liquid (usually of water)	FREEZE THE BUSHINGS AS FOLLOWS : IF YOU THINK THAT THE WATER WILL FREEZE, ADD ANTIFREEZE.	
FREQUENT (adj)	That occurs or is found often at short intervals	FREQUENT INSPECTIONS OF THESE AREAS ARE NECESSARY.	
FREQUENTLY (adv)	At frequent or short intervals	MONITOR THE INDICATORS FREQUENTLY.	
fresh (adj)	CLEAN (adj)	FLUSH THE TUBES WITH CLEAN WATER.	Flush the tubes with fresh water.
	NEW (adj)	FILL WITH NEW DESICCANT.	Recharge with fresh desiccant.
FROM (prep)	Function word that shows a point of departure for movement, time, distance, action, or separation	REMOVE THE PROTECTIVE COVER FROM THE NEW ASSEMBLY.	
FRONT (adj)	Nearer to the person that looks or a reference point 💡 Refer also to IN FRONT OF.	THERE IS A "FAULT" LIGHT ON THE FRONT FACE OF THE COMPUTER.	
FRONT (n)	The front part or the front surface	CLEAN THE FRONT OF THE MOUNTING FLANGE WITH SOLVENT.	
fuel (v)	REFUEL (v)	REFUEL THE AIRCRAFT.	Fuel the aircraft.

Word (part of speech)	Approved meaning / ALTERNATIVES	APPROVED EXAMPLE	Not approved example
fulfill (v)	OBEY (v)	OBEY THE INSTRUCTIONS IN THE TEST PROCEDURE.	Fulfill the instructions in the test procedure.
		THIS PROCEDURE OBEYS ALL THE REQUIREMENTS OF SERVICE BULLETIN No. 97.	This procedure fulfills all the requirements of Service Bulletin No. 97.
FULL (adj) (FULLER, FULLEST)	At or related to maximum travel, length, quantity, or detail	MAKE SURE THAT THE RESERVOIR IS FULL.	
FULLY (adv)	At or related to maximum travel, length, quantity, or detail	TURN THE CONTROL TO THE FULLY CLOSED POSITION.	
FUNCTION (n)	The purpose of an operation or an item	THE PRIMARY FUNCTION OF THIS UNIT IS TO CONTROL THE FUEL FLOW.	
function (v)	OPERATE (v)	THE ELEVATOR CONTROLS MUST OPERATE SMOOTHLY.	The elevator controls must function smoothly.
	MOVE (v)	THE SYSTEM CONTROLS MUST MOVE FREELY.	The system controls must function freely.
fundamental (adj)	IMPORTANT (adj)	IT IS IMPORTANT TO KEEP ALL PARTS CLEAN DURING THIS PROCEDURE.	Cleanliness of all parts is fundamental in this procedure.
furnish (v)	GIVE (v)	GIVE THE TECHNICIAN SUFFICIENT PROTECTIVE CLOTHING.	Furnish the technician with sufficient protective clothing.
	SUPPLY (v)	A JACK IS SUPPLIED WITH THE TOOL ASSEMBLY	A jack is furnished with the tool assembly.

Word (part of speech)	Approved meaning / ALTERNATIVES	APPROVED EXAMPLE	Not approved example
further (adj)	MORE (adj)	IF NECESSARY, ADD MORE GASKETS.	If required, add further gaskets.
further (adv)		IF IT IS NECESSARY TO DECREASE THE CABLE TENSION MORE, USE THE TURNBUCKLE.	Cable tension can be further reduced if necessary by means of the turnbuckle.

Word (part of speech)	Approved meaning / ALTERNATIVES	APPROVED EXAMPLE	Not approved example
gain (n)	INCREASE (v)	THE RESULT IS THAT THE TEMPERATURE INCREASES.	The result is a gain in temperature.
gain (v)	GET (v)	GET ACCESS TO THE CONNECTORS AT THE REAR OF THE INSTRUMENT.	Gain access to the connectors at the back of the instrument.
gall (v)	GALLING (TN)	THERE MUST BE NO SCRATCHES OR GALLING ON THE SURFACE.	The surface must not be scratched or galled.
gap (n)	CLEARANCE (n)	MEASURE THE CLEARANCE BETWEEN THE IMPELLER AND THE BODY.	Measure the gap between the impeller and the body.
	DISTANCE (n)	MEASURE THE DISTANCE BETWEEN THE ROTARY ACTUATOR AND THE STOP BOLT.	Measure the gap between the rotary actuator and the stop bolt.
	SPACE (n)	PUT THE BLADE OF A SMALL SCREWDRIVER INTO THE SPACE BETWEEN THE BALL MAT AND THE BALL UNIT.	Put the blade of a small screwdriver into the gap between the ball mat and the ball unit.
garble (adj)	CLEAR (adj)	IF THE RADIO SIGNAL IS NOT CLEAR, ADJUST THE FREQUENCY.	If the radio signal is garbled, adjust the frequency.
	CLEARLY (adv)	YOU MUST HEAR THE ANNOUNCEMENT CLEARLY.	The announcement must be audible and not garbled.

Word (part of speech)	Approved meaning / ALTERNATIVES	APPROVED EXAMPLE	Not approved example
garner (v)	COLLECT (v)	THESE COMPUTERS COLLECT DATA FROM THE VHF SYSTEM.	These computers garner data from the VHF system.
		THE BITE FUNCTION COLLECTS THE FAILURES AND SENDS THE FAILURE MESSAGE TO THE CENTRAL MAINTENANCE COMPUTER.	The BITE function garners the failures and sends the failure message to the Central Maintenance Computer.
GAS (n)	A fluid that has no shape or volume and that can expand	THE TEMPERATURE SENSING UNIT IS A CAPILLARY TUBE FILLED WITH GAS.	
gaseous (adj)	GAS (n)	THE TOOL CYLINDER CONTAINS A MIXTURE OF GASES (10% HELIUM AND 90% NITROGEN).	The tool cylinder contains a gaseous mixture of 10% helium and 90% nitrogen.
gash (v)	DAMAGED (adj)	IF THE THERMAL BLANKET IS DAMAGED, DO REPAIR No. 9.	If the thermal blanket is gashed, do repair No. 9.
gather (v)	COLLECT (v)	ALL FLUIDS COLLECT AT THE LOWEST POINT IN THE COMPARTMENT.	All fluids gather at the lowest point in the compartment.
		THREE COMPUTERS COLLECT DATA AND PARAMETERS FROM THE SYSTEMS AND PUT THEM TOGETHER ON THE DATA LINK TO THE DISPLAY UNIT.	Three computers gather data and parameters from the systems and put them together on the data link to the display unit.
gauge (v)	MEASURE (v)	MEASURE THE DISTANCE BETWEEN THE FUSELAGE AND THE KRUEGER FLAP.	Gauge the width of the gap between the fuselage and the Krueger flap.
GENERAL (adj)	Of, or related to something as a whole, not detailed	THIS SECTION GIVES GENERAL MAINTENANCE PROCEDURES	

Word (part of speech)	Approved meaning / ALTERNATIVES	APPROVED EXAMPLE	Not approved example
generally (adv)	USUALLY (adv)	YOU USUALLY REPLACE MEMORY MODULES ON AIRCRAFT.	Memory modules are generally replaced on aircraft.
generate (v)	BE (v)	THERE MUST BE NO ERRORS WHEN YOU OPEN THE FILE.	The file opening must not generate errors.
	GIVE (v)	IF THE HYDRAULIC PUMP DOES NOT GIVE A PRESSURE OF 3000 PSI, USE THE ELECTRIC PUMP.	If the hydraulic pump fails to generate a pressure of 3000 psi, use the electric pump.
	SUPPLY (v)	THE BATTERIES SUPPLY 28 VDC.	The batteries generate 28 VDC.
generous (adj)	LARGE (adj)	A LARGE QUANTITY OF COMPOUND IS NECESSARY.	A generous amount of compound will be necessary.
	THICK (adj) 💡 Be specific if possible.	APPLY A THICK LAYER OF GREASE.	Apply a generous amount of grease.
generously (adv)	LARGE (adj)	APPLY A LARGE QUANTITY OF SEALANT TO THE REPAIR PATCH.	Apply sealant generously to the repair patch.
	THICK (adj) 💡 Be specific if possible	APPLY A THICK LAYER OF GREASE.	Apply grease generously.
gentle (adj)	CAREFULLY (adv)	TURN THE POTENTIOMETER CAREFULLY.	Rotate the potentiometer with a gentle movement.
	LIGHTLY (adv)	TAP THE SURFACE LIGHTLY.	Give the surface a gentle tap.
gently (adv)	CAREFULLY (adv)	CAREFULLY PULL THE ELECTRICAL WIRE OUT FROM THE RUBBER SEAL.	Gently pull out the electrical wire from the rubber seal.
	LIGHTLY (adv)	LIGHTLY TAP THE FLAP SURFACE.	Gently tap the flap surface.

Word (part of speech)	Approved meaning / ALTERNATIVES	APPROVED EXAMPLE	Not approved example
genuine (adj)	CORRECT (adj)	MAKE SURE THAT THE INDICATION ON THE GAUGE IS CORRECT.	Make sure that the reading on the gauge is genuine.
GET (v), GETS, GOT ⚫ No other forms of this verb.	To obtain, to come into the state of having 💡 Do not use this word to mean BECOME, GO, DECREASE, INCREASE. Refer to rule 9.2 and the entries from "get" until "get to" that follow.	IF YOU GET THE FLUID ON YOUR SKIN, FLUSH YOUR SKIN IMMEDIATELY WITH CLEAN WATER.	
get (v)	BECOME (v)	DO NOT LET THE HEATER BECOME TOO HOT.	Do not let the heater get too hot.
get away (v)	GO AWAY (v)	BEFORE THE ENGINE STARTS, GO AWAY FROM THE EXHAUST AREA.	Get away from the exhaust area before the engine starts.
get down (v)	DECREASE (v)	IF THE TEMPERATURE DECREASES TO LESS THAN ZERO, DRAIN THE WATER SYSTEM.	If the temperature gets down to below zero, drain the water system.
	GO DOWN (v)	BE CAREFUL WHEN YOU GO DOWN THE LADDER FROM THE COCKPIT TO THE AVIONICS COMPARTMENT.	Be careful when you get down the ladder from the cockpit into the avionics compartment.
get into (v)	GO INTO (v)	INSTALL CAPS ON THE RECEPTACLES TO MAKE SURE THAT UNWANTED MATERIAL DOES NOT GO INTO THE RECEPTACLES.	IInstall caps to make sure that foreign objects do not get into the receptacles.
get off (v)	MOVE OFF (v)	BEFORE YOU MOVE THE AILERONS, TELL ALL PERSONS TO MOVE OFF THE WINGS.	Before you move the ailerons, tell all persons to get off the wings.

Word (part of speech)	Approved meaning / ALTERNATIVES	APPROVED EXAMPLE	Not approved example
get to (v)	BE (v)	THE MOTOR STOPS WHEN THE FLAPS ARE AT THE END OF THEIR TRAVEL.	The motor stops when the flaps get to the end of their travel.
	GO (v)	GO TO THE AFT CARGO COMPARTMENT TO DO THIS TEST.	Get to the aft cargo compartment to do this test.
	INCREASE (v)	WHEN THE TEMPERATURE OF THE VENTILATION AIR INCREASES TO 27 °C, THE DISCHARGE VALVE OPENS	When the temperature of the ventilation air gets to 27 °C, the discharge valve opens.
GIVE (v), GIVES, GAVE, GIVEN	To provide	THIS SECTION GIVES YOU THE PROCEDURES FOR THE DISASSEMBLY.	
gleam (v)	SHINY (adj)	POLISH THE SURFACE WITH A SOFT CLOTH UNTIL IT BECOMES SHINY	Polish the surface with a soft cloth until it gleams.
glitch (n)	ERROR (n)	IF THERE IS AN ERROR IN THE SYSTEM, THE SCREEN SHOWS : "NO GO".	If there is a glitch in the shows: NO GO.
	FAILURE (TN)	IF THERE IS A FAILURE IN THE SYSTEM, THE SCREEN SHOWS : "NO GO".	If there is a glitch in the shows: NO GO.
	UNSERVICEABLE (adj)	IF THE SYSTEM IS UNSERVICEABLE, THE SCREEN SHOWS : "NO GO".	If there is a glitch in the shows: NO GO.
gloss (n)	SHINY (adj)	POLISH THE SURFACE UNTIL IT IS VERY SHINY.	Polish the surface to a high gloss.
GLOSSY (adj) (GLOSSIER, GLOSSIEST)	Smooth and shiny	APPLY THE PATCH WITH THE MATT SIDE AGAINST THE GLOSSY SURFACE.	

Word (part of speech)	Approved meaning / ALTERNATIVES	APPROVED EXAMPLE	Not approved example
glow (v)	BE (v)	MAKE SURE THAT THE INDICATOR LIGHT IS ON.	Make sure that the indicator light glows.
		ADJUST THE POTENTIOMETER UNTIL THE LIGHT IS DIM.	Adjust the potentiometer until the light glows dimly.
glue (v)	BOND (v)	BOND THE PATCH TO THE SURFACE WITH THE APPLICABLE GLUE.	Glue the patch to the surface.
	ATTACH (v)	ATTACH THE PROTECTIVE PLATE TO THE SURFACE WITH ADHESIVE MATERIAL.	Glue the protective plate to the surface.
GO (v), GOES, WENT	To move to or from something	MAKE SURE THAT THE POINTER GOES OUT OF VIEW.	
GO OFF (v), GOES OFF, WENT OFF	To become dark when an internal power source is de-energized	THE ANNUNCIATOR LIGHT GOES OFF.	
GOOD (adj) (BETTER, BEST)	That is satisfactory	THIS MATERIAL GIVES GOOD PROTECTION FROM CORROSION.	
gouge (v)	GOUGE (TN)	IF A GOUGE OCCURS IN THE BLADE DURING REMOVAL, REPLACE THE BLADE.	If the blade was gouged during removal, replace it.
govern (v)	CONTROL (v)	THIS COMPONENT CONTROLS THE ENGINE SPEED.	This component governs the engine speed.
grab (v)	USE (v)	USE A SCREWDRIVER TO RELEASE THE CLIPS.	Grab a screwdriver to release the clips.
	HOLD (v)	HOLD THE HANDLE.	Grab the handle.
gradient (n)	SLOPE (n)	IF YOU MUST PARK THE AIRCRAFT ON A SLOPE, MAKE SURE THAT WHEEL CHOCKS ARE IN FRONT OF THE WHEELS.	If you have to park the aircraft on a gradient, make sure that wheel chocks are in front of the wheels.

Word (part of speech)	Approved meaning / ALTERNATIVES	APPROVED EXAMPLE	Not approved example
gradual (adj)	GRADUALLY (adv)	GRADUALLY ADJUST THE TEMPERATURE.	Make a gradual adjustment to the temperature.
GRADUALLY (adv)	Slowly and continuously	GRADUALLY OPEN THE COCKS ON THE RECHARGING UNIT.	
graduated (adj)	GRADUATION (TN)	MEASURE THE DIMENSIONS WITH A METAL RULE THAT HAS GRADUATIONS IN MILLIMETERS.	The measurements are obtained by means of a millimeter-graduated metal rule.
graph (v)	GRAPH (TN)	MAKE A GRAPH OF THE TEST RESULTS.	Graph the test results.
grasp (v)	HOLD (v)	HOLD THE HANDLE.	Grasp the handle.
grave (adj)	DANGEROUS (adj)	HYDRAULIC FLUID IS DANGEROUS FOR YOUR SKIN.	Hydraulic fluid can cause grave skin problems.
grease (v)	LUBRICATE (v)	BEFORE YOU INSTALL THE O-RING, LUBRICATE IT WITH GREASE.	Grease the O-ring before installation.
	GREASE (TN)	APPLY GREASE TO THE FASTENERS.	Grease the fasteners.
great (adj)	LARGE (adj)	AN INDICATION OF A LARGE QUANTITY OF FUEL SHOWS AN INCORRECT ADJUSTMENT OF THE FLOAT SWITCH.	A great amount of fuel indicates incorrect setting of the float switch.
	MORE THAN	IF THE PRESSURE IS MORE THAN 200 PSI, CLOSE THE VALVE.	If the pressure is greater than 200 psi, close the valve.
	VERY (adv)	BE VERY CAREFUL WHEN YOU RELEASE THE PRESSURE.	Take the greatest care when you release the pressure.
greatly (adv)	VERY MUCH	THIS METHOD CAN INCREASE THE RISK OF INJURY VERY MUCH.	This method can greatly increase the risk of injury.
grip (n)	HOLD (v)	HOLD THE JACK BODY TIGHTLY WHILE YOU TURN IT.	Make sure you have a tight grip of the jack body while turning it.

Word (part of speech)	Approved meaning / ALTERNATIVES	APPROVED EXAMPLE	Not approved example
grip (v)	HOLD (v)	HOLD THE HANDLE LIGHTLY WITH ONE HAND.	Grip the handle lightly with one hand.
GROOVE (n)	A long channel that is not wide	INSTALL THE O-RING IN ITS GROOVE ON THE PISTON.	
GROUND (n)	The surface of the earth	YOU CAN ONLY DO THIS PROCEDURE ON THE GROUND.	
GROUND (v), GROUNDS, GROUNDED, GROUNDED	To connect to the ground or to a large object of zero potential	GROUND THE FUEL TANKS.	
GROUP (n)	Objects that are related	THIS GROUP OF SEALING COMPOUNDS IS ALSO APPLICABLE IN AN EMERGENCY.	
grow (v)	BECOME (v)	IF THE BATTERY BECOMES TOO HOT, DISCONNECT IT.	If the battery grows too hot, disconnect it.
guard (v)	GUARD (TN)	MAKE SURE THAT THE GUARDS ARE INSTALLED ON THE SWITCHES.	Make sure that the switches are guarded.
guide (v)	PUT (v)	PUT THE CABLE THROUGH THE GROMMET.	Guide the cable through the grommet.
	MOVE (v)	WHILE YOU LOWER THE PUMP, MOVE IT ONTO THE MOUNTING BRACKET.	As you lower the pump, guide it onto the mounting bracket.
gush (v)	FLOW (n)	IF YOU TURN THE HANDLE TO "FULL", THERE WILL BE A STRONG FLOW OF WATER FROM THE OUTLET.	If you turn the valve handle to FULL, water will gush from the outlet.

Word (part of speech)	Approved meaning / ALTERNATIVES	APPROVED EXAMPLE	Not approved example
halt (v)	STOP (v)	IF YOU HEAR AN UNUSUAL NOISE, STOP THE PROCEDURE.	If you hear an unusual noise, halt the procedure.
halve (v)	HALF (TN)	MAKE SURE THAT THE PITCH DECREASES TO HALF ITS VALUE.	Check that the deviation in pitch is halved.
hamper (v)	PREVENT (v)	STRONG WINDS CAN PREVENT THE CORRECT DEPLOYMENT OF THE ESCAPE SLIDES.	Strong winds can hamper the correct deployment of the escape slides.
handle (v)	MOVE (v)	MOVE THE ACTUATOR WITH A HOIST.	Handle the actuator with a hoist.
	TOUCH (v)	DO NOT TOUCH THE PRINTED CIRCUIT CARD.	Do not handle the printed circuit card.
	CAREFUL (adj) This word can be part of safety sign (rule 8.6).	BE CAREFUL WITH INSTRUMENTS.	Handle instruments with care.
hand-tight (adj)	TIGHTEN ⋯ WITH YOUR HAND	INSTALL THE FILTER CASE AND TIGHTEN IT WITH YOUR HAND.	Install the filter case hand-tight.
hand-tighten (v)	TIGHTEN ⋯ WITH YOUR HAND	TIGHTEN THE SWIVEL NUT WITH YOUR HAND.	Hand-tighten the swivel nut.
HANG (v), HANGS, HUNG, HUNG	To attach or to be attached to something above with no support from below	HANG THE SHACKLE ON THE HOIST. LOWER THE PLATFORM ASSEMBLY UNTIL IT HANGS ON THE SUPPORT FRAME.	
happen (v)	OCCUR (v)	IF AN ACCIDENT OCCURS, GET MEDICAL AID.	If an accident happens, get medical attention.
HARD (adj) (HARDER, HARDEST)	Not easy to cut, not easy to go into or through	IF THE SURFACE IS HARD, USE A CARBIDE DRILL.	

Word (part of speech)	Approved meaning / ALTERNATIVES	APPROVED EXAMPLE	Not approved example
harden (v)	HARD (adj)	LET THE ADHESIVE BECOME HARD.	Let the adhesive harden.
	CURE (TV) 💡 Refer to rule 1.12.	LET THE BONDING MATERIAL CURE.	Let the bonding material harden.
harm (v)	INJURY (n)	BE CAREFUL WHEN YOU CUT LOCKWIRE. IT CAN CAUSE INJURY TO YOUR EYES.	Be careful when you cut lockwire. It can harm your eyes.
	IRRITATION (TN) 💡 Refer to rule 1.5.	HYDRAULIC FLUID CAN CAUSE SKIN IRRITATION.	Hydraulic fluid can harm your skin.
harmful (adj)	DANGEROUS (adj)	SOLVENT FUMES ARE DANGEROUS.	Solvent fumes are harmful to your health.
	INJURY (n)	THIS ADHESIVE COMPOUND CAN CAUSE INJURY TO YOUR SKIN.	This adhesive compound is harmful to your skin.
harmonize (v)	AGREE (v)	MAKE THE POSITIONS OF THE VALVES AGREE.	Harmonize the positions of the valves.
	ALIGN (v)	ALIGN THE CENTERLINE ON THE FLUX VALVE.	Harmonize the centerline on the flux valve.
haul (v)	TOW (v)	TOW THE HYDRAULIC CART AWAY FROM THE AIRCRAFT BEFORE YOU START THE ENGINE.	Haul the hydraulic cart away from the aircraft before you start the engine.
	MOVE (v)	MOVE THE HYDRAULIC CART AWAY FROM THE AIRCRAFT BEFORE YOU START THE ENGINE.	Haul the hydraulic cart away from the aircraft before you start the engine.
HAVE (v), HAS, HAD 💡 No other forms of this verb.	To possess as a part or quality	THE SYSTEM HAS AN EMERGENCY WARNING DEVICE.	

ASD STE 100

Word (part of speech)	Approved meaning / ALTERNATIVES	APPROVED EXAMPLE	Not approved example
have to (v)	MUST (v)	YOU MUST USE EAR PROTECTION WHEN YOU ARE NEAR AN ENGINE THAT IS IN OPERATION.	You have to use ear protection when you are near an engine that is in operation.
hazard (n)	DANGEROUS (adj)	TRICHLOROETHYLENE IS DANGEROUS.	Trichloroethylene is a health hazard.
hazardous (adj)	DANGEROUS (adj)	ALL PERSONNEL WHO DO WORK WITH DANGEROUS MATERIALS MUST OBEY THE SAFETY INSTRUCTIONS THAT FOLLOW.	All personnel who work with hazardous materials must obey the following safety instructions.
hazy (adj)	HAZE (TN)	IF THERE IS HAZE, NOT DO THE TEST.	DO If the weather is hazy, do not do the test.
HEAD (n)	The top of something	MAKE SURE THAT THE HEAD OF THE BOLT IS DOWN.	
head (v)	POINT (v)	POINT THE AIRCRAFT INTO THE WIND.	Head the aircraft into the wind.
HEAR (v), HEARS, HEARD, HEAR	To know by sound in the ear	MAKE SURE THAT YOU HEAR THE AUDIO SIGNALS IN ALL THE CREW HEADSETS.	
HEAT (n)	The condition or quality of being hot	USE HEAT TO CURE THE POLYSULPHIDE SEALANT.	
heat (v)	HEAT (n)	USE HEAT TO INCREASE THE TEMPERATURE OF THE OIL TO 40 ℃.	Heat the oil to 40 ℃.
	HOT (adj)	WHEN THE OIL IS HOT, IT FLOWS FREELY.	When you heat the oil, it flows freely.
HEAVY (adj) (HEAVIER, HEAVIEST)	That has a large mass, weight, or force	A SUPPORT WILL BE NECESSARY BECAUSE THE CONTROL UNIT IS HEAVY.	
HEIGHT (n)	The vertical distance	THE HEIGHT FROM THE GROUND TO THE TOP OF THE FIN CAN CHANGE.	

Word (part of speech)	Approved meaning / ALTERNATIVES	APPROVED EXAMPLE	Not approved example
heighten (v)	INCREASE (v)	STRONG WINDS WILL INCREASE THE RISK OF DAMAGE.	Strong winds will heighten the risk of damage.
help (n)	AID (n)	GET MEDICAL AID IMMEDIATELY.	You must get medical help immediately.
HELP (v), HELPS, HELPED, HELPED	To make something easier or better	PETROLATUM HELPS TO PREVENT CORROSION OF THE TERMINALS.	
helpful (adj)	HELP (v)	RECORD THE LOCKWIRE POSITIONS. THIS WILL HELP YOU DURING THE ASSEMBLY PROCEDURE.	Record the lockwire positions. This will be helpful during the assembly procedure.
HERE (adv)	In this position	TO DOWNLOAD THE FILE, CLICK HERE.	
hesitation (n)	SMOOTHLY (adv)	MAKE SURE THAT THE SOLENOID OPERATES SMOOTHLY.	Make sure that the solenoid operates without hesitation.
	CORRECTLY (adv)	THE VALVE MUST OPERATE CORRECTLY.	The valve must operate without hesitation.
	IMMEDIATELY (adv)	WHEN YOU OPEN THE CIRCUIT BREAKER, THE LIGHT MUST COME ON IMMEDIATELY.	When you open the circuit breaker, the light must come on without hesitation.
HIGH (adj) (HIGHER, HIGHEST)	That is of large value	USE THE SPECIAL PROTECTION FOR STORAGE IN HIGH TEMPERATURES.	
highly (adv)	VERY (adv)	TOLUENE IS VERY FLAMMABLE.	Toluene is highly flammable.

ASD STE 100

Word (part of speech)	Approved meaning / ALTERNATIVES	APPROVED EXAMPLE	Not approved example
hinder (v)	PREVENT (v)	SCRATCHES CAN PREVENT THE FREE MOVEMENT OF THE PISTON IN THE SLEEVE.	Scratches can hinder the movement of the piston in the sleeve
	DECREASE (v)	A CLOGGED DUCT WILL DECREASE AIRFLOW.	A clogged duct will hinder airflow.
	BLOCKAGE (n)	MAKE SURE THAT THERE IS NO BLOCKAGE IN THE PIPE THAT PREVENTS AIRFLOW.	Make sure that there is nothing in the pipe to hinder airflow.
	CLOGGED (adj)	MAKE SURE THAT THE PIPE IS NOT CLOGGED.	Make sure that there is nothing in the pipe to hinder airflow.
hinge (v)	TURN (v)	THE PANELS TURN ON TWO NYLON STRAPS.	Panels hinge on two nylon straps.
HIT (v), HITS, HIT, HIT	To touch suddenly and with much force	DO NOT HIT THE CARTRIDGE.	
hitch (v)	CONNECT (v)	CONNECT THE TOWING ARM TO THE NOSEWHEEL.	Hitch the towing arm to the nosewheel.
hoist (v)	LIFT (v)	LIFT THE MODULE INTO POSITION.	Hoist the module into position.
hold (n)	HOLD (v)	MAKE SURE THAT YOU HOLD THE ROD TIGHTLY.	Make sure that you have a tight hold on the rod.
HOLD (v), HOLDS, HELD, HELD	1. To continue to have in the hand or grip	HOLD THE ROD TIGHTLY.	
	2. To continue to have in a specified location, position, or condition	HOLD THE AIRSPEED INDICATION AT THE SAME VALUE FOR 2 MINUTES.	

Word (part of speech)	Approved meaning / ALTERNATIVES	APPROVED EXAMPLE	Not approved example
hold back (v)	PREVENT (v)	AT FULL THRUST, THE BRAKES MUST PREVENT MOVEMENT OF THE AIRCRAFT.	At full thrust, the brakes must hold the aircraft back.
hold off (v)	PREVENT (v)	THE PROTECTIVE PAINT WILL PREVENT CORROSION FOR SIX MONTHS.	The protective paint will hold off corrosion for six months.
HOLE (n)	An empty space in a solid object	MAKE SURE THAT THE HOLES IN THE BUSHING ALIGN WITH THOSE IN THE HOUSING	
hook (v)	PUT (v)	PUT THE SLING ON THE SHACKLE.	Hook the sling on the shackle.
hook up (v)	CONNECT (v)	CONNECT THE TOWING ARM TO THE NOSE GEAR.	Hook the towing arm up to the nose gear.
HORIZONTAL (adj)	Parallel to the horizon or a baseline	ADJUST THE SLING UNTIL THE FLAP IS HORIZONTAL.	
HORIZONTALLY (adv)	In a horizontal position	THE VALVE IS INSTALLED HORIZONTALLY.	
HOT (adj) (HOTTER, HOTTEST)	At a high temperature	DRY THE SURFACE WITH HOT AIR.	
house (v)	CONTAIN (v)	THE MODULE CONTAINS FIVE COMPONENTS.	The module houses five components.
HOW (adv)	By which manner	PARAGRAPH 7.0 TELLS YOU HOW TO INSTALL THE UNIT.	
however (adv)	BUT (conj)	BUT WE RECOMMEND THIS STEP TO DECREASE THE DRYING TIME.	However, we recommend this step to decrease the drying time.

ASD STE 100

Word (part of speech)	Approved meaning / ALTERNATIVES	APPROVED EXAMPLE	Not approved example
huge (adj)	LARGE (adj)	TO REMOVE THE PAINT STRIPPER, FLUSH THE SURFACE WITH LARGE QUANTITIES OF WATER.	To remove the paint stripper, flush the surface with huge quantities of water.
hum (v)	HUM (TN)	ADJUST THE POTENTIOMETER UNTIL YOU DO NOT HEAR A HUM FROM THE LOUDSPEAKER.	Adjust the potentiometer until the loudspeaker no longer hums.
hurt (v)	INJURY (n)	BE CAREFUL WHEN YOU DO THIS PROCEDURE. IF THE UNIT FALLS, IT CAN CAUSE INJURY TO PERSONNEL.	Be careful when you do this procedure. If the unit falls, it can hurt personnel.
HYDRAULIC (adj)	Related to, or operated by, pressurized liquid	CONNECT THE FITTINGS TO THE HYDRAULIC TEST BENCH.	
HYDRAULICALLY (adv)	With hydraulic power	MAKE SURE THAT THE LINES ARE HYDRAULICALLY OPERATED.	

Word (part of speech)	Approved meaning / ALTERNATIVES	APPROVED EXAMPLE	Not approved example
identical (adj)	SAME (adj)	THE SAME PROCEDURE IS APPLICABLE TO THE TWO VHF SETS.	The procedure is identical for both VHF sets.
IDENTIFICATION (n)	Something that identifies an object	MAKE SURE THAT THE NAMEPLATE SHOWS THE CORRECT IDENTIFICATION OF THE UNIT.	
IDENTIFY (v), IDENTIFIES, IDENTIFIED, IDENTIFIED	To use a specified code or marking to supply with an identity	IDENTIFY THE WIRES WITH SLEEVES OF DIFFERENT COLORS.	
	2. To show an identity	A 406 MHz DIGITAL SIGNAL IDENTIFIES THE EMERGENCY LOCATOR TRANSMITTER AND ITS LOCATION.	
	For other meanings, use: FIND (v)	FIND THE DAMAGED AREAS	Identify the damaged areas.
idle (v)	IDLE (TN)	OPERATE THE ENGINE AT IDLE FOR 20 MINUTES.	Idle the engine for 20 minutes.
IF (conj)	In the event that, on the condition that, in case of	IF YOU USE A REPLACEMENT FAIRING PLATE, CUT IT UNTIL YOU GET THE CORRECT MATING DIMENSION.	
ignite(v)	IGNITION (TN)	FUEL GOES THROUGH THE ATOMIZERS INTO THE COMBUSTION CHAMBER, WHERE IGNITION OCCURS.	Fuel passes through the atomizers to the combustion chamber, where it is ignited.
IGNORE (v), IGNORES, IGNORED, IGNORED	Not to think about something, not to do something about	IGNORE THE VIBRATION INDICATIONS. CLICK "CANCEL" TO IGNORE ALL CHANGES.	

Word (part of speech)	Approved meaning / ALTERNATIVES	APPROVED EXAMPLE	Not approved example
ILLUMINATE (v), ILLUMINATES, ILLUMINATED, ILLUMINATED	To make something visible by an external source such as light	MAKE SURE THAT THE STROBE LIGHT ILLUMINATES THE TRACKING PLATES	
	For lights or lamps, use : COME ON	WHEN THE PRESSURE LIGHT COMES ON, READ THE VALUE ON THE PRESSURE GAUGE.	When the pressure light illuminates, read the value on the pressure gauge.
		MAKE SURE THAT THE LAMP COMES ON.	Ensure the lamp illuminates.
	BE ON	MAKE SURE THAT THE LAMP IS ON.	Ensure the lamp is illuminated.
immediate (adj)	IMMEDIATELY (adv)	MAKE SURE THAT THE SPEEDBRAKE RETRACTS IMMEDIATELY.	Check the speedbrake for immediate retraction.
IMMEDIATELY (adv)	Without a gap of time or space	MAKE SURE THAT THE EMERGENCY LIGHT IMMEDIATELY GOES BACK TO "OFF".	
immerse (v)	SOAK (v)	SOAK THE FILTER IN THE CLEANING SOLUTION FOR 4 HOURS.	Immerse the filter in the cleaning solution for 4 hours.
	PUT FULLY INTO	PUT THE FILTER FULLY INTO THE SOLVENT.	Immerse the filter in solvent.
immobilize (v)	LOCK (v)	LOCK THE PULLEY WITH THE RIGGING PIN.	Immobilize the pulley with the rigging pin.
	PREVENT MOVEMENT	WHEN YOU REPAIR THE UNIT, PREVENT MOVEMENT OF THE ASSEMBLIES.	Immobilize the assemblies when repairing the unit.
impact (n)	HIT (v)	MAKE SURE THAT METAL OBJECTS DO NOT HIT THE MATING SURFACE.	Avoid impact between metal objects and the mating surface.

Word (part of speech)	Approved meaning / ALTERNATIVES	APPROVED EXAMPLE	Not approved example
impact (v)	HIT (v)	DO NOT LET THE VIBRATOR TOOL HIT THE SURFACE OF THE SEAL.	Do not allow the vibrator tool to impact the seal surface.
	EFFECT (n)	THESE REPAIRS HAVE AN EFFECT ON THE PERFORMANCE OF THE ENGINE.	These repairs impact engine performance.
impair (v)	DECREASE (v)	THE LIFE OF THE UNIT WILL DECREASE IF YOU LET THE UNIT BECOME DIRTY.	The life of the unit is impaired if the unit is allowed to get dirty.
	OPERATE INCORRECTLY	DAMAGE WILL CAUSE THE INSTRUMENT TO OPERATE INCORRECTLY.	Damage will impair operation of the instrument.
	CAUSE DAMAGE	CONTAMINATION OF THE GREASE CAN CAUSE DAMAGE TO THE BEARING.	Contaminants in the grease may impair the bearing.
imperative (adj)	NECESSARY (adj)	REMOVAL OF THE COVER IS NECESSARY.	Removal of the cover is imperative.
	MANDATORY (adj)	THE STEPS THAT FOLLOW ARE MANDATORY.	The following steps are imperative
	MUST (v)	YOU MUST DO THESE STEPS.	The following steps are imperative.
implement (v)	DO (v)	IF THE TEST DOES NOT GIVE SATISFACTORY RESULTS, DO THE FAULT ISOLATION PROCEDURE.	If the test does not give satisfactory results, implement the fault isolation procedure.
implementation (n)	DO (v)	IT IS MANDATORY TO DO THE PROCEDURE IN THIS SERVICE BULLETIN.	The implementation of the procedure in this Service Bulletin is mandatory.
IMPORTANT (adj)	That has a significant effect	THESE PROCEDURES ARE VERY IMPORTANT.	

Word (part of speech)	Approved meaning / ALTERNATIVES	APPROVED EXAMPLE	Not approved example
impossible (adj)	NOT POSSIBLE	THUS, IT IS NOT POSSIBLE TO GIVE A STANDARD VALUE.	Thus, it is impossible to give a standard value.
	CANNOT (v)	YOU CANNOT FILL THE CONTAINERS WHILE THEY ARE INSTALLED ON THE AIRCRAFT.	It is impossible to recharge containers while installed on aircraft.
impregnate (v)	SOAK (v)	SOAK THE FILTER ELEMENTS IN OIL.	The filter elements must be impregnated with oil.
impression (n)	THINK (v)	IF YOU THINK THAT A TIRE HAS LOW PRESSURE, DO THE STEPS THAT FOLLOW:	If you have the impression that a tire has low pressure, do the steps that follow:
improper (adj)	INCORRECT (adj)	INCORRECT ADJUSTMENT OF THE STOP BOLTS ON THE RUDDER PEDALS CAN CAUSE DAMAGE.	Improper adjustment of the stop bolts on the rudder pedals can cause damage.
improperly (adv)	INCORRECTLY (adv)	IF THE HINGE IS INCORRECTLY ADJUSTED, YOU CANNOT CLOSE THE PANEL.	If the hinge is improperly adjusted, the panel will not close.
improve (v)	BETTER (adj)	DO NOT ADJUST THE PARTS AGAIN TO MAKE THEIR POSITION BETTER.	Do not readjust the parts to improve their position.
impurity (n)	UNWANTED MATERIAL	USE A FILTER TO REMOVE UNWANTED MATERIAL FROM THE HYDRAULIC OIL.	Filter the hydraulic oil to remove impurities.
	CONTAMINATION (n)	CONTAMINATION CAN CAUSE A FAILURE.	Impurities may cause a failure.
IN (adv)	To, or into a location or position	MAKE SURE THAT THE SWITCHES ARE PUSHED IN.	

Word (part of speech)	Approved meaning / ALTERNATIVES	APPROVED EXAMPLE	Not approved example
IN (prep)	Function word that shows location, position, condition, time, or limits	LET THE SWITCH STAY IN THE SET POSITION.	
		THE COMPENSATORS ARE IN THE WING BAY.	
		DO NOT PARK THE AIRCRAFT IN STRONG WINDS.	
		MAKE SURE THAT THE LIGHT COMES ON IN 5 SECONDS.	
		MAKE SURE THAT THE CRACKS ARE IN THE LIMITS.	
IN FRONT OF (prep)	In a position ahead of	PUT CHOCKS IN FRONT OF THE WHEELS.	
IN PROGRESS (adv)	Occurring	IF AN INTERACTIVE SESSION IS IN PROGRESS, LET IT CONTINUE UNTIL IT IS FULLY COMPLETED.	
inactive (adj)	OFF (adj)	BEFORE YOU DRAIN THE FUEL, MAKE SURE THAT THE SYSTEM IS OFF.	Before you drain the fuel, make sure that the system is inactive.
	NO EFFECT	IN THIS CONFIGURATION, THE LINE KEY HAS NO EFFECT.	In this configuration, the line key is inactive.
	NOT IN OPERATION	THE AUTOTHRUST SYSTEM IS ON BUT NOT IN OPERATION.	The autothrust system is on but inactive.
	NOT OPERATE	MAKE SURE THAT THE PUMP DOES NOT OPERATE.	Make sure that the pump is inactive.
inadvertent (adj)	ACCIDENTAL (adj)	ACCIDENTAL OPERATION OF THE SYSTEM CAN KILL YOU.	Inadvertent operation of the system could cause fatal injuries.

Word (part of speech)	Approved meaning / ALTERNATIVES	APPROVED EXAMPLE	Not approved example
inadvertently (adv)	ACCIDENTALLY (adv)	IF YOU ACCIDENTALLY PUT TOO MUCH FUEL IN THE TANK, OPEN THE DRAIN VALVE.	If the tank is inadvertently overfilled, open the drain valve.
INBOARD (adj)	Nearer to the longitudinal axis	REMOVE THE INBOARD FAIRING OF THE FLAP HINGE.	
INBOARD (adv)	In or to a position nearer to the longitudinal axis	THE LANDING GEAR RETRACTS INBOARD INTO THE BAY.	
INBOARD OF (prep)	At a position nearer to the longitudinal axis	PUT THE ACCESS PLATFORM IN POSITION BELOW THE ACCESS PANEL THAT IS INBOARD OF THE FLAP TRACK.	
INCIDENT (n)	An important occurrence that can cause damage or have dangerous results	RECORD ALL INCIDENTS OF WATER FOUND IN THE FUEL.	
incline (n)	SLOPE (n)	YOU CAN ADJUST THE SLOPE OF THE RAMP.	You can adjust the incline of the ramp.
INCLUDE (v), INCLUDES, INCLUDED, INCLUDED	To make, or to be, part of	THIS CHAPTER INCLUDES THE PROCEDURES FOR THE REMOVAL OF THE COMPONENTS.	
including (prep)	THRU (prep)	DO TESTS 4 THRU 8 AGAIN.	Repeat from test 4 up to and including test 8.
	WITH (prep)	SEND THE DEFECTIVE COVER, WITH THE OIL SAMPLES, TO THE REPAIR CENTER.	Return the defective cover, including the oil samples, to the repair center.
incompatible (adj)	NOT COMPATIBLE	THIS SOFTWARE IS NOT COMPATIBLE WITH OTHER OPERATING SYSTEMS.	This software is incompatible with other operating systems.
		THIS COOLANT IS NOT COMPATIBLE WITH ALUMINUM ALLOYS.	This coolant is incompatible with aluminum alloys.

Word (part of speech)	Approved meaning / ALTERNATIVES	APPROVED EXAMPLE	Not approved example
incomplete (adj)	NOT FULL	IF THE ACTUATOR TRAVEL IS NOT FULL, ADJUST THE RODS AGAIN.	If the actuator travel is incomplete, readjust the rods.
	NOT COMPLETED	IF THE ADJUSTMENT IS NOT COMPLETED, THE VALUES SHOWN ON THE INDICATOR WILL BE INCORRECT.	If the adjustment is incomplete, the values shown on the indicator will be incorrect.
	ALL (adj)	IF YOU DO NOT HAVE ALL THE RESULTS, DO THE TEST AGAIN.	If the results are incomplete, do the test again.
incorporate (v)	INCLUDE (v)	ALL MODELS INCLUDE A MICROPROCESSOR CONTROL UNIT.	All models incorporate a microprocessor control unit.
	HAVE (v)	SOME RELAYS HAVE A POTENTIOMETER.	Some relays incorporate a potentiometer.
incorporation (n)	INCLUDE (v)	THE MANUFACTURER INCLUDED A SECOND DIODE TO INCREASE THE RELIABILITY OF THE MOTOR.	Incorporation of a second diode increased the reliability of the motor.
INCORRECT (adj)	Not correct	IF THE TRIM TAB ADJUSTMENT IS INCORRECT, DO STEPS 7 THRU 10.	
INCORRECTLY (adv)	In an incorrect manner	IF YOU SEE THE RED MARK, THE PART IS INSTALLED INCORRECTLY.	

ASD STE 100

Word (part of speech)	Approved meaning / ALTERNATIVES	APPROVED EXAMPLE	Not approved example
increase (n)	INCREASE (v)	THE TEMPERATURE MUST INCREASE.	There must be an increase in temperature.
INCREASE (v), INCREASES, INCREASED, INCREASED	To make or become larger or higher in value	INCREASE THE VANE ANGLE TO 90 DEGREES.	
		MAKE SURE THAT THE TEMPERATURE INCREASES TO 30 °C.	
INCREMENT (n)	One of a sequence of regular operations done one after the other, to increase or decrease an adjustable quantity	ADJUST THE STOP BOLT IN INCREMENTS OF 5 mm.	
incur (v)	CAUSE (v)	REMOVAL OF THE UNIT BEFORE 24 HOURS CAN CAUSE DAMAGE.	Removal of the unit before 24 hours can incur damage.
independent (adj)	INDEPENDENTLY (adv)	THIS UNIT OPERATES INDEPENDENTLY.	The operation of this unit is independent.
INDEPENDENTLY (adv)	Without a relation with	THE EMERGENCY SYSTEM IS CONTROLLED INDEPENDENTLY.	
indicate (v)	SHOW (v)	THE POINTER SHOWS ZERO FEET.	The pointer indicates zero feet.
	IDENTIFY (v)	A 406 MHz DIGITAL SIGNAL IDENTIFIES THE EMERGENCY LOCATOR TRANSMITTER AND ITS LOCATION.	A 406 MHz digital signal indicates the emergency locator transmitter and its location.
INDICATION (n)	Something that is shown	MAKE SURE THAT THE INDICATION IS CORRECT.	
induce (v)	CAUSE (v)	SCRATCHES IN THE WINDSCREEN CAN CAUSE CRACKS.	Scratches in the windscreen may induce cracks.

Word (part of speech)	Approved meaning / ALTERNATIVES	APPROVED EXAMPLE	Not approved example
ineffective (adj)	UNSERVICEABLE (adj)	IF THE PUMP IS UNSERVICEABLE, REPLACE IT.	If the pump is ineffective, replace it.
	UNSATISFACTORY (adj)	IF THE OPERATION OF THE PUMP IS UNSATISFACTORY, REPLACE IT.	If the operation of the pump is ineffective, replace it.
	NOT OPERATE	IF THE PUMP DOES NOT OPERATE CORRECTLY, REPLACE IT.	If the pump is ineffective, replace it.
inflammable (adj)	FLAMMABLE (adj)	SOLVENT IS VERY FLAMMABLE.	Solvent is highly inflammable.
INFLATE (v), INFLATES, INFLATED, INFLATED	To make or become larger as a result of pressurization by a gas	INFLATE THE TIRES WITH NITROGEN. OPERATION OF THE HANDLE RELEASES THE GAS, AND THE SLIDE-RAFT INFLATES.	
inform (v)	TELL (v)	TELL THE MANUFACTURER ABOUT THE PROBLEM.	Inform the manufacturer about the problem.
INFORMATION (n)	Data collected and made available for a specified function	THIS MANUAL CONTAINS INFORMATION ABOUT MAINTENANCE PROCEDURES.	
ingest (v)	SWALLOW (v)	IF YOU SWALLOW HYDRAULIC FLUID, GET MEDICAL AID IMMEDIATELY.	If you ingest hydraulic fluid, get medical aid immediately.
ingress (n)	GO INTO	IF WATER GOES INTO THE COMPONENT, DAMAGE WILL OCCUR.	Water ingress will damage the component.

ASD STE 100

Word (part of speech)	Approved meaning / ALTERNATIVES	APPROVED EXAMPLE	Not approved example
inhale (v)	BREATHE (v)	DO NOT BREATHE THE SOLVENT FUMES.	Do not inhale the solvent fumes.
inhibit (v)	PREVENT (v)	ALODINE PREVENTS CORROSION.	Alodine inhibits corrosion.
INITIAL (adj)	That is related to the start	MOVE THE LEVER BACK TO ITS INITIAL POSITION.	
INITIALLY (adv)	At the start	INITIALLY, THE SPEED INCREASES TO 3000 RPM.	
initiate (v)	START (v)	START THE TEST AT 2000 RPM.	Initiate the test at 2000 rpm.
inject (v)	PUT (v)	PUT OIL INTO THE GEARBOX WITH A SYRINGE.	Inject oil into the gearbox with a syringe.
injection (n)	PUT (v)	PUT THE CORROSION PREVENTIVE OIL INTO THE PUMP WITH A SYRINGE.	The injection of the corrosion preventive oil into the pump must be done with a syringe.
injure (v)	INJURY (n)	MAKE SURE THAT THE END OF THE SAFETY WIRE WILL NOT CAUSE INJURY TO PERSONNEL.	Make sure that the end of the safety wire will not injure personnel.
INJURY (n)	Damage to a person	BEND THE ENDS OF THE LOCKING WIRE TO PREVENT INJURY.	
INNER (adj)	Nearer to the center of an object	THE INNER SURFACE OF THE PART IS BLACK.	
inoperative (adj)	OFF (adj)	BEFORE YOU DRAIN THE FUEL, MAKE SURE THAT THE SYSTEM IS OFF.	Before you drain the fuel, make sure that the system is inoperative.
	NOT OPERATE	MAKE SURE THAT THE DEMISTING SYSTEM DOES NOT OPERATE.	Make sure that the demisting system is inoperative.
INPUT (n)	The data, power, or energy put into equipment or a system	THE UNIT COMPARES THE INPUTS FROM THE TWO SENSORS TO THE COMPUTER.	

Word (part of speech)	Approved meaning / ALTERNATIVES	APPROVED EXAMPLE	Not approved example
insert (v)	PUT (v)	PUT THE SLEEVE INTO THE OPENING.	Insert the sleeve into the opening.
	ENGAGE (v)	MAKE SURE THAT THE SHAFT ENGAGES IN THE MATING PART.	Check that the shaft is inserted in the mating part.
inside (adj)	INNER (adj)	CLEAN THE INNER SURFACE OF THE CONTAINER.	Clean the inside surface of the container.
inside (n)	INNER (adj)	PAINT THE INNER SURFACE OF THE PUMP ASSEMBLY.	Paint the inside surface of the pump assembly.
inside (prep)	IN (prep)	THERE MUST BE LUBRICANT IN THE HOLE.	There must be lubricant inside the hole.
	INTO (prep)	SAFETY ALL COMPONENTS BEFORE YOU PUT THEM INTO THE FUEL TANK.	Safety all components before you place them inside the fuel tank.
inspect (v)	EXAMINE (v)	EXAMINE ALL THE DRAIN HOLES.	Inspect all the drain holes.
	INSPECTION (n)	DO AN INSPECTION OF THE WORK.	Inspect the work.
INSPECTION (n)	The procedure which compares an object with its standard or specification	USE A VOLTMETER TO DO THIS INSPECTION.	
INSTALL (v), INSTALLS, INSTALLED, INSTALLED	To attach an item in or to a second item	INSTALL THE NEW O-RINGS ON THE SPINDLE.	
INSTALLATION (n)	The procedure which installs an item	REFER TO PARAGRAPH 3 FOR THE INSTALLATION OF THE UNIT.	
instead (adv)	ALTERNATIVE (n)	USE A SPATULA AS AN ALTERNATIVE.	Use a spatula instead.

ASD STE 100

Word (part of speech)	Approved meaning / ALTERNATIVES	APPROVED EXAMPLE	Not approved example
instead of (prep)	ALTERNATIVE (n)	YOU CAN USE A CLEAN PLASTIC BAG AS AN ALTERNATIVE TO THE SPECIFIED CONTAINER.	You can use a clean plastic bag instead of the specified container.
INSTRUCTION (n)	A command that you must obey	IF YOU DO NOT OBEY THIS INSTRUCTION, DAMAGE CAN OCCUR.	
INSTRUMENT (n)	An item which measures and/or shows	ALL THE INSTRUMENTS ARE ON THE LEFT QUARTER PANEL.	
insufficient (adj)	NOT SUFFICIENT	IF THIS STEP IS NOT SUFFICIENT TO STOP THE LEAKAGE, REPLACE THE ACTUATOR.	If this step is insufficient to stop the leakage, replace the actuator.
INSULATION (n)	A material that helps to prevent the movement of energy	MAKE SURE THAT YOU DO NOT CAUSE DAMAGE TO THE INSULATION.	
insure (v)	MAKE SURE (v)	MAKE SURE THAT THE WORK BENCH IS CLEAN.	Insure that the work bench is clean.
intact (adj)	NOT DAMAGED	MAKE SURE THAT THE WINDSCREEN IS NOT DAMAGED.	Make sure the windscreen is intact.
integral (adj)	PART (n)	THE PIN IS A PART OF THE PUMP.	The pin is integral with the pump.
INTENSITY (n)	The quantity of strength, force, or energy	OPERATE THE DIMMER SWITCH AND MAKE SURE THAT THE INTENSITY OF THE LIGHT CHANGES.	
INTERCHANGE (v), INTERCHANGES, INTERCHANGED, INTERCHANGED	To put or use each of two things in the place of the other without change	INTERCHANGE THE No. 1 AND No. 2 COMPUTERS. THEN DO THE TEST AGAIN.	

Word (part of speech)	Approved meaning / ALTERNATIVES	APPROVED EXAMPLE	Not approved example
INTERCHANGE-ABLE (adj)	That you can interchange	RELAYS 2YG AND 8YG ARE FULLY INTERCHANGEABLE ITEMS.	
interconnect (v)	CONNECT (v)	THE PIPES CONNECT SYSTEM A TO SYSTEM B.	The pipes interconnect system A and system B.
INTERFACE (n)	The connection between two systems or components	CLEAN THE INTERFACE BETWEEN THE COMPUTER AND THE SENSOR.	
interfere (v)	HIT (v)	IF YOU INSTALL THE UPPER DRAG STRUT WITH THE HEAD DOWN, IT WILL HIT THE LOWER DRAG STRUT DURING RETRACTION.	Placing the upper drag strut upside down makes it interfere with the lower drag strut.
	CATCH (v)	MAKE SURE THAT THE RODS CANNOT CATCH ON THE FLAPS.	Make sure the rods cannot interfere with the flaps.
	TOUCH (v)	IF THE BRACKET TOUCHES THE PLATE, REMOVE THE UNWANTED MATERIAL WITH A FILE.	Should the bracket interfere with the plate, remove surplus material with a file.
	INTERFERENCE (TN)	MAKE SURE THAT THERE IS NO INTERFERENCE BETWEEN THE RADAR AND THE TACTICAL AIR NAVIGATION SYSTEM (TACAN).	Ensure that the radar does not interfere with the Tactical Air Navigation System (TACAN).

ASD STE 100

Word (part of speech)	Approved meaning / ALTERNATIVES	APPROVED EXAMPLE	Not approved example
interference (n)	HIT (v)	IF YOU INSTALL THE UPPER DRAG STRUT WITH THE HEAD DOWN, IT WILL HIT THE LOWER DRAG STRUT DURING RETRACTION.	Placing the upper drag strut upside down causes interference with the lower drag strut.
	CATCH (v)	MAKE SURE THAT THE RODS CANNOT CATCH ON THE FLAPS.	Make sure that there is no interference between the rods and the flaps.
	TOUCH (v)	MAKE SURE THAT THE LOCKING WIRE DOES NOT TOUCH THE LEVER.	Ensure that there is no interference between the locking wire and the lever.
	💡 This word can be a technical name or part of a technical name.	MAKE SURE THAT YOU DO NOT HEAR INTERFERENCE IN THE 400 Hz BAND.	
		INTERFERENCE BOLTS ATTACH THE STRAP AND THE BOTTOM SKIN PANEL TO THE TRIFORM MEMBER.	
interior (n)	INTERNALLY (adv)	EXAMINE THE TANK INTERNALLY.	Examine the interior of the tank.
	INTERNAL (adj)	APPLY A SMALL QUANTITY OF LUBRICANT TO THE INTERNAL SIDE OF THE VALVE HOUSING.	Apply a small quantity of lubricant to the interior of the valve housing.
intermediate (adj)	MIDDLE (adj)	PUT THE LEVER IN THE MIDDLE POSITION.	Put the lever in intermediate position.
	BETWEEN (prep) 💡 Give the limits.	WHEN THE INPUT LEVER IS BETWEEN 5 AND 10 mm, MEASURE THE PISTON EXTENSION.	When the input lever is in an intermediate position, measure the piston extension.

Word (part of speech)	Approved meaning / ALTERNATIVES	APPROVED EXAMPLE	Not approved example
INTERMITTENT (adj)	That stops and starts again, not continuous	THIS CAUSES INTERMITTENT OPERATION OF THE WARNING LIGHTS.	
INTERMITTENTLY (adv)	In an intermittent manner	THE LIGHT COMES ON INTERMITTENTLY.	
INTERNAL (adj)	Of, or on, the inner side and inner space	MAKE SURE THAT FUEL COMES OUT OF THE INTERNAL EJECTORS.	
INTERNALLY (adv)	Of, or on, the inner side and inner space	USE A BORESCOPE TO EXAMINE THE COMBUSTOR INTERNALLY.	
interrupt (v)	STOP (v)	DO NOT STOP THE TEST.	Do not interrupt the test.
intersect (v)	INTERSECTION (TN)	DRILL A HOLE AT THE INTERSECTION OF THE TWO LINES.	Drill a hole where the two lines intersect.
INTERVAL (n)	A distance or gap between two points in space or time	DO THE TEST AT FIVE-MINUTE INTERVALS.	
INTO (prep)	Movement to something and access to it	IF AN OBJECT FALLS INTO THE OPENING, DAMAGE TO THE ENGINE CAN OCCUR.	
	Function word that shows change, condition, result	THE PARTS OF THE STRUCTURE ARE DIVIDED INTO THREE GROUPS.	
investigate (v)	INVESTIGATION (n)	DO AN INVESTIGATION TO FIND THE CAUSE OF THE FUEL LEAKAGE.	Investigate the cause of the fuel leakage.
INVESTIGATION (n)	An official and accurate enquiry or research	THE TASK TEAM STARTED THE INVESTIGATION TO FIND THE CAUSE OF THE ACCIDENT.	

ASD STE 100

Word (part of speech)	Approved meaning / ALTERNATIVES	APPROVED EXAMPLE	Not approved example
inward (adj)	INNER (adj)	MEASURE THE INNER DIAMETER OF THE HOLE.	Measure the inward diameter of the hole.
inward (adv)	IN (adv)	MOVE THE DOOR IN AND REARWARD.	Move the door inward and rearward.
IRREGULAR (adj)	Not regular	IF THE SIGNALS ARE IRREGULAR, REPLACE THE UNIT.	
irregularity (n)	DAMAGE (n)	THERE MUST BE NO DAMAGE TO THE SURFACE FINISH.	There must be no irregularities in the surface finish.
	DEFECT (TN)	THERE MUST BE NO DEFECTS IN THE SURFACE FINISH.	There must be no irregularities in the surface finish.
	IRREGULAR (adj)	IF YOU GET IRREGULAR RESULTS, DO THE TEST AGAIN.	If you get irregularities in the results, do the test again.
	UNUSUAL (adj)	IF YOU GET UNUSUAL RESULTS, DO THE TEST AGAIN.	If you get irregularities in the results, do the test again.
IRREGULARLY (adv)	Not regularly	IF THE UNIT RECEIVES THE SIGNALS IRREGULARLY, REPLACE IT.	
ISOLATE (v), ISOLATES, ISOLATED, ISOLATED	To prevent a supply or connection to	ISOLATE THE ELECTRICAL POWER SUPPLY.	
isolation (n)	ISOLATE (v)	ISOLATE SYSTEM No. 1 TO DO THE LEAKAGE CHECKS.	Isolation of system No. 1 is necessary to do the leakage checks.
IT (pron)	That thing	CAREFULLY MOVE THE DEFLECTOR UNIT DOWN UNTIL IT ENGAGES.	
ITEM (n)	A thing that is determined or specified	LUBRICATE THESE ITEMS WITH GREASE.	
ITS (adj)	Belonging to a thing	REMOVE THE UNIT AND ITS WIRING.	

Word (part of speech)	Approved meaning / ALTERNATIVES	APPROVED EXAMPLE	Not approved example
jack (v)	JACK (TN)	DO NOT LIFT THE AIRCRAFT ON JACKS IF THE WIND SPEED IS MORE THAN 20 MPH.	Do not jack the aircraft if the wind speed exceeds 20 mph.
jam (v)	FREELY (adv)	MAKE SURE THAT THE VALVE SPINDLE MOVES FREELY.	Check that the valve spindle does not bind or jam.
job (n)	WORK (n)	DO THIS WORK IN A CLEAN AREA.	Do this job in a clean area.
	TASK (n)	DO THIS TASK IN A CLEAN AREA.	Do this job in a clean area.
join (v)	BOND (v)	USE ADHESIVE No. 35 TO BOND METAL TO METAL.	Use adhesive No. 35 to join metal to metal.
	ATTACH (v)	ATTACH SMOKE DETECTOR 1 TO SMOKE DETECTOR 2.	Join smoke detectors 1 and 2.
	CONNECT (v)	CONNECT THE HOSE TO THE PIPE WITH A CLIP	Join the hose to the pipe with a clip.
JOINT (n)	The area at which two surfaces or edges touch or are attached	SEAL THE JOINT WITH SEALING COMPOUND.	
just (adv)	IMMEDIATELY (adv)	KEEP THE RING IMMEDIATELY ABOVE THE JACK COLLARS.	Keep the ring just above the jack collars

ASD STE 100

Word (part of speech)	Approved meaning / ALTERNATIVES	APPROVED EXAMPLE	Not approved example
KEEP (v), KEEPS, KEPT, KEPT	To continue to have or hold	KEEP THE COMPOUND IN A CLOSED CONTAINER.	
key (v)	REFER (v)	THE ILLUSTRATION REFERS TO EACH STEP.	The illustration will be keyed to each of the steps.
	KEY (TN)	INSTALL THE KEY BETWEEN THE PULLEY AND THE SHAFT.	The pulley must be keyed to the shaft.
KILL (v), KILLS, KILLED, KILLED	To cause death	HIGH VOLTAGES CAN KILL YOU.	
kind (n)	TYPE (n)	YOU CAN USE TWO TYPES OF SEALING COMPOUND.	Two kinds of sealing compound can be used.
kink (v)	KINK (TN)	DO NOT MAKE KINKS IN THE CABLES.	Do not kink the cables.
knock (v)	HIT (v)	HIT THE CLAMP ON THE RIGHT SIDE WITH A HAMMER.	Knock the clamp on the right side with a hammer.
KNOW (v), KNOWS, KNEW, KNOWN	To be sure of data, to have data ready to use	IF YOU KNOW THE CLEARANCE, YOU CAN CALCULATE THE THICKNESS OF THE WASHER.	

Word (part of speech)	Approved meaning / ALTERNATIVES	APPROVED EXAMPLE	Not approved example
label (v)	IDENTIFY (v)	IDENTIFY THE COMPONENT WITH A CODE TO HELP YOU INSTALL IT AGAIN CORRECTLY.	Label the component with a code to help you install it again correctly.
	LABEL (TN)	PUT A LABEL ON THE RELAY ASSEMBLY.	Label the relay assembly.
lack (n)	NOT SUFFICIENT	DAMAGE CAN OCCUR TO THE PUMP IF THERE IS NOT SUFFICIENT OIL IN THE RESERVOIR.	Damage can occur to the pump if there is a lack of oil in the reservoir.
LAMINATED (adj)	Made of laminations	THIS PANEL IS MADE OF LAMINATED CARBON FIBER.	
LAMINATION (n)	Layers of one or more materials bonded together	IF THE LAMINATION IS DAMAGED, REPLACE THE PANEL.	
land (v)	LANDING (TN)	AFTER A HEAVY LANDING, DO THE HEAVY LANDING INSPECTION.	If the aircraft landed heavily, do the Heavy Landing Inspection.
LARGE (adj) (LARGER, LARGEST)	More than average in dimension, quantity, or capacity	CLEAN YOUR SKIN WITH A LARGE QUANTITY OF CLEAN WATER.	
LAST (adj)	That comes at the end	IMMEDIATELY AFTER THE LAST FLIGHT OF THE DAY, INSTALL ALL COVERS.	
LAST (adv)	After other persons or things	FILL THE OUTER TANKS LAST.	
last (v)	CONTINUE (v)	THE SIGNALS CONTINUE FOR 0.8 SECONDS.	The signals last 0.8 seconds.
LATCH (v), LATCHES, LATCHED, LATCHED	To hold something in position with a latching device	MAKE SURE THAT YOU LATCH THE DOOR CORRECTLY.	
		MAKE SURE THAT THE DOOR LATCHES CORRECTLY.	

ASD STE 100

Word (part of speech)	Approved meaning / ALTERNATIVES	APPROVED EXAMPLE	Not approved example
later (adj)	SUBSEQUENT (adj)	A SUBSEQUENT REPAIR WILL BE FOR THE NEW CONFIGURATION.	A later repair will be for the new configuration.
	THEN (adv)	DO THIS STEP FIRST. THEN, DISCONNECT THE CABLES.	Do this step first. At a later time, disconnect the cables.
later (adv)	SUBSEQUENTLY (adv)	MAKE SURE THAT THE TOOL IS SUBSEQUENTLY AVAILABLE FOR THE INSTALLATION PROCEDURE.	Make sure that the tool is available later for the installation procedure.
	WHEN (conj)	DO STEPS (3) THRU (5). DO STEP (6) WHEN THE AILERON MOVEMENT STOPS.	Do steps (3) to (5). Do step (6) later.
	Give the condition or time, if possible AFTER (prep)	THE BAR MOVES DOWN AFTER 20 SECONDS.	The bar moves down later.
LATERAL (adj)	Related to or on the side	ADJUST THE LATERAL LEVEL	
LATERALLY (adv)	In a lateral direction	PUSH THE UNIT OUT, AND THEN MOVE IT LATERALLY.	
lay (v)	PUT (v)	PUT COVERS ON THE FLOOR.	Lay covers on the floor.
LAYER (n)	A material applied to a surface or put on, or below, a second material	APPLY A THIN LAYER OF SEALING COMPOUND ON THE BARE METAL.	
lead (v)	PUT (v)	PUT THE TELEFLEX CABLE THROUGH THE BULKHEAD.	Lead the Teleflex cable through the bulkhead.
LEAK (n)	A crack, gap or hole which lets fluid or light go into or come out of something	EXAMINE THE SWIVEL COUPLINGS FOR LEAKS.	

Word (part of speech)	Approved meaning / ALTERNATIVES	APPROVED EXAMPLE	Not approved example
leak (v)	LEAK (n)	IF THERE ARE LEAKS IN THE SYSTEM, REPAIR THEM.	If the system is leaking, repair it.
LEAKAGE (n)	The quantity of material that goes through a leak	MEASURE THE LEAKAGE FROM THE OUTLET PORT.	
least (adv)	MINIMUM (adj)	REPAIR THE AREA WITH THE MINIMUM DAMAGE FIRST.	Repair the least damaged area first.
least (at least) (adv)	MINIMUM (adj)	THE MINIMUM TIME BETWEEN CHECKS IS TWO MINUTES.	The time between checks is at least two minutes.
	MINIMUM (n)	DO STEPS 13 THRU 16 FOR A MINIMUM OF THREE TIMES.	Do steps 13 thru 16 at least three times.
leave (v)	KEEP (v)	KEEP THE VENT VALVES OPEN.	Leave the vent valves open.
	LET ···. STAY (v)	LET THE VENT VALVES STAY OPEN.	Leave the vent valves open.
	GO (v)	IF FUEL SPILLS ON THE GROUND, IMMEDIATELY GO TO A SAFE AREA.	If fuel spills on the ground, immediately leave the contaminated area.
LEFT (adj)	On the west side when you look north	INSTALL THE CONTROL PANEL IN THE LEFT CONSOLE	
left-hand (adj)	LEFT (adj)	SET THE LEFT SWITCH TO "ON".	Set the left-hand switch to ON.
legible (adj)	READ (v)	MAKE SURE THAT YOU CAN READ THE IDENTIFICATION PLATES.	Make certain that the identification plates are legible.
LENGTH (n)	The distance from one end to the other end	MEASURE THE LENGTH OF THE JACK RAM.	
	The longer or longest of the three dimensions of an object	THE DIMENSIONS OF THE UNIT ARE: - LENGTH 300 mm - WIDTH 90 mm - THICKNESS 60 mm.	

251

Word (part of speech)	Approved meaning / ALTERNATIVES	APPROVED EXAMPLE	Not approved example
lengthen (v)	INCREASE (v)	DO NOT TRY TO INCREASE THE LENGTH OF THIS ROD.	Do not try to lengthen this rod.
LESS (adj) 💡 No other forms of this adjective.	Of smaller dimension, value, quantity, volume, or number	THE FLOW RATE MUST NOT BE LESS THAN 4.0 GPM.	
less (prep)	WITHOUT (prep)	THE JUNCTION BOX IS SUPPLIED WITHOUT THE TEST LEADS.	The junction box is supplied less the test leads.
LET (v), LETS, LET, LET	To give opportunity	LET THE ADHESIVE BECOME TACKY.	
lethal (adj)	KILL (v)	THE ELECTRICAL DISCHARGE FROM THESE POWER UNITS CAN KILL YOU.	The electrical discharge from these power units can be lethal.
LEVEL (adj)	Horizontal to a known datum	PARK THE VEHICLE ON LEVEL GROUND.	
LEVEL (n)	A horizontal line, plane, surface, or condition	FILL THE TANK TO THE CORRECT LEVEL (REFER TO FIG. 105).	
level (v)	LEVEL (adj)	MAKE THE AIRCRAFT LEVEL.	Level the aircraft.
liberal (adj)	LARGE (adj)	CLEAN THE WINDOW WITH LARGE QUANTITIES OF WATER AND SOAP.	Clean the window with liberal quantities of water and soap.
	THICK (adj)	APPLY A THICK LAYER OF THE COMPOUND.	Apply a liberal amount of the compound.
liberally (adv)	LARGE (adj)	APPLY A LARGE QUANTITY OF THE SOLUTION.	Apply the solution liberally.
		APPLY A THICK LAYER OF THE COMPOUND.	Apply the compound liberally.
lie (v)	BE (v)	THE OTHER PART OF THE CLIP IS ALONG THE BARREL.	The other part of the clip lies along the barrel.

Word (part of speech)	Approved meaning / ALTERNATIVES	APPROVED EXAMPLE	Not approved example
LIFE (n)	The time during which you can use an item or object	THE LIFE OF THE CARTRIDGE IN THE FIRE EXTINGUISHER IS 3 YEARS.	
LIFT (v), LIFTS, LIFTED, LIFTED	To move something up	LIFT THE COVER CAREFULLY.	
LIGHT (adj) (LIGHTER, LIGHTEST)	That has a small mass, weight, or force	APPLY A LIGHT FORCE ON THE RUDDER PEDALS.	
	For other meanings, use: THIN (adj)	APPLY A THIN LAYER OF SEALANT ON THE SEALING SURFACES OF THE CONTAINER.	Apply a light layer of sealant on the sealing surfaces of the container.
	SMALL (adj)	APPLY A SMALL QUANTITY OF LUBRICANT ON EACH O-RING BEFORE YOU INSTALL IT.	Apply a light quantity of lubricant on each O-ring before its installation.
light (v)	COME ON	MAKE SURE THAT THE FLUID INDICATOR LIGHT COMES ON.	Ensure that the fluid indicator light lights.
LIGHTING (n)	That which gives light to	A DIMMER UNIT CONTROLS THE PANEL LIGHTING.	
LIGHTLY (adv)	In a light manner	LIGHTLY RUB THE DEFECTIVE AREA WITH WET ABRASIVE PAPER.	
LIMIT (n)	A specified maximum or minimum quantity, number, time, or distance	IF THE CLEARANCES ARE NOT IN THE LIMITS GIVEN IN FIG. 4, REFER TO REPAIR SCHEME No. 2.	

ASD STE 100

Word (part of speech)	Approved meaning / ALTERNATIVES	APPROVED EXAMPLE	Not approved example
limitation (n)	LIMIT (n)	WHEN YOU LIFT THE AIRCRAFT ON JACKS, KEEP THE CENTER OF GRAVITY BETWEEN THESE LIMITS :	When you lift the aircraft on jacks, observe these center of gravity limitations :
limited (adj)	SMALL (adj)	THERE IS ONLY A SMALL NUMBER OF REPAIRS THAT YOU CAN DO.	There is only a limited number of repairs that you can do.
LINEAR (adj)	In a straight line	MAKE SURE THAT THE RESULTS ARE LINEAR.	
LINEARLY (adv)	In a straight line	INCREASE THE PRESSURE LINEARLY.	
link (v)	CONNECT (v)	CONNECT THE CABLES.	Link the cables.
	ATTACH (v)	ATTACH THE HOIST TO THE POWER UNIT.	Link the hoist to the power unit.
LIQUID (adj)	That has the properties of a liquid	DURING SERVICING, LIQUID OXYGEN FLOWS THROUGH THE STABILIZING CONTAINER.	
LIQUID (n)	A material that is not a gas or a solid	THE CONVERTER CHANGES THE LIQUID INTO A GAS.	
list (v)	RECORD (v)	RECORD THE TEST RESULTS.	List the test results.
		TABLE 1 SHOWS ALTERNATIVE ADHESIVES THAT YOU CAN USE.	Table 1 lists alternative adhesives that you can use.
LISTEN (v), LISTENS, LISTENED, LISTENED	To use your ears to hear of find.	LISTEN FOR THE SIGNAL	

Word (part of speech)	Approved meaning / ALTERNATIVES	APPROVED EXAMPLE	Not approved example
little (adj)	SMALL (adj)	THE DIAMETER OF THE TUBE IS TOO SMALL.	The diameter of the tube is too little.
	SHORT (adj)	INSTALL A SHORT LENGTH OF NEW TUBE.	Install a little length of new tube.
	NOT SUFFICIENT	IF THE PRESSURE IS NOT SUFFICIENT, THE TEST WILL STOP.	If the pressure is too little, the test will stop.
little (a little) (adj)	SMALL QUANTITY	ADD A SMALL QUANTITY OF DISINFECTANT TO THE SOLUTION.	Add a little disinfectant to the solution.
little (a little) (adv)	SMALL (adj)	AFTER YOU REMOVE THE NUT, THE RIB CAN MOVE DOWN A SMALL DISTANCE.	After you remove the nut, the rib can move down a little.
LIVE (adj)	That includes explosive material	SOME MAINTENANCE TASKS ARE NOT PERMITTED ON AIRCRAFT THAT HAVE LIVE AMMUNITION.	
	For electrical systems, use: ENERGIZE (v)	THE SYSTEM IS ENERGIZED.	The system has live electrical power.
load (v)	INSTALL (v)	INSTALL THE SPRING IN THE CARTRIDGE.	Load the spring in the cartridge.
	LOAD (TN)	PUT THE LOAD ON THE SPRING BALANCE.	Load the spring balance.
LOCAL (adj)	Applicable to a given location or position	SET THE "LAT" KNOB TO THE LOCAL LATITUDE.	
LOCALLY (adv)	Applicable to a given location or position	YOU CAN ALSO DO THIS TEST WITH A LOCALLY MADE TOOL	

Word (part of speech)	Approved meaning / ALTERNATIVES	APPROVED EXAMPLE	Not approved example
locate (v)	FIND (v)	USE TALCUM POWDER TO FIND EXTERNAL LEAKS.	Use talcum powder to locate external leaks.
	ENGAGE (v)	ENGAGE THE GEAR WHEEL ON THE SHAFT.	Locate the gear wheel on the shaft.
	PUT (v)	USE THE MARK TO HELP YOU PUT THE CLAMP IN ITS CORRECT POSITION.	Use the mark to locate the clamp.
LOCATION (n)	A place or site that you can find	FIGURES 1 THRU 4 SHOW THE LOCATIONS OF THE WALKWAYS.	
LOCK (v), LOCKS, LOCKED, LOCKED	To attach something, or hold it in position with a locking device	LOCK THE SWITCH AND REMOVE THE KEY.	
		MAKE SURE THAT THE SWITCH LOCKS BEFORE YOU CONTINUE.	
log (v)	RECORD (v)	RECORD THE COMPASS CORRECTIONS ON THE CARD.	Log the compass corrections on the card.
LONG (adj) (LONGER, LONGEST)	That has large length or duration	USE A TUBE WHICH IS 3.3 FEET LONG.	
long (as long as) (conj)	WHILE (conj)	WHILE THE DC SUPPLY IS ON, THE FAN MUST OPERATE.	As long as the DC supply is ON, the fan must operate.
long (no longer) (adv)	MAXIMUM LENGTH	USE A DRILL BIT THAT HAS A MAXIMUM LENGTH OF 45 mm.	Use a drill bit no longer than 45 mm.
	NOT··· AT THIS TIME	THIS PROCEDURE IS NOT APPLICABLE AT THIS TIME.	This procedure is no longer applicable.
	UNTIL···NOT	ADJUST THE POTENTIOMETER UNTIL YOU DO NOT HEAR A HUM FROM THE LOUDSPEAKER.	Adjust the potentiometer until the loudspeaker no longer hums.

Word (part of speech)	Approved meaning / ALTERNATIVES	APPROVED EXAMPLE	Not approved example
LONGITUDINAL (adj)	Related to the longitudinal axis	ADJUST THE LONGITUDINAL TRIM SYSTEM.	
LONGITUDINALLY (adv)	In a longitudinal direction	MOVE THE STAND LONGITUDINALLY.	
LOOK (v), LOOKS, LOOKED, LOOKED	To use your eyes to see or find	LOOK THROUGH THE INSPECTION WINDOW.	
LOOP (n)	A circular shape made in a flexible material	MAKE A LOOP OF WIRE AROUND THE UNIT.	
loop (v)	LOOP (n)	MAKE A LOOP OF WIRE AROUND THE UNIT.	Loop the wire around the unit.
LOOSE (adj)	On, in, but not attached	MAKE SURE THAT YOU REMOVE ALL TOOLS, EQUIPMENT, AND LOOSE OBJECTS FROM THE AIR INTAKE.	
	Not tight	DO A CHECK FOR LOOSE FASTENERS AND TIGHTEN THEM, IF NECESSARY.	
	For other meanings, use: TENSION (TN)	MAKE SURE THAT THERE IS TENSION IN THE CABLES.	Make sure that the cables are not loose.
LOOSELY (adv)	Not tightly	MAKE SURE THAT THE PARTS ARE LOOSELY ASSEMBLED.	
LOOSEN (v), LOOSENS, LOOSENED, LOOSENED	To cause to be not tight	LOOSEN THE SCREWS THAT ATTACH THE CLAMP TO THE SUPPORT.	
lose (v)	DECREASE (v)	THE EFFECT OF THE SOLVENT DECREASES QUICKLY.	The solvent loses its effectiveness quickly.

Word (part of speech)	Approved meaning / ALTERNATIVES	APPROVED EXAMPLE	Not approved example
lost (adj)	DECREASE (v)	IF THE PRESSURE DECREASES QUICKLY, THE SHEAR PINS IN THE LATCH WILL BREAK.	If the pressure is lost rapidly, the shear pins in the latch will break.
	NOT FIND	IT IS POSSIBLE THAT YOU CANNOT FIND THE RUBBER BUSHINGS.	The rubber bushings may be lost.
LOW (adj) (LOWER, LOWEST)	That is of small value	THE SWITCH SENSES LOW PRESSURE IN THE DISTRIBUTION CIRCUIT.	
LOWER (v), LOWERS, LOWERED, LOWERED	To move something down	LOWER THE ANTENNA TO GET ACCESS TO THE CABLE CONNECTOR.	
lowermost (adj)	BOTTOM (adj)	THE BOTTOM MARK ON THE BOARD IS RED.	The lowermost mark on the board is red.
LUBRICATE (v), LUBRICATES, LUBRICATED, LUBRICATED	To apply lubricant	LUBRICATE THE O-RINGS WITH HYDRAULIC FLUID (NATO CODE H-515)	
lukewarm (adj)	WARM (adj)	SOAK THE AREA WITH WARM WATER.	Soak the area with lukewarm water.

Word (part of speech)	Approved meaning / ALTERNATIVES	APPROVED EXAMPLE	Not approved example
MAGNETIC (adj)	Related to the properties of a magnet	REMOVE THE MAGNETIC DRAIN PLUG FROM THE OIL TANK.	
MAGNETICALLY (adv)	In a magnetic manner	RELEASE THE MAGNETICALLY LATCHED SWITCHES.	
magnetized (adj)	MAGNETIC (adj)	DO NOT USE MAGNETIC TOOLS TO ADJUST THE COMPASS.	Do not use magnetized tools to adjust the compass.
main (adj)	PRIMARY (adj)	THE PRIMARY CAUSE OF VALVE FAILURE IS CONTAMINATION OF THE HYDRAULIC FLUID.	The main cause of valve failure is contamination of hydraulic fluid.
maintain (v)	KEEP (v)	KEEP THE FLUID TEMPERATURE AT 70 °F.	Maintain the fluid temperature at 70 °F.
	HOLD (v)	TURN THE ROTATING TUBE 75 DEGREES. THEN HOLD THE TUBE IN THIS POSITION.	Turn the rotating tube 75 degrees. Then maintain the tube in this position.
	MAINTENANCE (n)	DO MAINTENANCE ON THE FUEL SYSTEM.	Maintain the fuel system.
MAINTENANCE (n)	The servicing and/or the repair of something to keep it in the correct condition	DO NOT REFUEL THE AIRCRAFT DURING MAINTENANCE.	
major (adj)	PRIMARY (adj)	THE PRIMARY FUNCTION OF THE POWER UNIT IS TO SUPPLY ELECTRICAL POWER.	The major function of the power unit is to supply electrical power.

Word (part of speech)	Approved meaning / ALTERNATIVES	APPROVED EXAMPLE	Not approved example
MAKE (v), MAKES, MADE, MADE	To manufacture, to cause to occur or to become	MAKE A RECESS FOR THE STUDS OF 5 mm.	
		MAKE THE CLOTH MOIST WITH WATER.	
		TILT THE FITTING TO MAKE THE BARREL NUT FALL OUT OF IT.	
make certain (v)	MAKE SURE (v)	MAKE SURE THAT THE VALVE IS OPEN.	Make certain that the valve is open.
MAKE SURE (v), MAKES SURE, MADE SURE, MADE SURE	To verify and/or do the necessary steps	MAKE SURE THAT NO LEAK DETECTION FLUID GOES INTO THE OXYGEN SYSTEM.	
maladjusted (adj)	INCORRECTLY ADJUSTED	IF THE WARNING LIGHT IS ON WHEN THE DOOR IS CLOSED, THE MICROSWITCH IS INCORRECTLY ADJUSTED.	If the warning light is on when the door is closed, the microswitch is maladjusted.
MALFUNCTION (n)	Incorrect operation	REFER TO TABLE 104 TO CORRECT THE MALFUNCTION.	
MANDATORY (adj)	That which you must do, use, or obey	THIS SERVICE BULLETIN IS MANDATORY.	
manipulate (v)	MOVE (v)	MOVE THE FLEXIBLE PIPE TO GET ACCESS TO THE BOTTOM BOLTS.	Manipulate the flexible pipe to get access to the bottom bolts.
	ADJUST (v)	ADJUST THE FLEXIBLE PIPE TO GET ACCESS TO THE BOTTOM BOLTS.	Manipulate the flexible pipe to get access to the bottom bolts.
MANUAL (adj)	Operated with the hands	USE THE MANUAL CONTROLS IF THE AUTOMATIC CONTROLS DO NOT OPERATE.	

Word (part of speech)	Approved meaning / ALTERNATIVES	APPROVED EXAMPLE	Not approved example
MANUAL (n)	A publication that supplies data related to a special subject	THIS MANUAL IDENTIFIES AND SUPPLIES THE PERFORMANCE DATA.	
MANUALLY (adv)	With your hands	MOVE THE LEVER MANUALLY.	
manufacture (v)	MAKE (v)	YOU CAN MAKE THE CLEARING TOOL LOCALLY.	The clearing tool can be manufactured locally.
MANY (adj) (MORE, MOST)	Of large number If possible, give the range, number, or quantity.	CORROSION CAN HAVE MANY CAUSES.	
MARK (n)	Something that you make or is made to show an identification, location, or direction	THE RED MARKS SHOW A MAXIMUM STEERING ANGLE OF 35 DEGREES.	
mark (v)	IDENTIFY (v)	IDENTIFY THE COMPONENT WITH A CODE TO HELP YOU INSTALL IT AGAIN CORRECTLY.	Mark the component with a code to help you install it again correctly.
	MARK (n)	PUT MARKS ON THE OUTER TUBE TO SHOW THE CLAMP LOCATIONS.	Mark the clamp locations on the outer tube.
mask (v)	APPLY (v)	APPLY MASKING TAPE TO THE TRANSPARENT PANEL	Mask the transparent panel with masking tape.
MASS (n)	The quantity of matter that is in an object and relates to its weight. The equivalent of inertia	STRUCTURAL OR EQUIPMENT MODIFICATIONS CAN CHANGE THE BASIC MASS AND THE CENTER-OF-GRAVITY COORDINATES.	

ASD STE 100

Word (part of speech)	Approved meaning / ALTERNATIVES	APPROVED EXAMPLE	Not approved example
match (v)	ALIGN (v)	FOLD THE GIRT ONTO THE CONTAINER UNTIL IT IS ALIGNED WITH THE VELCRO TAPE.	Fold the girt over the container so that the Velcro tape matches.
	AGREE (v)	MAKE SURE THAT THE SEAL AGREES WITH THE SHAPE OF THE PANEL.	Ensure the seal matches the panel shape.
mate (v)	CONNECT (v)	CONNECT THE PLUG TO THE RECEPTACLE.	Mate the plug to the receptacle.
	ENGAGE (v)	ENGAGE THE SPLINES ON THE SHAFT WITH THOSE IN THE GEARBOX.	Mate the splines on the shaft with those in the gearbox.
	TOGETHER (adv)	PUT THE SMOOTH SURFACES TOGETHER.	Mate the smooth surfaces.
MATERIAL (n)	1. A substance or something from which a thing is made	BEFORE YOU INSTALL THE SEAL, REMOVE THE UNWANTED MATERIAL.	
	2. Something made to do a task	YOU CAN USE EQUIVALENT ALTERNATIVES FOR THESE MATERIALS.	
MATING (adj)	Made to touch	APPLY GREASE ON THE MATING SURFACES OF THE STARTER GENERATOR.	
MATT (or MATTE) (adj)	Not glossy	APPLY MATT PAINT ON THE PANEL.	
matter (n)	MATERIAL (n)	REMOVE THE GLOSSY MATERIAL FROM THE SURFACE OF THE BLADE.	Remove the glossy matter from the surface of the blade.
MAXIMUM (adj)	Related to the largest dimension, quantity, number, or value	THE MAXIMUM VALUE THAT THE VOLTMETER SHOWS IS 199.9 V.	
MAXIMUM (n)	The largest dimension, quantity, number, or value	MOVE THE LEVER A MAXIMUM OF 45 DEG.	

Word (part of speech)	Approved meaning / ALTERNATIVES	APPROVED EXAMPLE	Not approved example
may (v)	CAN (v)	IF YOU USE INCORRECT EQUIPMENT, YOU CAN CAUSE DAMAGE TO THE VANES.	The vanes may be damaged by using incorrect equipment.
	POSSIBLY (adv)	IF YOU CANNOT ENGAGE THE ROD AND THE PISTON, THE LENGTH OF THE NEW ROD IS POSSIBLY INCORRECT.	If you cannot engage the rod and the piston, the length of the new rod may be incorrect.
MEASURE (v), MEASURES, MEASURED, MEASURED	To find the dimensions, capacity, or quantity of something	MEASURE THE LOAD.	
MECHANICAL (adj)	Related to or operated with a mechanism	THE STANDBY SYSTEM IS MECHANICAL.	
MECHANICALLY (adv)	In a mechanical manner	OPERATE THE HORIZONTAL STABILIZER MECHANICALLY.	
MECHANISM (n)	An assembly of mechanical parts that are made to operate together	USE WHITE SPIRIT TO CLEAN A HINGE MECHANISM THAT HAS A GREASE NIPPLE.	
MEDICAL (adj)	Related to medicine	IF YOU GET HYDRAULIC FLUID IN YOUR EYES, FLUSH THEM WITH WATER AND GET MEDICAL AID.	
medium (adj)	MODERATE (adj)	APPLY MODERATE PRESSURE.	A medium amount of pressure must be applied.
meet (v)	ENGAGE (v)	PUSH THE PIN IN UNTIL IT ENGAGES IN THE RETAINING CLIP.	Push the pin in until it meets with the retaining clip.
	TOUCH (v)	THE ROD MUST TOUCH THE CENTER OF THE STRIP.	The rod should meet the center of the strip.

ASD STE 100

Word (part of speech)	Approved meaning / ALTERNATIVES	APPROVED EXAMPLE	Not approved example
MELT (v), MELTS, MELTED, MELTED	To change or to cause something to change from solid to liquid because of heat	THE FUSIBLE PLUGS MUST MELT IN 20 SECONDS OR LESS. DO NOT USE A FLAME TO MELT THE ICE.	
mention (v)	GIVE (v)	THE REPAIR LIMITS ARE NOT GIVEN BECAUSE SPECIAL EQUIPMENT IS NECESSARY.	The repair limits are not mentioned as special equipment is required.
mesh (v)	ENGAGE (v)	IF THE GEARS DO NOT ENGAGE CORRECTLY, ADD A SHIM.	If the gears do not mesh correctly, add a shim.
metallic (adj)	METAL (TN)	EXAMINE THE FILTER FOR METAL PARTICLES.	Examine the filter for metallic particles.
meteorological (adj)	WEATHER (n)	DO THE TEST IN GOOD WEATHER.	Carry out the test in good meteorological conditions.
METHOD (n)	A special type of procedure used to get a specified result	THIS PROCEDURE GIVES TWO METHODS FOR THE TEMPORARY REPAIR OF THE WATER TUBES.	
mid (adj)	MIDDLE (adj)	PUT THE THROTTLE LEVER IN THE MIDDLE POSITION.	Place the throttle lever in mid position.
MIDDLE (adj)	At a point that is between two other points	REMOVE THE MIDDLE BELLCRANK UNIT.	
MIDDLE (n)	A point that is at or near the center	LIFT THE SEAT TO THE MIDDLE OF THE TRAVEL	
mild (adj)	WEAK (adj)	USE A WEAK SOAP SOLUTION TO CLEAN THE SIDEWALL PANEL	Use a mild soap solution to clean the sidewall panel.
minimize (v)	MINIMUM (n)	USE A TRESTLE TO KEEP THE LOADS ON THE WING TO A MINIMUM.	Use a trestle to minimize the loads on the wing.

Word (part of speech)	Approved meaning / ALTERNATIVES	APPROVED EXAMPLE	Not approved example
MINIMUM (adj)	Related to the smallest dimension, quantity, number, or value	MAKE SURE THAT THE FLUID IN THE HYDRAULIC RESERVOIR IS ABOVE THE MINIMUM LEVEL.	
MINIMUM (n)	The smallest dimension, quantity, number, or value	LET THE PAINT DRY FOR A MINIMUM OF 1 HOUR.	
minor (adj)	SMALL (adj)	YOU CAN IGNORE SMALL DIFFERENCES IN TEMPERATURE.	Minor differences in temperature can be ignored.
MINUS (prep)	With the subtraction of	INCREASE THE PRESSURE IN THE SHOCK ABSORBER TO 85.5 BAR, PLUS OR MINUS 2.7 BAR.	
miscellaneous (adj)	OTHER (adj)	REMOVE THE TOOLS AND THE OTHER RELATED ITEMS.	Remove the tools and the related miscellaneous items.
	ALL (adj)	REMOVE ALL EQUIPMENT.	Remove miscellaneous equipment.
misrigged (adj)	INCORRECTLY ADJUSTED	IF THE MARKS ARE NOT ALIGNED, THE LINKAGE IS INCORRECTLY ADJUSTED.	If the marks are not aligned, the linkage is misrigged.
MISSING (adj)	That is not there	IF SEALS ARE MISSING, INSTALL NEW SEALS	
mix (n)	MIXTURE (n)	THE POTLIFE OF THE MIXTURE IS APPROXIMATELY 4 HOURS.	The potlife of the mix is approximately 4 hours.
MIX (v), MIXES, MIXED, MIXED	1. To put together two or more materials to become one	MIX THE COMPOUND.	
	2. To become combined	IF METHANE AND AIR MIX, THERE IS A RISK OF EXPLOSION.	
MIXTURE (n)	The result that you get when you mix materials	DO NOT USE THIS MIXTURE WHEN THE TEMPERATURE IS LESS THAN 15 °C.	

Word (part of speech)	Approved meaning / ALTERNATIVES	APPROVED EXAMPLE	Not approved example
MOBILE (adj)	That is made to move easily	CONNECT THE MOBILE GROUND POWER UNIT.	
MODE (n)	A special condition of operation	MAKE SURE THAT THE "HEADING SELECT" MODE OPERATES.	
MODERATE (adj)	Between low and high values	APPLY A MODERATE LOAD ON THE BRAKE PEDALS.	
MODERATELY (adv)	In a moderate manner	YOU CAN APPLY A SECOND LAYER WHEN THE SURFACE IS MODERATELY DRY.	
modify (v)	CHANGE (v)	SERVICE BULLETIN NO. 105 CHANGES THE BOLTS THAT ATTACH THE POWER CONTROL UNIT.	Service Bulletin No. 105 modifies the power control unit attachment bolts.
MOIST (adj)	Moderately wet	CLEAN THE PANEL WITH A MOIST CLOTH.	
moisten (v)	MOIST (adj)	MAKE THE CLOTH MOIST WITH SOLVENT.	Moisten the cloth with solvent.
MOMENTARILY (adv)	For a short time	STOP THE PUMP MOMENTARILY. THEN START IT AGAIN.	
momentary (adj)	MOMENTARILY (adv)	MAKE SURE THAT THE SPEED INCREASES MOMENTARILY.	Check for momentary increase in speed.
MONITOR (v), MONITORS, MONITORED, MONITORED	To do a check at something for a period of time to find if there is a change	MONITOR THE INDICATORS ON THE OVERHEAD PANEL. HEAT SENSORS MONITOR THE AMBIENT TEMPERATURE.	
MOOR (v), MOORS, MOORED, MOORED	To hold something in position with ropes and cables	IN BAD WEATHER CONDITIONS, MOOR THE BOAT.	
MORE (adj)	Refer to MANY (adj) and MUCH (adj)		

Word (part of speech)	Approved meaning / ALTERNATIVES	APPROVED EXAMPLE	Not approved example
MORE (adv)	By a larger dimension, value, quantity, number, or degree	IF IT IS NECESSARY TO DECREASE THE CABLE TENSION MORE, USE THE TURNBUCKLE.	
MOST (adj)	Refer to MANY (adj) and MUCH (adj)		
motion (n)	MOVEMENT (n)	MAKE SURE THAT THE STABILIZER MOVEMENT CONTINUES	Check that the stabilizer motion continues.
motor (v)	DRY-MOTOR (TV)	DRY-MOTOR THE ENGINE.	Motor the engine without fuel.
	WET-MOTOR (TV)	WET-MOTOR THE ENGINE.	Motor the engine without ignition.
	MOTORING (TN)	DO A MOTORING PROCEDURE.	Motor the engine.
mount (v)	INSTALL (v)	INSTALL THE MANIFOLD.	Mount the manifold.
	ATTACH (v)	ATTACH THE SEATS TO THE SEAT TRACKS.	Mount the seats on the seat tracks.
	PUT (v)	PUT THE WHEEL ON THE AXLE.	Mount the wheel on the axle.
MOVABLE (adj)	That can move if necessary	TURN THE MOVABLE HALF-COLLAR OF THE SUPPORT.	
MOVE (v), MOVES, MOVED, MOVED	To change or cause to change position or location	MAKE SURE THAT THE POINTER MOVES FREELY.	
		MOVE THE VALVE UNTIL IT ALIGNS WITH THE ACTUATOR SHAFT.	
MOVEMENT (n)	A change of position or location	SUDDEN OPERATION OF THE GYRO CAN CAUSE UNWANTED MOVEMENT OF THE HORIZONTAL STABILIZER.	

ASD STE 100

Word (part of speech)	Approved meaning / ALTERNATIVES	APPROVED EXAMPLE	Not approved example
MUCH (adj) (MORE, MOST)	Of relatively large dimension, value, quantity, or volume	DO NOT APPLY TOO MUCH PRESSURE.	
MUCH (adv)	To a great degree or extent	BE CAREFUL THAT YOU DO NOT TURN THE INNER RACES TOO MUCH.	
MULTIPLY (v), MULTIPLIES, MULTIPLIED, MULTIPLIED	To use multiplication to get a result	MULTIPLY THE INDICATOR VALUE BY THE SCALE VALUE.	
	💡 For other meanings, use: INCREASE (v)	THE NUMBER OF CRACKS CAN INCREASE.	Cracks can multiply.
MUST (v)	Helping verb that shows obligation	THE BAT 1 SWITCH MUST BE IN THE ON POSITION.	

Word (part of speech)	Approved meaning / ALTERNATIVES	APPROVED EXAMPLE	Not approved example
NAME (n)	The identification you give to a person or an object	PUSH THE LINE KEY ADJACENT TO THE NAME OF THE SYSTEM.	
		ENTER YOUR NAME AND YOUR PASSWORD.	
NEAR (adj) (NEARER, NEAREST)	At or to a relatively short distance	PUT THE TOOL ON THE NEAR FACE OF THE COMPONENT	
NEAR (prep)	Approaching in space or condition	BALANCE THE ELEVATOR NEAR ITS MAXIMUM LIMIT.	
		THE FLIGHT DATA RECORDER IS NEAR THE DOOR.	
nearly (adv)	ALMOST (adv)	MOVE THE POINTER UNTIL IT IS ALMOST IN THE GREEN BAND.	Move the pointer until nearly in the green band.
NECESSARY (adj)	That must be	TWO HOURS ARE NECESSARY TO COMPLETE THE PROCEDURE	
need (v)	NECESSARY (adj)	IT IS NOT NECESSARY TO REPLACE THE BACKING RINGS.	The backing rings do not need to be replaced.
neither (adj)	TWO (TN)···NOT	THE TWO UNITS MUST NOT OPERATE.	Neither unit must operate.
neither (pron)	TWO (TN)···NOT	THE TWO UNITS MUST NOT OPERATE.	Neither of the units must operate.
NEUTRAL (adj)	1. That has no effect	MAKE SURE THAT THE CONTROLS ARE IN THE NEUTRAL POSITION.	
	2. That is not acid or alkaline	CLEAN THE SCREEN WITH A NEUTRAL SOLUTION.	

269

Word (part of speech)	Approved meaning / ALTERNATIVES	APPROVED EXAMPLE	Not approved example
neutralize (v)	NEUTRAL (adj)	MAKE THE ELECTROLYTE NEUTRAL WITH VINEGAR OR BORIC ACID.	Neutralize the electrolyte with vinegar or boric acid.
never (adv)	DO NOT	DO NOT LET THE LEVEL IN THE TANK DECREASE TO LESS THAN HALF.	Never allow the level in the tank to drop below half.
NEW (adj) (NEWER, NEWEST)	Not used before	INSTALL A NEW GASKET ON THE FLANGE.	
NEXT (adj)	The first occurrence that follows immediately after in time or sequence.	REMOVE THE UNIT BEFORE THE NEXT FLIGHT.	
next (adv)	THEN (adv)	HOLD THE FLANGE IN ITS POSITION. THEN, INSTALL THE BOLT.	Hold the flange in its position. Next, install the bolt.
next to (prep)	ADJACENT TO (prep)	THE PUMP IS ADJACENT TO THE MIDDLE RIB.	The pump is next to the middle rib.
NO (adj)	Not any	MAKE SURE THAT THERE IS NO FUEL LEAKAGE.	
NO (adv)	Function word that shows the negative answer to a question	DOES THE LIGHT COME ON? YES OR NO?	
NOISE (n)	An unwanted sound	WHILE THE ENGINE CONTINUES TO TURN, LISTEN FOR UNUSUAL NOISES.	
noisy (adj)	NOISE (n)	IF THERE IS NOISE WHEN THE PUMP OPERATES, EXAMINE THE FILTER FOR METAL PARTICLES.	If pump operation is noisy, check the pump filter for metal particles.
NONE (pron)	Not one, not anyone	IF NONE OF THE BRACKETS ARE DAMAGED, CONTINUE THE INSPECTION.	

Word (part of speech)	Approved meaning / ALTERNATIVES	APPROVED EXAMPLE	Not approved example
nor (conj)	NOT (adv)	IN THESE CONDITIONS, THE MECHANICAL AND ELECTRICAL PITCH TRIM SYSTEMS WILL NOT OPERATE.	In these conditions, neither the mechanical nor the electrical pitch trim systems will operate.
normal (adj)	USUAL (adj)	THE ARMED POSITION IS THE USUAL POSITION OF THE SWITCH.	The ARMED position is the normal position of the switch.
	CORRECT (adj)	THE CORRECT PRESSURE FOR OPERATION IS 3000 PSI.	Normal operating pressure is 3000 psi.
normally (adv)	USUALLY (adv)	THE SWITCH IS USUALLY IN THE ARMED POSITION.	The switch is normally in the ARMED position.
	CORRECTLY (adv)	IF THE SYSTEM DOES NOT OPERATE CORRECTLY, REFER TO THE FAULT ISOLATION PROCEDURE.	If the system does not operate normally, refer to the fault isolation procedure.
NOSE (n)	The front end or part, a part that protrudes	PULL THE TRANSPARENT PLASTIC COLLAR AWAY FROM THE NOSE OF THE ELECTRICAL LATCH.	
NOT (adv)	Adverb of negation	DO NOT LET THE PRESSURE INCREASE TO MORE THAN 3000 PSI.	
NOTCH (n)	An area in the shape of a "V"	MAKE SURE THAT THE BOGIE ROLLERS ARE ALIGNED WITH THE NOTCHES IN THE TRACK.	

ASD STE 100

Word (part of speech)	Approved meaning / ALTERNATIVES	APPROVED EXAMPLE	Not approved example
note (v)	RECORD (v)	RECORD DIMENSION "A".	Note dimension A.
notify (v)	TELL (v)	IF YOU FIND CRACKS, TELL THE CHIEF INSPECTOR.	If cracks are found, notify the chief inspector.
	WRITE (v)	IF THE UNIT DOES NOT OPERATE CORRECTLY, WRITE TO THE MANUFACTURER.	If the unit does not operate correctly, notify the manufacturer.
now (adv)	AT THIS TIME	DO NOT TIGHTEN THE NUTS AT THIS TIME.	Do not tighten the nuts now.
NUMBER (n)	1. A symbol or word that identifies an integer and/or decimal	NEGATIVE NUMBERS SHOW THAT THE PRESSURE DECREASES.	
	2. An amount that you can count or calculate	IF THE NUMBER OF FAILURES IS MORE THAN THREE, REPLACE THE UNIT.	

Word (part of speech)	Approved meaning / ALTERNATIVES	APPROVED EXAMPLE	Not approved example
OBEY (v), OBEYS, OBEYED, OBEYED	To do that which the procedures or instructions tell you	OBEY THE PRECAUTIONS THAT FOLLOW.	
OBJECT (n)	Something that you can see or touch	MAKE SURE THAT THERE ARE NO LOOSE OBJECTS IN THE AIR INTAKE.	
observe (v)	MONITOR (v)	MONITOR THE RADIO ALTIMETER INDICATOR.	Observe the radio altimeter indicator.
	SEE (v)	IF YOU SEE OIL IN THE DRAIN, STOP THE TEST.	If you observe oil in the drain, stop the test.
	OBEY (v)	OBEY ALL SAFETY PRECAUTIONS.	Observe all safety precautions.
obstruct (v)	CATCH (v)	MAKE SURE THAT THE DRAG STRUTS DO NOT CATCH ON THE LANDING GEAR.	Make sure that the drag struts do not obstruct the landing gear.
	PREVENT (v)	ADJUST THE LEVER ARMS IF THEY PREVENT MOVEMENT.	Adjust the lever arms if they obstruct movement.
	BLOCKAGE (n)	REMOVE THE DIRT THAT CAUSES THE BLOCKAGE IN THE TUBE.	Remove the dirt obstructing the tube.
obstructed (adj)	BLOCKED (adj)	IF THE DRAIN HOLE IS BLOCKED, REMOVE THE UNWANTED MATERIAL.	If the drain hole is obstructed, remove the unwanted material.
	CLOGGED (adj)	IF THE DRAIN HOLE IS CLOGGED, CLEAN IT.	If the drain hole is obstructed, clean it.
obstruction (n)	BLOCKAGE (n)	EXAMINE THE DRAIN HOLES FOR BLOCKAGE.	Examine the drain holes for obstruction.
obtain (v)	GET (v)	ADD 0.05 mm TO GET THE CORRECT CLEARANCE FOR A STANDARD SPHERICAL COUPLING.	Add 0.05 mm to obtain the correct clearance for a standard spherical coupling.

Word (part of speech)	Approved meaning / ALTERNATIVES	APPROVED EXAMPLE	Not approved example
OCCUR (v), OCCURS OCCURRED	To be found or to take place, to come to be	A SUDDEN MOVEMENT OF THE CONTROL SURFACES CAN OCCUR.	
		IF THE SYMPTOMS OCCUR AGAIN, DO A SYSTEM TEST.	
OF (prep)	Function word that shows: from, belonging to, having, or containing	REMOVE THE SPLIT PINS FROM THE BOLTS IN THE BOTTOM ENDS OF THE CONTROL RODS.	
OFF (adj)	Not in operation	MAKE SURE THAT THE BATTERIES ARE OFF.	
OFF (adv)	1. Not in operation	MAKE SURE THAT THE WARNING LIGHT GOES OFF.	
	2. Not in contact	THE HANDLE MUST COME OFF EASILY.	
OFF (prep)	Not in contact with	MAKE SURE THAT THE TIRE IS FULLY OFF THE GROUND.	
often (adv)	FREQUENTLY (adv)	IF A FAILURE OCCURS FREQUENTLY, DO THE SYSTEM TEST.	If a failure occurs often, do the system test.
oil (v)	LUBRICATE (v)	LUBRICATE THE LINKAGE WITH OIL.	Oil the linkage.
	OIL (TN)	PUT OIL ON THE LINKAGE.	Oil the linkage.
oil-free (adj)	OIL (TN)	USE A SOLUTION THAT CONTAINS NO OIL.	Use an oil-free solution.
old (adj)	REMAINING (adj)	REMOVE THE REMAINING SEALANT.	Remove the old sealant.
	USED (adj)	DRAIN THE USED OIL INTO A CONTAINER.	Drain the old oil into a container.
	EXPIRED (adj)	MAKE SURE THAT THE SHELF LIFE OF THE MATERIAL IS NOT EXPIRED.	Make sure that the material is not too old.

Word (part of speech)	Approved meaning / ALTERNATIVES	APPROVED EXAMPLE	Not approved example
omit (v)	DO NOT DO	DO NOT DO STEPS 3 THRU 5.	Omit steps 3 to 5.
	IGNORE (v)	IGNORE STEPS 3 THRU 5.	Omit steps 3 to 5.
ON (adj)	In operation	MAKE SURE THAT THE BATTERIES ARE ON.	
ON (adv)	1. In operation	MAKE SURE THAT THE WARNING LIGHT COMES ON.	
	2. In contact	MAKE SURE THAT THE LID GOES ON EASILY.	
ON (prep)	Function word that shows contact, support, direction	PUT THE ASSEMBLED PARTS ON THE SUPPORT FITTING.	
once (adv)	ONE (TN) TIME	PUSH THE SWITCH ONE TIME.	Press the switch once.
once (conj)	WHEN (conj)	WHEN THE UNIT IS ON ITS MOUNTING, LOCK IT.	Once the unit is on its mounting, lock it.
ONE (pron)	That refers to a single person or object You can also use this word as a technical name.	IF THE LABEL IS NOT THERE, ATTACH A NEW ONE.	
ONLY (adj)	Nothing more or different	THIS IS THE ONLY APPROVED CONFIGURATION.	
ONLY (adv)	Exclusively	TO TIGHTEN THE NUTS, USE ONLY A TORQUE WRENCH.	
ONTO (prep)	To a position on or upon	WHEN YOU LOWER THE PUMP, MOVE IT ONTO THE MOUNTING BRACKETS.	
opaque (adj)	NOT TRANSPARENT	CLEAN THE PLASTIC SURFACES THAT ARE NOT TRANSPARENT	Clean the opaque plastic surfaces.
OPEN (adj)	That lets something go in or out	PUT A PLUG ON THE OPEN END OF EACH PIPE.	

ASD STE 100

Word (part of speech)	Approved meaning / ALTERNATIVES	APPROVED EXAMPLE	Not approved example
OPEN (v), OPENS, OPENED, OPENED	1. To move or cause to move from the closed position	OPEN THE PRESSURE VALVE.	
		WHEN THE RELIEF VALVE OPENS, THE PRESSURE DECREASES.	
	2. To operate a circuit breaker to interrupt an electrical circuit	OPEN THE CIRCUIT BREAKER.	
OPENING (n)	An aperture or hole in a surface	MAKE SURE THAT THE OPENING IS CLEAR.	
operable (adj)	OPERATE (v)	MAKE SURE THAT THE VALVE CAN OPERATE.	Check that the valve is operable.
		MAKE SURE THAT YOU CAN OPERATE THE VALVE.	Check that the valve is operable.
OPERATE (v), OPERATES, OPERATED, OPERATED	To put, keep, or be in action	OPERATE THE PLUNGER TO DRAIN THE SYSTEM.	
		DO NOT GO NEAR THE ENGINE WHEN IT OPERATES.	
OPERATION (n)	That which occurs when something operates or is operated	THIS PROCEDURE IS IMPORTANT FOR THE CORRECT OPERATION OF THE VALVE.	
operational (adj)	SERVICEABLE (adj)	MAKE SURE THAT THE OTHER MICROSWITCH IS SERVICEABLE.	Check that the other microswitch is operational.
	OPERATE (v)	MAKE SURE THAT THE GROUND-PROXIMITY WARNING SYSTEM CAN OPERATE.	Check that the ground-proximity warning system is operational.
opportunity (n)	Be specific if possible.	REPLACE THE UNIT AT THE NEXT CHECK.	Replace the unit at the first opportunity.

Word (part of speech)	Approved meaning / ALTERNATIVES	APPROVED EXAMPLE	Not approved example
OPPOSITE (adj)	1. In the other direction	THE RESET DEVICE OPERATES IN THE OPPOSITE DIRECTION.	
	2. Across from	THE BOLTS ARE ON THE OPPOSITE SIDE OF THE FLANGE.	
OPPOSITE (prep)	Across from	THE UNIT IS IN THE WHEEL BAY OPPOSITE THE LANDING GEAR.	
option (n)	POSSIBLE (adj)	IF POSSIBLE, DO THE INSPECTION IN DAYLIGHT.	If you have the option, do the inspection in daylight.
OPTIONAL (adj)	Not mandatory	THIS TOOL IS OPTIONAL.	
OR (conj)	Function word that shows a choice	DO NOT TOUCH THE HIGH TENSION LEADS OR THE IGNITER PLUGS.	
	⊙ Do not use this word with the meaning of otherwise. Use a different construction.	MAKE SURE THAT THE L-SHAPED SEAL STAYS BONDED. IF THE SEAL DOES NOT STAY BONDED, A LEAK CAN OCCUR.	Make sure that the L-shaped seal stays bonded or a leak can occur.
order (n)	SEQUENCE (n)	DO THE WEIGHING PROCEDURE IN THIS SEQUENCE:	Do the weighing procedure in the following order:
order (v)	TELL (v)	TELL ALL PERSONNEL TO GO OUT OF THE MAINTENANCE AREA.	Order all personnel out of the maintenance area.
	ORDER (TN)	SEND AN ORDER FOR THE SPECIFIED PAINT DIRECTLY TO THE MANUFACTURER.	Order the required paint directly from the manufacturer.
orient (v)		MAKE SURE THAT THE BOLT HEADS POINT TO THE REAR.	The bolt heads must be oriented toward the rear.
origin (n)	SOURCE (n)	THE SOURCE OF THE PROBLEM IS IN THE FUEL SYSTEM.	The origin of the problem is in the fuel system.

Word (part of speech)	Approved meaning / ALTERNATIVES	APPROVED EXAMPLE	Not approved example
original (adj)	INITIAL (adj)	THE SLIDE GOES BACK TO ITS INITIAL POSITION.	The slide returns to the original position.
originate (v)	SOURCE (n)	IF THE VALVE IS THE SOURCE OF THE FUEL LEAK, REPLACE THE VALVE SEALS.	If the fuel leak originates at the valve, replace the valve seals.
OTHER (adj)	Not the same as that given before	CONNECT ONE OF THE STUDS TO THE GROUND AND THE OTHER STUDS TO THE PINS.	
OTHER (pron)	That which is not the same as that given before	CONNECT ONE PLUG, THEN CONNECT THE OTHER.	
otherwise (adv)	IF ···NOT	MAKE SURE THAT THE RODS ARE ADJUSTED CORRECTLY. IF THE ADJUSTMENT IS NOT CORRECT, ADJUST THEM AS FOLLOWS:	Check that the rods are adjusted correctly, otherwise adjust them as follows:
	DIFFERENTLY (adv)	UNLESS THE INSTRUCTIONS TELL YOU DIFFERENTLY, DO REPAIR SCHEME No. 4.	Unless the instructions tell you otherwise, do repair scheme No. 4.
OUT (adj)	Away from, or not in, a location or position	IF THE INDICATOR BUTTON IS OUT, REPLACE THE FILTER.	
OUT (adv)	To a position away from the inside	WHEN THE INDICATOR BUTTON COMES OUT, REPLACE THE FILTER.	
OUT OF (prep)	1. Through or from the inside to the outside	TILT THE FITTING TO MAKE THE BARREL NUT FALL OUT OF IT.	
	2. Not in	KEEP THE COMPOUND OUT OF THE SUNLIGHT.	

Word (part of speech)	Approved meaning / ALTERNATIVES	APPROVED EXAMPLE	Not approved example
OUTBOARD (adj)	Farther from the longitudinal axis of something	MEASURE THE MOVEMENT OF THE INBOARD AND OUTBOARD FLAPS.	
OUTBOARD (adv)	In, or to, a position farther from the longitudinal axis of something	MOVE THE JACK OUTBOARD TO DISENGAGE IT FROM THE JACKING POINT.	
OUTBOARD OF (prep)	At a position farther from the longitudinal axis	PUT THE ACCESS PLATFORM IN A POSITION THAT IS OUTBOARD OF THE FLAP TRACK.	
OUTDOORS (adv)	Not in a building	DO THIS WORK OUTDOORS.	
OUTER (adj)	Located on the outside or farther from the center of an object	APPLY SEALANT ON THE OUTER SURFACE.	
outline (v)	GIVE (v)	THIS SECTION GIVES YOU THE PROCEDURES THAT ARE NECESSARY TO FIND THE FAULTS.	This section outlines the procedures needed to find the faults.
OUTPUT (n)	The data, power, energy that comes out of equipment or a system	THE IMPEDANCE MATCHING TRANSFORMERS SUPPLY 60 W OUTPUT TO THE LOUDSPEAKERS.	
outside (adj)	EXTERNAL (adj)	THE EXTERNAL TEMPERATURE IS SHOWN ON THE CENTRAL DISPLAY UNIT.	The outside temperature is indicated on the central display unit.
	OUTER (adj)	CLEAN THE OUTER SURFACE WITH WARM WATER.	Clean the outside surface with warm water.

Word (part of speech)	Approved meaning / ALTERNATIVES	APPROVED EXAMPLE	Not approved example
outside (adv)	OUTDOORS (adv)	DO THIS PROCEDURE OUTDOORS.	Do this procedure outside.
outside (n)	EXTERNAL (adj)	FOLD THE EDGING AGAINST THE EXTERNAL SIDE OF THE INSULATION BLANKET.	Fold the edging against the outside of the insulation blankets.
	OUTER (adj)	FOLD THE EDGING AGAINST THE OUTER SIDE OF THE INSULATION BLANKET.	Fold the edging against the outside of the insulation blankets.
outside (prep)	NEAR (prep)	WHEN YOU DO WORK IN A FUEL TANK, A SECOND PERSON MUST BE NEAR THE TANK AT ALL TIMES.	When you do work in a fuel tank, a second person must be outside the tank at all times.
outwards (adv)	OUT (adv)	MOVE THE DOOR OUT AND FORWARD.	Move the door outwards and forwards.
OVER (prep)	To indicate a position higher than or above land or water 💡 Use this word only for movement above land or water. Not permitted for other meanings. Refer to the word "over (prep)" below.	BEFORE FLIGHT OPERATIONS OVER WATER AT LOW ALTITUDES, APPLY CORROSION-PREVENTIVE FLUID TO THE DOOR HINGES OF THE LANDING GEAR.	
over (prep)	ABOVE (prep)	MAKE SURE THAT THE HYDRAULIC FLUID LEVEL IS NOT ABOVE FULL THE "FULL" MARK.	Make sure the hydraulic fluid level is not over the mark.
	ALONG (prep)	APPLY THE WEIGHT EQUALLY ALONG THE STABILIZER SPAN.	The weight must be evenly spread over the stabilizer span.
	ON (prep)	INSTALL THE STOP SLEEVE ON THE SLIDING MEMBER.	Install the stop sleeve over the sliding member.
	MORE THAN	DO NOT INSTALL SHIMS WITH A THICKNESS MORE THAN 0.1 mm.	Do not install shims over 0.1 mm thick.

Word (part of speech)	Approved meaning / ALTERNATIVES	APPROVED EXAMPLE	Not approved example
OVERBOARD (adv)	Out of a vessel	RELEASE THE AIR OVERBOARD.	
overfill (v)	TOO MUCH	DO NOT PUT TOO MUCH FLUID IN THE LUBRICATION HOLE.	Do not overfill the lubrication hole.
overfull (adj)	TOO FULL	IF THE TANK IS TOO FULL, YOU CANNOT PRESSURIZE IT CORRECTLY.	If the tank is overfull, you cannot pressurize it correctly.
overhaul (v)	OVERHAUL (TN)	DO AN OVERHAUL OF THE No. 2 ENGINE	Overhaul the No. 2 engine.
overheat (v)	TOO HOT	IF YOU PRESSURIZE THE OXYGEN BOTTLE QUICKLY, IT WILL BECOME TOO HOT.	Rapid charging overheats the oxygen bottle.
OVERLAP (n)	The area in which a part of one surface is on a part of a second surface	REPLACE THE PART IF THE OVERLAP IS MORE THAN 0.01 mm.	
overlap (v)	OVERLAP (n)	MAKE AN OVERLAP OF 10 mm.	Overlap the surfaces by 10 mm.
OVERRIDE (v), OVERRIDES, OVERRODE, OVERRIDDEN	To prevent the automatic operation of a part or system	MANUALLY OVERRIDE THE START SEQUENCE.	
overtighten (v)	TIGHTEN TOO MUCH	DO NOT TIGHTEN THE FITTINGS TOO MUCH.	Do not overtighten the fittings.
	TOO TIGHT	DO NOT MAKE THE FITTINGS TOO TIGHT.	Do not overtighten the fittings.
	TOO TIGHTLY	DO NOT INSTALL THE FITTINGS TOO TIGHTLY.	Do not overtighten the fittings.

Word (part of speech)	Approved meaning / ALTERNATIVES	APPROVED EXAMPLE	Not approved example
pack (v)	PUT (v)	PUT THE ASSEMBLY INTO THE BOX.	Pack the assembly into the box.
	FILL (v)	FILL THE GROOVE WITH GREASE.	Pack grease into the groove.
PAINT (v), PAINTS, PAINTED, PAINTED	To apply paint to something	PAINT ALL THE SURFACES.	
PAIR (n)	Two objects that are the same or almost the same, and/or that you use together	MEASURE THE DISTANCE BETWEEN EACH PAIR OF AXLES.	
PARALLEL (adj)	Along lines that stay a constant distance apart at all points	MAKE SURE THAT THE TURNBUCKLE IS PARALLEL TO THE AXIS OF THE AIR OUTLET.	
PARK (v), PARKS, PARKED, PARKED	To stop a vehicle and to let it stay in one position on the ground	PARK THE CAR.	
PART (n)	1. A constituent of a machine or other equipment		
	2. A piece or section of a whole	REFER TO PART 2 FOR THE APPLICABLE PROCEDURE	
part (v)	DISCONNECT (v)	DISCONNECT THE DUCTING.	Part the ducting.
partial (adj)	NOT FULLY	IF THE FLAPS DO NOT FULLY EXTEND, DO THE TEST AGAIN.	If only partial extension of the flap occurs, do the test again.
partially (adv)	NOT FULLY	IF THE FLAPS DO NOT FULLY EXTEND, DO THE TEST AGAIN.	If the flaps only partially extend, do the test again.
PARTICLE (n)	A very small piece of material	IF YOU FIND METAL PARTICLES IN THE DISASSEMBLED PUMP, FIND THEIR SOURCE AND REPAIR THE DEFECTIVE PART.	

Word (part of speech)	Approved meaning / ALTERNATIVES	APPROVED EXAMPLE	Not approved example
particular (adj)	ONLY APPLICABLE	THIS PROCEDURE IS ONLY APPLICABLE TO TYPE A PARTS.	This procedure is particular to type A parts.
	VERY (adv)	THIS STEP IS VERY IMPORTANT.	This step is of particular importance.
particularly (adv)	VERY (adv)	THIS STEP IS VERY IMPORTANT.	This step is particularly important.
partly (adv)	NOT FULLY	IF THE VALVE DOES NOT FULLY OPEN, EXAMINE THE POSITIONS OF THE END STOPS ON THE ACTUATOR.	If the valve opens only partly, examine the positions of the end stops on the actuator.
pass (v)	GO (v)	MAKE SURE THAT THE CABLE GOES ONTO THE PULLEY.	Make sure that the cable passes over the pulley.
	THROUGH (prep)	PUT THE ANTENNA CABLE THROUGH THE TOP SLOTS.	Pass the antenna cable through the top slots.
	GIVE (v)	GIVE ONE END OF THE CABLE TO A SECOND PERSON.	Pass one end of the cable to another person.
passage (n)	FLOW (n)	THE FLOW OF FLUID THROUGH THE VALVE MUST BE CONTINUOUS.	The passage of fluid through the valve must be continuous.
	HOLE (n)	CAREFULLY PUT THE TUBE THROUGH THE HOLE.	Carefully put the tube through the passage.
	OPENING (n)	CAREFULLY PUT THE TUBE THROUGH THE OPENING.	Carefully put the tube through the passage.
past (prep)	AROUND (prep)	IF YOU INSTALL THE SEAL INCORRECTLY, LEAKS CAN OCCUR AROUND THE VALVE.	If you install the seal incorrectly, leaks can occur past the valve.
	THROUGH (prep)	IF YOU INSTALL THE SEAL INCORRECTLY, THE FLUID WILL GO THROUGH IT.	An incorrect installation of the seal will let fluid go past it.

ASD STE 100

Word (part of speech)	Approved meaning / ALTERNATIVES	APPROVED EXAMPLE	Not approved example
PASTE (n)	A wet, flexible mixture or compound	MIX THE MATERIALS UNTIL THEY MAKE A PASTE.	
PATCH (n)	A piece of material that you use to repair a surface or hole	BOND THE PATCH TO THE TUBE WITH ADHESIVE.	
penetrate (v)	GO THROUGH	IF THE SCRATCH DOES NOT GO THROUGH THE PROTECTIVE LAYER, THE UNIT IS SERVICEABLE.	If the scratch does not penetrate the protective layer, the unit is serviceable.
	GO INTO	MAKE SURE THAT THE HYDRAULIC FLUID DOES NOT GO INTO THE RECEPTACLES.	Make sure that the hydraulic fluid does not penetrate the receptacles.
people (n)	PERSONS (n)	KEEP ALL PERSONS OUT OF THE WORK AREA.	Keep all people out of the work area.
	PERSONNEL (n)	TELL YOUR PERSONNEL ABOUT THESE NEW REGULATIONS.	Tell your people about these new regulations.
per (prep)	FOR EACH	DO NOT USE MORE THAN TWO WASHERS FOR EACH BOLT.	Do not use more than two washers per bolt.
	REFER (v)	DO THE LEAK TEST: (REFER TO PARAGRAPH 7.0).	Do the leak test as per paragraph 7.0.
perforated (adj)	HOLE (n)	MAKE SURE THAT THERE ARE NO HOLES IN THE MEMBRANE.	Make sure that the membrane is not perforated.
perform (v)	DO (v)	DO THE LEAK TEST.	Perform the leak test.
	You can use a more specific command verb.	MEASURE THE VOLTAGE BETWEEN PINS A AND B.	Perform the voltage measurement between pins A and B.

Word (part of speech)	Approved meaning / ALTERNATIVES	APPROVED EXAMPLE	Not approved example
PERFORMANCE (n)	The ability of a part, a mechanism, or system to do its necessary function when you compare it with a standard or specification	SOME REPAIRS CAN DECREASE THE PERFORMANCE OF THE ENGINE.	
	For other meanings, use: DO (v)	DO THE TEST. THEN GO TO PARAGRAPH C.	After performance of the test, go to paragraph C.
PERIOD (n)	A quantity of time	THE EMERGENCY LOCATOR TRANSMITTER HAS A STANDBY PERIOD OF 30 SECONDS.	
periodically (adv)	INTERVAL (n) Give the value.	EXAMINE THE SERVO CONTROLS AT INTERVALS OF 400 FLIGHT HOURS.	Examine the servo controls periodically.
PERMANENT (adj)	Without a limit in time	MAKE A PERMANENT REPAIR.	
PERMANENTLY (adv)	In a permanent manner	THE "NO SMOKING" SIGNS WILL STAY ON PERMANENTLY DURING THE FLIGHT.	
permissible (adj)	PERMITTED (adj)	EQUIVALENT MATERIALS ARE ALSO PERMITTED.	Equivalent materials are also permissible.
permit (v)	LET (v)	DO NOT LET THE FLUID TOUCH YOU.	Do not permit the fluid to touch you.
PERMITTED (adj)	Allowed	A MAXIMUM OF TWO WASHERS IS PERMITTED FOR EACH BOLT.	
PERPENDICULAR (adj)	At a 90 degree angle to a given line or plane	MAKE SURE THAT THE TOOL AND FASTENER ARE PERPENDICULAR TO THE WORK SURFACE.	

ASD STE 100

Word (part of speech)	Approved meaning / ALTERNATIVES	APPROVED EXAMPLE	Not approved example
persist (v)	CONTINUE (v)	IF THE FAULT MESSAGE CONTINUES, PUSH THE AUDIO CANCEL SWITCH ON THE AVIONICS TEST PANEL.	If the fault message persists, push the AUDIO CANCEL switch on the avionics test panel.
persistent (adj)	CONTINUOUS (adj)	IF YOU HEAR CONTINUOUS BACKGROUND NOISE, FIND THE CAUSE.	If you hear persistent background noise, find the cause.
PERSON (n)	A human being	MAKE SURE THAT THERE IS A PERSON NEAR THE TANK.	
PERSONNEL (n)	Persons employed in a group or organization	INJURY TO PERSONNEL AND/OR DAMAGE TO EQUIPMENT CAN OCCUR.	
picket (v)	MOOR (v)	IF STRONG WINDS OCCUR, MOOR THE AIRCRAFT.	Picket the aircraft in strong winds.
PIECE (n)	A quantity or segment of a whole that you can use on its own, or that can operate as an individual item	REMOVE ALL PIECES OF THE BROKEN SEAL.	
pierced (adj)	HOLE (n)	MAKE SURE THAT THERE ARE NO HOLES IN THE MEMBRANE.	Make sure that the membrane is not pierced.
placard (v)	PUT (v) (A PLACARD [TN])	PUT A PLACARD ON THE CONTROLS BEFORE YOU START THE TEST.	Placard the controls before you start the test.
place (n)	POSITION (n)	MAKE SURE THAT THE COVERS ARE IN POSITION.	Ensure that covers are in place.
	AREA (n)	REPAIR THE DAMAGED AREAS.	Repair the damaged places.
place (v)	PUT (v)	PUT THE MANIFOLD IN POSITION.	Place the manifold in position.

Word (part of speech)	Approved meaning / ALTERNATIVES	APPROVED EXAMPLE	Not approved example
PLAY (n)	Free movement, the length or dimension of this movement	THE PLAY BETWEEN THE TWO GEARS MUST BE LESS THAN 0.05 mm.	
plot (v)	MAKE (v) (A PLOT [TN])	MAKE A PLOT OF THESE POINTS.	Plot these points.
plug (v)	CONNECT (v)	CONNECT THE MICRO-PHONE TO THE JACK.	Plug the microphone into the jack.
	SEAL (v) (WITH A PLUG [TN] OR PLUGS [TN])	SEAL THE TUBE WITH A PLUG.	Plug the tube.
PLUS (prep)	With the addition of	INCREASE THE PRESSURE IN THE SHOCK ABSORBER TO 85.5 BAR, PLUS OR MINUS 2.7 BAR.	
PNEUMATIC (adj)	Related to, or operated by gas pressure	INSTALL THE PNEUMATIC CONTROLLER.	
PNEUMATICALLY (adv)	With pneumatic power	SOME VALVES OPERATE PNEUMATICALLY.	
POINT (n)	1. A sharp or tapered end	PUT THE POINT OF THE TOOL IN THE SLOT.	
	2. An accurate location	ON THE FLANGE, MEASURE THE DISTANCE BETWEEN POINTS "A" AND "B".	
POINT (v), POINTS, POINTED, POINTED	1. To show the position or direction of	MAKE SURE THAT THE ARROW ON THE CHECK VALVE POINTS AWAY FROM THE GROUND SUPPLY DUCT.	
	2. To turn something in a specified direction	DO NOT POINT THE COMPRESSED AIR OUTLET AT YOUR SKIN.	
POISONOUS (adj)	That contains poison	DO NOT SWALLOW HYDRAULIC FLUID. IT IS POISONOUS.	

ASD STE 100

Word (part of speech)	Approved meaning / ALTERNATIVES	APPROVED EXAMPLE	Not approved example
POLISH (v), POLISHES, POLISHED, POLISHED	To make smooth or shiny	POLISH THE WINDOW PANE WITH A SOFT CLOTH.	
poor (adj)	UNSATISFACTORY (adj)	IF SYSTEM PERFORMANCE IS UNSATISFACTORY, DO A TEST OF CIRCUIT A.	If system performance is poor, test circuit A.
	DEFECTIVE (adj)	DEFECTIVE CONTACTS CAN CAUSE A FAILURE OF THE UNIT.	Poor contacts can cause a failure of the unit.
	UNSERVICEABLE (adj)	IF THE PART IS UNSERVICEABLE, REPLACE IT.	If the condition of the part is poor, replace it.
pop (v)	OPEN (v)	IF THE CIRCUIT BREAKER OPENS, DE-ENERGIZE THE CIRCUIT.	If the circuit breaker pops, de-energize the circuit.
	OUT (adv)	IF THE INDICATOR BUTTON CAME OUT, REPLACE THE FILTER.	If the indicator button popped out, replace the filter.
port (adj)	LEFT (adj)	REMOVE THE WING TIP BRAKE FROM THE LEFT WING.	Remove the wing tip brake from the port wing.
portion (n)	PIECE (n)	REMOVE ALL THE PIECES OF THE DAMAGED SEAL.	Remove all portions of the damaged seal.
	PART (n)	ISOLATE THE DEFECTIVE PART OF THE CIRCUIT.	Isolate the defective portion of the circuit.
POSITION (n)	The attitude or setting of something that you can adjust, or the place or site where you put something	SET THE SWITCH TO THE CORRECT POSITION.	
		MAKE SURE THAT THE WARNING NOTICES ARE IN POSITION BEFORE YOU START THE TASK.	

Word (part of speech)	Approved meaning / ALTERNATIVES	APPROVED EXAMPLE	Not approved example
position (v)	PUT (v)	PUT THE BRACKET ON THE FRAME.	Position the bracket on the frame.
	SET (v)	SET THE SWITCH TO "ON".	Position the switch to ON.
POSSIBLE (adj)	That can occur	IF POSSIBLE, PUT THE RIGGING PIN IN THE HOLE.	
POSSIBLY (adv)	That can occur	IF YOU CANNOT ENGAGE THE ROD AND THE PISTON, THE LENGTH OF THE NEW ROD IS POSSIBLY INCORRECT.	
potential (adj)	POSSIBLE (adj)	PUT BARRIERS AROUND ALL THE POSSIBLE DANGER AREAS.	Put barriers around all the potential danger areas.
pour (v)	PUT (v)	PUT THE MIXTURE INTO THE CYLINDER.	Pour the mixture into the cylinder.
power (v)	SUPPLY (v)	THE HYDRAULIC SYSTEM SUPPLIES POWER TO THE ACTUATORS.	The hydraulic system powers the actuators.
practice (n)	PROCEDURE (n)	IT IS STANDARD PROCEDURE TO TIGHTEN THE BOLTS IN THIS SEQUENCE.	It is common practice to tighten the bolts in this sequence.
PRECAUTION (n)	That which you do to prevent injury and/or damage	OBEY THESE PRECAUTIONS.	
precautionary (adj)	PRECAUTION (n)	OBEY THESE PRECAUTIONS.	Take these precautionary measures.
precede (v)	BEFORE (conj)	BEFORE YOU APPLY THE TAPE, CLEAN THE SURFACE	Application of the tape must be preceded by cleaning of the surface.
precise (adj)	ACCURATE (adj)	THE GYRO ADJUSTMENT MUST BE ACCURATE.	The gyro requires precise adjustment.
precisely (adv)	ACCURATELY (adv)	ADJUST THE GYRO ACCURATELY.	The gyro must be adjusted precisely.

Word (part of speech)	Approved meaning / ALTERNATIVES	APPROVED EXAMPLE	Not approved example
PRECISION (n)	The quality of being accurate	THE TEMPERATURE OF THE OIL HAS AN EFFECT ON THE PRECISION OF THE OIL LEVEL INDICATOR.	
preferable (adj)	RECOMMEND (v)	IT IS POSSIBLE TO MIX APPROVED ENGINE OILS OF THE SAME TYPE. BUT WE RECOMMEND THAT YOU ALWAYS USE THE SAME TYPE OF ENGINE OIL FROM THE SAME MANUFACTURER.	It is possible to mix approved engine oils of the same type, but it is always preferable to use the same type of engine oil from the same manufacturer.
preferably (adv)	RECOMMEND (v)	WE RECOMMEND THAT YOU REFUEL THE VEHICLE OUTDOORS.	Preferably, refueling should be done outdoors.
preheat (v)	HEAT (n)	BEFORE YOU START THIS PROCEDURE, APPLY HEAT TO THE AREA WITH A HEAT LAMP.	Preheat the area with a heat lamp.
preload (v)	LOAD (TN)	BEFORE YOU START THIS PROCEDURE, APPLY A LOAD OF 10 LBS. TO THE SPRING.	Preload the spring to 10 lbs.
premature (adj)	BEFORE (conj)	IF THE VALVE OPENS BEFORE THE SET PRESSURE, STOP THE TEST.	If the valve opening is premature, stop the test.
prematurely (adv)	BEFORE (conj)	IF THE VALVE OPENS BEFORE THE SET PRESSURE, STOP THE TEST.	If the valve opens prematurely, stop the test.
preparation (n)	PREPARE (v)	PREPARE THE MIXTURE 20 MINUTES BEFORE YOU USE IT.	Mixture preparation must be accomplished 20 minutes before use.

Word (part of speech)	Approved meaning / ALTERNATIVES	APPROVED EXAMPLE	Not approved example
PREPARE (v), PREPARES, PREPARED, PREPARED	To make or become ready	PREPARE THE TUBE FOR THE LEAK TEST.	
		PREPARE FOR ELECTRICAL BONDING.	
prescribed (adj)	SPECIFIED (adj)	FILL THE HYDRAULIC TANK WITH THE SPECIFIED HYDRAULIC FLUID.	Fill the hydraulic tank with the prescribed hydraulic fluid.
presence (n)	BE (v)	THIS INSPECTION IS NECESSARY WHEN THERE ARE DEFECTS.	This inspection is necessary in the presence of defects.
present (adj)	BE (v)	IF THERE IS A VOLTAGE AT PIN C OF CONNECTOR F7, THE UNIT IS UNSERVICEABLE.	If a voltage is pin C of connector F7, the unit is faulty.
present (v)	GIVE (v)	THIS SECTION GIVES THE APPLICABLE TORQUE VALUES.	The applicable torque values are presented in this section.
	SHOW (v)	THE TABLE THAT FOLLOWS SHOWS THE TEST DATA.	The test data is presented in the following table.
preserve (v)	PRESERVATION (TN)	THIS PROCEDURE IS FOR THE PRESERVATION OF STEEL CABLES.	This procedure will preserve the steel cables.
preset (v)	SET (v)	SET THE TENSION INDICATOR TO ZERO.	Preset the tension indicator to zero.
press (v)	PUSH (v)	PUSH AND HOLD THE TEST BUTTON.	Press and hold the TEST button.
PRESSURI-ZATION (n)	The procedure that supplies or increases the pressure	CONTINUE THE PRESSURIZATION FOR 10 MINUTES.	
PRESSURIZE (v), PRESSURIZES, PRESSURIZED, PRESSURIZED	To supply pressure	PRESSURIZE THE HYDRAULIC SYSTEM	

Word (part of speech)	Approved meaning / ALTERNATIVES	APPROVED EXAMPLE	Not approved example
PREVENT (v), PREVENTS, PREVENTED, PREVENTED	To make sure that something does not occur	TO PREVENT DAMAGE TO THE ENGINE, IMMEDIATELY INSTALL PROTECTIVE COVERS ON ALL OPENINGS.	
prevent (from) (v)	LET (v)	DO NOT LET THE DOOR OPEN.	Prevent the door from opening.
preventive (adj)	PREVENT (v)	THIS PREVENTS CORROSION.	This is a corrosion preventive measure.
previous (adj)	BEFORE (conj)	REMOVE THE PLATE BEFORE YOU ADJUST THE CABLE.	Adjustment of the cable requires previous removal of the plate.
previously (adv)	BEFORE (conj)	IF THE CONTROL WAS ADJUSTED BEFORE YOU STARTED THIS PROCEDURE, DO NOT DO THE VALVE TEST.	If the control was adjusted previously, omit the valve test.
primarily (adv)	PRIMARY (adj)	THE PRIMARY FUNCTION OF THE HYDRAULIC SYSTEM IS TO SUPPLY THE PRESSURE TO OPERATE THE FLIGHT CONTROLS.	The hydraulic system primarily supplies the pressure to operate the flight controls.
PRIMARY (adj)	First in importance	THE PRIMARY FUNCTION OF THE POWER UNIT IS TO SUPPLY ELECTRICAL POWER.	
prime (v)	FILL (v)	FILL THE FILLER HOSE.	Prime the filler hose.
	PUT (v)	PUT FUEL IN THE FUEL PUMP.	Prime the fuel pump.
principal (adj)	PRIMARY (adj)	THIS IS THE PRIMARY FUNCTION OF THE SYSTEM.	This is the principal function of the system.
prior to (prep)	BEFORE (conj)	DRAIN THE SYSTEM BEFORE YOU DISCONNECT THE COMPONENTS.	Drain the system prior to disconnecting the components.

Word (part of speech)	Approved meaning / ALTERNATIVES	APPROVED EXAMPLE	Not approved example
priority (n)	IMPORTANT (adj)	THIS PROCEDURE IS VERY IMPORTANT.	This procedure has high priority.
	BEFORE (prep)	FILL THE INNER TANK BEFORE YOU FILL THE OUTER TANK.	The inner tank filling procedure has priority over the outer tank filling procedure.
	FIRST (adv)	DURING THE PROCEDURE THAT FOLLOWS, REPAIR THE UPPER FLANGE FIRST.	During the following repair procedure, the upper flange has priority.
probability (n)	RISK (n)	OBEY THE SAFETY PRECAUTIONS TO DECREASE THE RISK OF FIRE.	Obey the safety precautions to decrease the probability of fire.
probable (adj)	POSSIBLE (adj)	IF YOU DO NOT SAFETY THE DOOR, IT IS POSSIBLE THAT STRONG WINDS WILL CAUSE DAMAGE TO THE STRUCTURE.	If you do not safety the door, damage to the structure due to strong winds is probable.
	RISK (n)	IF YOU DO NOT SAFETY THE DOOR, THERE IS A RISK THAT STRONG WINDS WILL CAUSE DAMAGE TO THE STRUCTURE.	If you do not safety the door, damage to the structure due to strong winds is probable.
probe (v)	FIND (v) (WITH A PROBE [TN])	USE A PROBE TO FIND THE BLOCKAGE IN THE TUBE.	Probe the tube to find the blockage.
PROBLEM (n)	Something that is difficult and for which you must find the correct answer	IF YOU FIND A PROBLEM, REFER TO PROBLEM, REFER TO	
PROCEDURE (n)	Steps that are in a sequence	THESE MAINTENANCE PROCEDURES ARE APPLICABLE TO THE MAIN LANDING GEAR ONLY.	
proceed (v)	CONTINUE (v)	CONTINUE WITH THE ELECTRICAL TEST.	Proceed with the electrical test.

Word (part of speech)	Approved meaning / ALTERNATIVES	APPROVED EXAMPLE	Not approved example
process (in the process of) (prep)	DURING (prep)	DURING THIS REPAIR, APPLY SUFFICIENT HEAT TO THE UNIT.	Apply sufficient heat to the unit in the process of doing this repair.
	WHILE (conj)	WHILE YOU DO THIS REPAIR, APPLY SUFFICIENT HEAT TO THE UNIT.	Apply sufficient heat to the unit in the proc
process (n)	PROCEDURE (n) This word is a technical name when it means a sequence of changes that occur and cause a result.	THE ASSEMBLY PROCEDURES ARE ALMOST THE SAME. CORROSION IS AN ELECTROLYTIC PROCESS.	The assembly processes are almost the same.
process (v)	PUT (v)	PUT THE PARTS IN AN ELECTROLYTIC BATH AND DO THE ELECTROPLATING PROCEDURE.	Process the parts in an electrolytic bath.
produce (v)	CAUSE (v)	ELECTRICAL EQUIPMENT CAN CAUSE INTERFERENCE IN TELEPHONE COMMUNICATION.	Electrical equipment can produce interference in telephone communication.
	GIVE (v)	A USED SOLUTION WILL NOT GIVE YOU THE CORRECT RESULTS.	An old solution does not produce the correct results.
	MAKE (v)	THE LEVER MAKES A CLICK WHEN IT ENGAGES.	The lever produces a click when engaged.
	SUPPLY (v)	THE POWER UNIT SUPPLIES THE SYSTEM WITH A VOLTAGE OF 28 VDC.	The power unit produces a voltage of 28 VDC.
product (n)	MATERIAL (n)	WASH PRIMER IS A DANGEROUS MATERIAL.	Wash primer is a dangerous product.

Word (part of speech)	Approved meaning / ALTERNATIVES	APPROVED EXAMPLE	Not approved example
profile (n)	CONTOUR (n)	MAKE SURE THAT THE CONTOUR OF THE TEMPLATE IS THE SAME.	Make sure that the profile of the template is the same.
program (n)	SEQUENCE (n)	DISASSEMBLE THE ROTOR IN THIS SEQUENCE:	Disassemble the rotor according to the following program:
progress (n)	CONTINUE (v) Also refer to IN PROGRESS (adv).	MAKE SURE THAT THE TEST CONTINUES SATISFACTORILY.	Monitor the progress of the test.
progress (v)	CONTINUE (v)	YOU CAN CONTINUE THE TEST.	You can progress with the test.
progressive (adj)	GRADUALLY (adv)	GRADUALLY TORQUE THE NUT.	Apply progressive torque to the nut.
progressively (adv)	GRADUALLY (adv)	TORQUE THE BOLTS GRADUALLY.	Torque the bolts progressively.
prohibit (v)	PREVENT (v)	PUT A WARNING NOTICE ON THE PANEL TO PREVENT OPERATION OF THE CONTROLS.	Display a warning notice on the panel prohibiting the operation of the controls.
	TELL (NOT TO) (v)	TELL THE PERSONNEL NOT TO USE ASBESTOS PARTS.	Prohibit the use of asbestos parts.
prolonged (adj)	LONG (adj)	OPERATION OF THE MOTOR FOR LONG PERIODS CAN CAUSE DAMAGE TO IT.	Prolonged motor operation can cause damage.
prompt (adj)	IMMEDIATELY (adv)	IF YOU SWALLOW SOLVENT, GET MEDICAL AID IMMEDIATELY.	Prompt action is required if you swallow solvent.

Word (part of speech)	Approved meaning / ALTERNATIVES	APPROVED EXAMPLE	Not approved example
propagation (n)	INCREASE (v)	IF THE DIMENSION OF A CRACK INCREASES, THE PART CAN BREAK.	Crack propagation can cause the part to break.
	⊙ Give the dimensions or limits.	IF THE DEPTH OF CRACK IS MORE THAN 0.2 mm, REJECT THE PART.	A Crack propagation can cause the rejection of the part.
		IF A CRACK IS LARGER THAN 0.2 mm, REJECT THE PART.	Crack propagation can cause the rejection of the part.
proper (adj)	CORRECT (adj)	DO A CHECK FOR THE CORRECT OPERATION OF THE UNIT.	Check the unit for proper operation.
properly (adv)	CORRECTLY (adv)	CLOSE THE DOORS CORRECTLY.	Close the doors properly.
PROPERTY (n)	A characteristic or attribute of an object	THE MAGNETIC PROPERTIES OF THIS METAL DECREASE AT HIGH TEMPERATURES.	
PROPORTION (n)	The ratio of something to something else	MAKE SURE THAT YOU ALWAYS MIX CLEANING AGENTS WITH COLD WATER, AND IN THE CORRECT PROPORTIONS.	
	⊙ For other meanings, use: RELATION (n)	THE TEMPERATURE DECREASES IN RELATION TO THE ALTITUDE.	The temperature decreases in proportion to the altitude.
proportional (adj)	RELATION (n)	THE CENTER OF GRAVITY MOVES IN RELATION TO THE LOADS ON THE WINGS.	Movement of the center of gravity is proportional to the loads on the wings.
	PROPORTION (n)	MIX THE PIGMENT AND SOLVENT IN THE CORRECT PROPORTIONS.	Mix the correct quantity of pigment proportional to the quantity of solvent.

Word (part of speech)	Approved meaning / ALTERNATIVES	APPROVED EXAMPLE	Not approved example
proportionally (adv)	RELATION (n)	THE CABLE TENSION CHANGES IN RELATION TO THE TEMPERATURE.	The cable tension changes proportionally with temperature.
protect (v)	PREVENT (v)	USE CELLOPHANE TO PREVENT DAMAGE TO THE SURFACE.	Use cellophane to protect the surface.
	PROTECTION (n)	MAKE SURE THAT ALL SHARP EDGES HAVE VINYL TAPE PROTECTION.	Make sure that all sharp edges are protected with vinyl tape.
PROTECTION (n)	Something to prevent injury, damage, or failure	APPLY TWO LAYERS OF SEALING COMPOUND ON THE SURFACES THAT HAVE NO PROTECTION.	
PROTECTIVE (adj)	That gives protection	REMOVE THE PROTECTIVE LAYER.	
protrude (v)	ABOVE (prep)	THE TOPS OF THE BOLT HEADS MUST NOT BE MORE THAN 5 mm ABOVE THE PLATE.	The tops of the bolt heads must not protrude from the plate more than 5 mm.
	OUT (adv)	REPLACE THE FILTER ELEMENT IF THE CLOGGING INDICATOR IS OUT.	Replace the filter element if the clogging indicator protrudes.
provide (v)	GIVE (v)	THIS SECTION GIVES THE PROCEDURES FOR THE TEST.	This section provides the procedures for the test.
	SUPPLY (v)	THE HYDRAULIC PRESSURE SYSTEM SUPPLIES PRESSURE FOR THE OPERATION OF THE FLIGHT CONTROLS.	The hydraulic pressure system provides pressure for operating the flight controls.
provided (that) (conj)	IF (conj)	IF A REPLACEMENT IS AVAILABLE, REPLACE THE DAMAGED FAIRING.	Provided that a replacement is available, replace the damaged fairing.

ASD STE 100

Word (part of speech)	Approved meaning / ALTERNATIVES	APPROVED EXAMPLE	Not approved example
providing (that) (conj)	IF (conj)	IF A NEW COMPONENT IS INSTALLED, YOU CAN CONTINUE THE OPERATION OF THE MACHINE.	Providing that a new component is installed, you can continue the operation of the machine.
proximity (n)	NEAR (prep)	DO NOT DO MAINTENANCE PROCEDURES NEAR AN ENGINE THAT IS IN OPERATION.	Do not do maintenance procedures in proximity to a running engine.
PULL (v), PULLS, PULLED, PULLED	To use a force on something to move it toward the source of the force 💡 Use this word together with a preposition or an adverb to show direction	PULL THE CABLE DOWN AND AWAY FROM THE BRACKET.	
pump (v)	PUMP (TN)	WHEN YOU REMOVE OIL FROM THE TANK, OPEN THE VALVE BEFORE YOU START THE PUMP.	Before you pump oil from the tank, open the valve.
puncture (v)	HOLE (n)	MAKE SURE THAT YOU DO NOT MAKE A HOLE IN THE BLADDER.	Take care not to puncture the bladder.
purge (v)	REMOVE (v)	REMOVE UNWANTED MATERIAL FROM THE SYSTEM.	Purge the system.
purify (v)	CLEAN (v)	CLEAN THE WATER.	Purify the water.
purpose (n)	FUNCTION (n)	THE FUNCTION OF THIS SPECIAL TOOL IS TO REMOVE THE BUSHING.	The purpose of this special tool is to extract the bushing.
	DO (v)	BE CAREFUL WHEN YOU OPEN THE COWLS TO DO A MAINTENANCE TASK.	Be careful when you open the cowls for maintenance purposes.

Word (part of speech)	Approved meaning / ALTERNATIVES	APPROVED EXAMPLE	Not approved example
providing (that) (conj)	IF (conj)	IF A NEW COMPONENT IS INSTALLED, YOU CAN CONTINUE THE OPERATION OF THE MACHINE.	Providing that a new component is installed, you can continue the operation of the machine.
proximity (n)	NEAR (prep)	DO NOT DO MAINTENANCE PROCEDURES NEAR AN ENGINE THAT IS IN OPERATION.	Do not do maintenance procedures in proximity to a running engine.
PULL (v), PULLS, PULLED, PULLED	To use a force on something to move it toward the source of the force Use this word together with a preposition or an adverb to show direction	PULL THE CABLE DOWN AND AWAY FROM THE BRACKET.	
pump (v)	PUMP (TN)	WHEN YOU REMOVE OIL FROM THE TANK, OPEN THE VALVE BEFORE YOU START THE PUMP.	Before you pump oil from the tank, open the valve.
puncture (v)	HOLE (n)	MAKE SURE THAT YOU DO NOT MAKE A HOLE IN THE BLADDER.	Take care not to puncture the bladder.
purge (v)	REMOVE (v)	REMOVE UNWANTED MATERIAL FROM THE SYSTEM.	Purge the system.
purify (v)	CLEAN (v)	CLEAN THE WATER.	Purify the water.
purpose (n)	FUNCTION (n)	THE FUNCTION OF THIS SPECIAL TOOL IS TO REMOVE THE BUSHING.	The purpose of this special tool is to extract the bushing.
	DO (v)	BE CAREFUL WHEN YOU OPEN THE COWLS TO DO A MAINTENANCE TASK.	Be careful when you open the cowls for maintenance purposes.

ASD STE 100

Word (part of speech)	Approved meaning / ALTERNATIVES	APPROVED EXAMPLE	Not approved example
PUSH (v), PUSHES, PUSHED, PUSHED	1. To apply a force to something to move it away from the source of the force	PUSH THE INSERT DOWN UNTIL IT TOUCHES THE BOTTOM OF THE HOLE.	
	2. To move with a force against something Use this word together with a preposition or an adverb to show direction.	THE SPRING UNIT PUSHES AGAINST THE BRAKE PEDAL.	
PUT (v), PUTS, PUT, PUT	To cause something to move or to be in a specified position or condition	PUT THE ADAPTER IN POSITION AGAINST ITS SUPPORT. PUT THE LEVER BACK TO ITS INITIAL POSITION.	
PUT ON (v), PUTS ON, PUT ON, PUT ON	To cover your skin or face with clothing, or other items that give protection	PUT ON SAFETY GOGGLES AND PROTECTIVE CLOTHING.	

Word (part of speech)	Approved meaning / ALTERNATIVES	APPROVED EXAMPLE	Not approved example
qualified (adj)	APPROVED (adj)	AN APPROVED PERSON MUST DO THE IMPORTANT CHECKS.	A qualified person must do the important checks.
QUALITY (n)	Condition, property, or type	THE CLEANING SOLVENT MUST BE OF GOOD QUALITY.	
QUANTITY (n)	A specified amount or number For an amount that you can count, use NUMBER (n).	APPLY A SMALL QUANTITY OF OIL ON THE THREADS OF THE BOLTS. MAKE SURE THAT YOU HAVE THE CORRECT NUMBER OF SHIMS AVAILABLE.	
quarterly (adv)	INTERVAL (n)	SEND REPORTS TO THE AUTHORITIES AT INTERVALS OF THREE MONTHS.	Send reports to the authorities quarterly.
questionable (adj)	NOT SURE	IF YOU ARE NOT SURE OF THEIR CONDITION, REJECT THE PARTS.	Reject the parts that are in a questionable condition.
quick (adj)	QUICKLY (adv)	MAKE SURE THAT THE ROD DOES NOT MOVE QUICKLY.	Make sure that there is no quick movement of the rod.
QUICKLY (adv)	In a fast manner	MAKE SURE THAT THE PRESSURE DECREASES QUICKLY.	
quit (v)	GO (v)	BEFORE YOU START THE ENGINE, MAKE SURE THAT ALL PERSONS GO AWAY FROM THE DANGER AREA.	Before you start the engine, make sure that all persons quit the danger area.
	STOP (v)	IF THE RED LIGHT COMES ON, STOP THE REFUEL PROCEDURE.	If the red light comes on, quit the refuel procedure.
quote (v)	GIVE (v)	THE TABLE GIVES THE MAXIMUM TOLERANCE FOR THE HOLE.	The table quotes the maximum tolerance for the hole.

301

Word (part of speech)	Approved meaning / ALTERNATIVES	APPROVED EXAMPLE	Not approved example
RADIAL (adj)	Along a radius	DO A CHECK FOR RADIAL CUTS, CRACKS, OR SPLITS.	
RADIALLY (adv)	Along a radius	THE FAN BLADES ARE INSTALLED RADIALLY.	
RADIOACTIVE (adj)	Related to radioactivity	DO A CHECK FOR RADIOACTIVE CONTAMINATION.	
raise (v)	LIFT (v)	DO NOT LIFT THE COVER MORE THAN NECESSARY.	Do not raise the cover more than necessary.
	INCREASE (v)	INCREASE THE TEMPERATURE BY 10 DEG.	Raise the temperature 10 deg.
	RETRACT (v)	RETRACT THE LANDING GEAR.	Raise the landing gear.
RANDOM (adj)	Not regular	DO RANDOM CHECKS OF THE TIRE PRESSURE DURING THIS PROCEDURE.	
RANDOMLY (adv)	Not regularly	DO THESE CHECKS RANDOMLY.	
RANGE (n)	The limits within which something operates	THE AUDIO SPECTRUM IS THE FREQUENCY RANGE AT WHICH HUMANS CAN HEAR.	
rapid (adj)	FAST (adj)	HYDRAULIC FLUID CAUSES FAST DETERIORATION OF PAINTED SURFACES.	Hydraulic fluid causes rapid deterioration of painted surfaces.
rapidly (adv)	QUICKLY (adv)	QUICKLY TURN THE AILERON CONTROL WHEEL CLOCKWISE.	Rapidly turn the aileron control wheel clockwise.
RATE (n)	A measurement of how frequently or how quickly something occurs	MAKE SURE THAT THE FLOW RATE IS CORRECT.	

Word (part of speech)	Approved meaning / ALTERNATIVES	APPROVED EXAMPLE	Not approved example
re- (prefix)	In general, use the word AGAIN (adv) or BACK(adv) with the basic word to replace words that have "re-" as a prefix.		
reach (v)	GET (v)	WHEN YOU GET THE CORRECT PRESSURE, CLOSE THE VALVE.	When the correct pressure is reached, close the valve.
	TOUCH (v)	MAKE SURE THAT THE EXTENSION BAR TOUCHES THE TARGET PLATE.	Make sure that the extension bar reaches the target plate.
	BE (v)	WHEN THE FLAPS ARE AT THE 30 DEGREE POSITION, INSTALL THE RIGGING PIN.	When the flaps reach the 30 degree position, install the rigging pin.
reactivate (v)	OPERATE (v)	OPERATE THE UNIT AGAIN.	Reactivate the unit.
	START (v)	START THE SYSTEM AGAIN.	Reactivate the system.
READ (v), READS, READ, READ	To come to know information with the eyes or electronically	READ THE INDICATORS ON THE CONTROL PANEL.	
reading (n)	INDICATION (n)	MAKE SURE THAT THE EXHAUST FROM THE GROUND CART DOES NOT CAUSE AN INCORRECT INDICATION.	Avoid an erroneous reading caused by exhaust from ground cart.
readjust (v)	ADJUST (v)	ADJUST THE LINKAGE AGAIN AFTER THE INSPECTION.	Readjust the linkage after the inspection.
ready (adj)	PREPARE (v)	MAKE SURE THAT THE CONTROL SYSTEM IS PREPARED FOR OPERATION.	Make sure that the control system is in an operational ready state.
ready (v)	PREPARE (v)	PREPARE THE REMOVAL KIT FOR THE REMOVAL OF THE STRUT.	Ready the removal kit for the removal of the strut.

ASD STE 100

Word (part of speech)	Approved meaning / ALTERNATIVES	APPROVED EXAMPLE	Not approved example
real (adj)	AGREE (v)	MAKE SURE THAT THE INDICATION ON THE GAUGE AGREES WITH THE QUANTITY THAT IS IN THE TANK.	Make sure that the gauge shows the real quantity that is in the tank.
REAR (adj)	Away from the person who looks or from a reference point	INSTALL THE TWO BOLTS IN THE REAR FITTINGS.	
REAR (n)	The rear part or rear surface	THE CIRCUIT BREAKERS ARE INSTALLED ON THE REAR OF THE UNIT.	
rear of (prep)	AFT OF	THE PUMP IS INSTALLED ON RIB 3, AFT OF THE FRONT SPAR.	The pump is located on rib 3, rear of the front spar.
	BEHIND (prep)	THE PUMP IS INSTALLED ON RIB 3, BEHIND THE FRONT SPAR.	The pump is located on rib 3, rear of the front spar.
rearmost (adj)	REAR (n)	YOU CANNOT REMOVE THE HALF CLAMP NEAREST TO THE REAR.	The rearmost half clamp is not removable.
REARWARD (adv)	In the direction of the rear	PULL THE LEVER REARWARD.	
reason (n)	CAUSE (n)	FIND THE CAUSE OF THE INCORRECT INDICATION.	Find the reason for the wrong indication.
	BECAUSE OF (prep)	BECAUSE OF THE POSSIBLE EFFECTS ON YOUR HEALTH, USE ONLY POTABLE WATER.	For health reasons, only use potable water.
reassemble (v)	ASSEMBLE (v)	ASSEMBLE THE ACTUATOR AGAIN.	Reassemble the actuator.
rebuild (v)	ASSEMBLE (v)	ASSEMBLE THE UNIT AGAIN. USE NEW PARTS IF NECESSARY.	Rebuild the unit if necessary.

Word (part of speech)	Approved meaning / ALTERNATIVES	APPROVED EXAMPLE	Not approved example
RECEIVE (v), RECEIVES, RECEIVED, RECEIVED	To get energy, material, or a signal from a different source	MAKE SURE THAT THE CAPTAIN'S BOOMSET RECEIVES THE SIGNALS CORRECTLY.	
RECESS (n)	An indentation in a surface	WHEN YOU CLEAN THE SURFACES, REMOVE THE STAINS FROM THE RECESSES.	
recess (v)	RECESS (n)	DO NOT MAKE A RECESS OF MORE THAN 5 mm FOR THE STUDS.	Do not recess studs more than 5 mm.
		THE FLANGE IS IN A RECESS IN THE FUSELAGE.	The flange is recessed into the fuselage.
recharge (v)	CHARGE (v)	CHARGE THE BATTERY AGAIN.	Recharge the battery.
	FILL (v)	FILL THE FLUID RESERVOIR.	Recharge the fluid reservoir.
	PRESSURIZE (v)	PRESSURIZE THE ACCUMULATOR.	Recharge the accumulator.
recheck (v)	MEASURE (v)	MEASURE THE DISTANCE BETWEEN THE FACES AGAIN.	Recheck the distance between the faces.
	EXAMINE (v)	EXAMINE THE CASTING FOR CORROSION AGAIN.	Recheck the casting for corrosion.
	CHECK (n)	DO A LEAKAGE CHECK OF THE FILTER ASSEMBLY AGAIN.	Recheck the filter assembly for leakage.
reclaim (v)	REPAIR (v)	REPAIR THE DAMAGED FABRIC AREA.	Reclaim the damaged fabric area.
recleat (v)	ATTACH (v) (TO A CLEAT [TN])	ATTACH THE TIEDOWN CORD TO A CLEAT.	Recleat the tiedown cord.
reclose (v)	CLOSE (v)	AFTER SERVICING, CLOSE THE COMPARTMENT AGAIN.	Reclose the compartment after servicing.

ASD STE 100

Word (part of speech)	Approved meaning / ALTERNATIVES	APPROVED EXAMPLE	Not approved example
recoil (v)	MOVE BACK	BE CAREFUL WHEN THE SLIDE MOVES BACK.	Be careful when the slide recoils.
	WIND (v)	WIND THE PROBE WIRE BACK ON THE SPOOL.	Recoil the probe wire back on the spool.
	RECOIL (TN)	MOVE THE BARREL OF THE GUN TO THE RECOIL POSITION.	Recoil the gun barrel.
RECOMMEND(v), RECOMMENDS, RECOMMENDED, RECOMMENDED	To advise that which is best	WE RECOMMEND THAT YOU DO THIS PROCEDURE IN A DEDICATED AREA.	
recondition (v)	REPAIR (v)	REPAIR THE SEATS.	Recondition the seats.
	OVERHAUL (TN)	DO AN OVERHAUL OF THE ENGINE.	Recondition the engine.
reconstruction (n)	REPAIR (n)	RECORD ALL REPAIRS TO THE SKIN SURFACE.	Record all reconstruction of the skin surface.
	REPAIR (v)	THIS PROCEDURE TELLS YOU HOW TO REPAIR THE SURFACE.	This procedure is for the reconstruction of the surface.
RECORD (v), RECORDS, RECORDED, RECORDED	1. To make notes of and keep data to use subsequently	RECORD THE RESULTS.	
	2. To put data on a storage medium	THE COCKPIT VOICE RECORDER RECORDS SIGNALS FROM FOUR AUDIO INPUTS DURING THE FLIGHT.	
recover (v)	COLLECT (v)	REMOVE THE NUT AND THE BOLT, AND COLLECT THE WASHER.	Remove the nut and the bolt, and recover the washer.
rectify (v)	CORRECT (v)	CORRECT THE DEFECT BEFORE YOU START THE PROCEDURE AGAIN.	Rectify the defect before you restart the procedure.
recur (v)	OCCUR (v)	IF THE SYMPTOMS OCCUR AGAIN, DO A SYSTEM TEST.	If the symptoms recur, do a system test.

Word (part of speech)	Approved meaning / ALTERNATIVES	APPROVED EXAMPLE	Not approved example
RECYCLE (v), RECYCLES, RECYCLED, RECYCLED	To put a used material through a process to make it possible to use it or its components again	MAKE SURE THAT YOU RECYCLE THE REMOVED INSULATION MATERIAL.	
	💡 For other meanings, use: CYCLE (n)	DO ONE MORE TEST CYCLE OF THE COMPONENT.	Recycle the component through a test.
reduce (v)	DECREASE (v)	SLOWLY DECREASE THE RATE OF DESCENT.	Slowly reduce the rate of descent.
REFER (v), REFERS, REFERRED, REFERRED	1. To tell a person where to find information	REFER TO CHAPTER 28 FOR THE TEST PROCEDURE.	
	2. To give information	BEFORE YOU DO THIS PROCEDURE, ENGAGE THE RAMP SERVICE DOOR SAFETY CONNECTOR PIN (THE PIN THAT HOLDS THE RAMP SERVICE DOOR, REFERRED TO IN THIS PROCEDURE AS THE "SAFETY CONNECTOR PIN").	
reference (n)	REFER (v)	REFER TO CHAPTER 20 FOR THE STANDARD TORQUE VALUES.	Reference is made to Chapter 20 for the standard torque values.
referenced (adj)	GIVEN (adj)	THIS POINT IS GIVEN ON THE GRAPH.	This point is referenced on the graph.
refill (v)	FILL (v)	FILL THE CONTAINER AGAIN.	Refill the container.
refit (v)	INSTALL (v)	INSTALL THE LINKAGE AGAIN.	Refit the linkage.
	REPAIR (v)	ON THE SUBMARINE, REPAIR ALL DAMAGE AND REPLACE ALL WORN PARTS.	Refit the submarine.

ASD STE 100

Word (part of speech)	Approved meaning / ALTERNATIVES	APPROVED EXAMPLE	Not approved example
reflect (v)	REFLECTION (n)	THE RETICLE IMAGE MAKES A REFLECTION ON THE BOTTOM SURFACE OF THE GLASS.	The reticle image reflects on the bottom surface of the glass.
REFLECTION (n)	Something that occurs when energy comes against a surface which sends it back	A CLEAN SURFACE GIVES A BETTER REFLECTION.	
REFUEL (v), REFUELS, REFUELED, REFUELED	To supply with fuel	REFUEL THE AIRCRAFT.	
register (v)	SHOW (v)	ADJUST THE "SET +40" CONTROL UNTIL THE POINTER SHOWS +40.	Adjust the "SET +40" control until the pointer registers +40.
regrease (v)	APPLY (v)	APPLY GREASE TO THE ROD AGAIN.	Regrease the rod.
	MORE (adj)	PUT MORE GREASE ON THE JOINT UNTIL YOU CAN MOVE IT.	Regrease the joint until you can move it.
REGULAR (adj)	At specified or equal intervals	THE COMPUTER GIVES REGULAR INPUTS TO THE CONTROL SYSTEM.	
REGULARLY (adv)	In a regular manner	IF THE FAILURE OCCURS REGULARLY, DO A SYSTEM TEST.	
regulate (v)	CONTROL (v)	CONTROL THE ELECTRICAL CURRENT.	Regulate the electrical current.
	ADJUST (v)	ADJUST THE TIRE PRESSURE AS NECESSARY.	Regulate the tire pressure as necessary.

Word (part of speech)	Approved meaning / ALTERNATIVES	APPROVED EXAMPLE	Not approved example
regulation (n)	ADJUSTMENT (n)	THE TEMPERATURE ADJUSTMENT IS AUTOMATIC.	The regulation of temperature is automatic.
	CONTROL (n)	THE TEMPERATURE CONTROL IS AUTOMATIC.	The regulation of temperature is automatic.
	CONTROL (v)	A SENSOR CONTROLS THE TEMPERATURE IN THE COMPARTMENT.	The regulation of temperature in the compartment is effected by a sensor
reinflate (v)	INFLATE (v)	INFLATE THE TIRE AGAIN.	Reinflate the tire.
reinforce (v)	MAKE ··· STRONGER	DOUBLERS MAKE THE JOINT STRONGER.	Doublers reinforce the joint
reinstall (v)	INSTALL (v)	INSTALL THE COVER AGAIN AFTER YOU ADJUST THE UNIT.	Reinstall the cover after you adjust the unit.
reinstallation (n)	INSTALLATION (n)	ONLY APPROVED PERSONNEL CAN DO THE INSTALLATION PROCEDURE.	This reinstallation must be performed by qualified personnel.
REJECT (v), REJECTS, REJECTED, REJECTED	To make a decision that something is unsatisfactory	REJECT THE PARTS THAT ARE DAMAGED.	
rejection (n)	REJECT (v)	REJECT THE COMPONENT IF THE TEST IS NOT SATISFACTORY.	Rejection is mandatory if the test proves the component to be defective.
relate (v)	RELATED (adj)	THE PROCEDURES ARE RELATED TO THE SYSTEM TEST.	The procedures relate to the system test.
RELATED (adj)	That has a relation	CLEAN THE BALLS OF THE ELECTRICAL LATCH AND ITS RELATED SOCKETS.	
RELATION (n)	The connection between two or more things caused by their functions, values, or conditions	THE RELATION BETWEEN THE TWO CONTROL SYSTEMS KEEPS THE AIRCRAFT STABLE.	

Word (part of speech)	Approved meaning / ALTERNATIVES	APPROVED EXAMPLE	Not approved example
relay (v)	SEND (v)	SEND THE INFORMATION TO PERSON B.	Relay the information to Person B.
RELEASE (v), RELEASES, RELEASED, RELEASED	To make free, to let go	RELEASE THE INSTRUMENT PANEL TO GET ACCESS TO THE CONNECTIONS.	
relevant (adj)	RELATED (adj)	REMOVE THE ROD END FROM THE RELATED PIVOT.	Withdraw the rod end from the relevant pivot.
	THEIR (pron)	INSTALL THE BOLTS IN THEIR HOLES.	Install the bolts in the relevant holes.
	ITS (pron)	INSTALL THE COMPUTER IN ITS RACK.	Install the computer in the relevant rack.
relieve (v)	RELEASE (v)	RELEASE THE TENSION IN THE CABLE.	Relieve the tension in the cable.
remain (v)	STAY (v)	THE FLAGS MUST STAY OUT OF VIEW.	The flags must remain out of view.
REMAINING (adj)	That continues to stay	USE A SOLVENT TO REMOVE THE REMAINING SEALANT.	
remnant (n)	REMAINING (adj)	REMOVE THE REMAINING SEALANT FROM THE FLOOR COVERING.	Remove sealant remnants from the floor covering.
removable (adj)	REMOVE (v)	FIND THE PART OF THE BARREL THAT YOU CAN REMOVE.	Find the removable part of the barrel.
REMOVAL (n)	A procedure which removes an object	THE SUPERVISOR MUST SUPPLY THE APPLICABLE PROCEDURE FOR CORROSION REMOVAL.	
REMOVE (v), REMOVES, REMOVED, REMOVED	To take or move something away from its initial position	REMOVE THE INDICATOR FROM THE PANEL.	
render (v)	MAKE (v)	MAKE THE SYSTEM ELECTRICALLY SAFE.	Render the system electrically safe.

Word (part of speech)	Approved meaning / ALTERNATIVES	APPROVED EXAMPLE	Not approved example
renew (v)	NEW (adj)	USE NEW ADHESIVE TAPE.	Renew the adhesive tape.
renovate (v)	REPAIR (v)	REPAIR ALL WORN SURFACES.	Renovate all worn surfaces.
	NEW (adj)	APPLY NEW PAINT TO THE CONTROL BOX IF ITS PAINT IS DAMAGED.	Renovate any damaged paint on the control box.
repack (v)	PUT (v)	PUT THE ASSEMBLY BACK IN THE BOX.	Repack the assembly in the box.
	FILL (v)	FILL THE HOLE WITH GREASE AGAIN.	Repack the hole with grease.
repaint (v)	PAINT (v)	PAINT ALL THE SURFACES AGAIN.	Repaint all the surfaces.
REPAIR (n)	The act of repairing or the result when something is repaired	AFTER THE REPAIR, THE SURFACE FINISH OF THE REPAIRED AREA MUST BE BETTER THAN 0.8 MICRONS.	
REPAIR (v), REPAIRS, REPAIRED, REPAIRED	To make an item serviceable	REPAIR THE DEFECTIVE WIRING.	
repairable (adj)	REPAIR (v)	IT IS POSSIBLE TO REPAIR THIS DAMAGE.	This damage is repairable.
repeat (v)	AGAIN (adv)	DO STEPS (10) THRU (14) AGAIN.	Repeat steps (10) to (14).
repeated (adj)	AGAIN AND AGAIN	IF YOU HEAR SIGNALS AGAIN AND AGAIN, DO A CHECK OF THE "AP ENGAGE" BUTTON ON THE FLIGHT MODE PANEL.	If repeated signals are heard, check the AP ENGAGE button on the flight mode panel.
repeatedly (adv)	AGAIN AND AGAIN	IF THE VOLTAGE DECREASES AGAIN AND AGAIN, ADJUST THE VOLTAGE REGULATOR.	If voltage drops repeatedly, adjust the voltage regulator.

Word (part of speech)	Approved meaning / ALTERNATIVES	APPROVED EXAMPLE	Not approved example
REPLACE (v), REPLACES, REPLACED, REPLACED	To remove an item and to install a new or serviceable item of the same type	REPLACE THE RELAY.	
REPLACEMENT (n)	The item you install when you replace an item	MAKE SURE THAT THE REPLACEMENT HAS THE CORRECT DIMENSIONS.	
replenish (v)	FILL (v)	FILL THE ACCUMULATOR WITH OIL.	Replenish the accumulator with oil.
	ADD (v)	ADD OIL TO THE ACCUMULATOR.	Replenish the oil in the accumulator.
	REFUEL (v)	REFUEL THE AIRCRAFT.	Replenish the aircraft with fuel.
REPORT (n)	The information that is recorded about a subject or occurrence	IF THERE IS A REPORT OF DAMAGE, DO AN ACCURATE INSPECTION.	
reposition (v)	MOVE (v)	MOVE THE LEVER BACK TO ITS INITIAL POSITION.	Reposition the lever.
	PUT (v)	PUT THE LEVER BACK TO ITS INITIAL POSITION.	Reposition the lever.
	SET (v)	SET THE SWITCH BACK TO THE OFF POSITION.	Reposition the switch to OFF.
represent (v)	SHOW (v)	THE SUCTION SHOWS AS AN ALTIMETER INDICATION.	The suction is represented by an altimeter reading.
repressurize (v)	PRESSURIZE (v)	PRESSURIZE THE TANK AGAIN.	Repressurize the tank.
request (n)	TELL (v)	TELL THE FIRE SERVICE TO HELP YOU.	Make a request for external fire support.
	WRITE (v)	IF AID IS NECESSARY, WRITE TO THE MANUFACTURER.	Any request for assistance should be addressed to the manufacturer.

Word (part of speech)	Approved meaning / ALTERNATIVES	APPROVED EXAMPLE	Not approved example
request (v)	TELL (v)	TELL THE FIRE SERVICE TO HELP YOU.	Request external fire support.
	WRITE (v)	WRITE TO THE MANUFACTURER FOR REPAIR INSTRUCTIONS.	Request repair instructions from the manufacturer.
require (v)	NECESSARY (adj)	IF NECESSARY, INSTALL CLEAN FILTERS.	Install clean filters if required.
reseal (v)	SEAL (v)	SEAL THE CONTAINER AGAIN.	Reseal the container.
reset (v)	SET (v)	SET THE INDICATOR TO A NEW POSITION.	Reset the indicator to a new position.
residual (adj)	REMAINING (adj)	REMOVE ALL THE REMAINING GREASE.	Remove all residual grease.
residue (n)	REMAINING (adj)	REMOVE THE REMAINING GREASE.	Remove the grease residues.
RESISTANT (adj)	That will help to prevent something	THE MATERIAL OF THE SEATS IS RESISTANT TO FIRE	
respective (adj)	RELATED (adj)	ATTACH THE CABLES TO THEIR RELATED SHACKLES.	Attach the cables to their respective shackles.
	CORRECT (adj)	INSTALL THE BOLTS IN THEIR CORRECT POSITIONS.	Install the bolts in their respective positions.
respectively (adv)	RELATED (adj)	ENGINES 1 AND 2 SUPPLY HOT AIR TO THEIR RELATED WINGS.	Engines 1 and 2 supply the left and right wings respectively with hot air.
respond (v)	RESULT (n)	IF THE INSTRUMENT DOES NOT GIVE A RESULT, DO A TEST.	If the instrument fails to respond, do a test.
rest (n)	REMAINING (adj)	THE REMAINING INSTRUCTIONS ARE APPLICABLE ONLY TO AIRCRAFT WITH FUSELAGE TANKS.	The rest of these instructions only apply to aircraft with fuselage tanks.

ASD STE 100

Word (part of speech)	Approved meaning / ALTERNATIVES	APPROVED EXAMPLE	Not approved example
rest (v)	BE (v)	THE AIRCRAFT MUST BE ON ITS WHEELS.	The aircraft must rest on its wheels.
	PUT (v)	PUT THE REMOVED PART ON A CLEAN SURFACE.	Rest the removed part on a clean surface.
restart (v)	START (v)	START THE UNIT AGAIN.	Restart the unit.
restore (v)	REPAIR (v)	DO NOT REPAIR THE CHROMIC ACID ANODIZING ON THE SKIN PANEL.	Do not restore the chromic acid anodizing on the skin panel.
	PUT (v)	PUT THE PINS BACK IN THEIR LOCATION.	Restore the pins to their location.
restrain (v)	HOLD (v)	HOLD THE HOSES IN POSITION.	Restrain the hoses in position.
	STOP (v)	STOP THE FLUID FLOW.	Restrain all fluid flow.
	PREVENT (v)	THE STOP PREVENTS THE MOVEMENT OF THE ROD.	The stop restrains the movement of the rod.
	LIMIT (n)	THE VALVE KEEPS THE AIRFLOW IN LIMITS.	The valve restrains the airflow.
restrict (v)	DECREASE (v)	THE METERING PLUG DECREASES THE FUEL FLOW.	The metering plug restricts the fuel flow.
	PREVENT (v)	THE STOP PREVENTS THE MOVEMENT OF THE ROD.	The stop restricts the movement of the rod.
	ONLY (adv)	USE THESE NUTS ONLY FOR THE TEST.	Restrict the use of these nuts to test only.
	LIMIT (n)	THE VALVE KEEPS THE AIRFLOW IN LIMITS.	The valve restricts the airflow.
RESULT (n)	Something that occurs when you do something	IF THESE TESTS DO NOT GIVE THE CORRECT RESULTS, REPLACE THE UNIT.	

Word (part of speech)	Approved meaning / ALTERNATIVES	APPROVED EXAMPLE	Not approved example
result (v)	CAUSE (v)	AN INCORRECT CONNECTION WILL CAUSE DAMAGE.	An incorrect connection will result in damage.
	RESULT (n)	REPAIR DAMAGE THAT IS THE RESULT OF CORROSION.	Repair any damage resulting from corrosion.
resume (v)	START (v)	IF THERE IS NO CONTAMINATION, START THE OPERATION AGAIN.	If there is no contamination, resume the operation.
	CONTINUE (v)	CONTINUE THE TEST.	Resume the test.
retain (v)	KEEP (v)	KEEP THE PLUG.	Retain the plug.
retorque (v)	TORQUE (v)	TORQUE THE FITTING AGAIN.	Retorque the fitting.
retouch (v)	APPLY (v)	APPLY ENAMEL ON THE AREAS WHERE IT IS MISSING.	Retouch the missing enamel areas.
	PAINT (v)	PAINT (v)	PAINT (v)
PAINT (v)	1. To pull in(to)	RETRACT THE LANDING GEAR.	
	2. To move in(to)	THE NOSE LANDING GEAR RETRACTS INTO THE FUSELAGE.	
retractable (adj)	RETRACT (v)	THE AIRCRAFT HAS A LANDING GEAR THAT RETRACTS.	The aircraft has a retractable landing gear.
RETRACTION (n)	The result when something retracts	DURING THE RETRACTION SEQUENCE, MAKE SURE THAT THE LANDING GEAR DOORS CLOSE.	
return (n)	GO (v)	AFTER THE AILERONS GO BACK TO NEUTRAL, MAKE SURE THAT THEY ARE FLUSH WITH THE FLAPS.	After the return of the ailerons to neutral, check that they are flush with the flaps.

ASD STE 100

Word (part of speech)	Approved meaning / ALTERNATIVES	APPROVED EXAMPLE	Not approved example
return (v)	GO (v)	THE PLUNGERS MUST GO BACK TO THE CLOSED POSITION.	Plungers must return to the closed position.
reusable (adj)	USE (v)	YOU CAN USE THE MIXTURE AGAIN.	The mixture is reusable.
reuse (v)	USE (v)	USE THE FABRIC AGAIN IF IT IS NOT DAMAGED.	Reuse the fabric if it is not damaged.
reveal (v)	SHOW (v)	IF THE FUEL SAMPLE SHOWS FREE WATER, DRAIN THE SYSTEM.	If the fuel sample reveals free water, drain the system.
reverse (adj)	OPPOSITE (adj) 💡 This word is part of a technical name when it refers to rearward thrust.	MOVE THE CONTROL IN THE OPPOSITE DIRECTION. MANUALLY TURN THE PROPELLER BLADES TO THE FULL REVERSE POSITION.	Move the control in the reverse direction.
reverse (v)	OPPOSITE (adj)	MOVE THE ROD IN THE OPPOSITE DIRECTION.	Reverse the movement of the rod.
review (n)	INSPECTION (n)	DO AN INSPECTION OF THE DAMAGED AREA.	Do a review of the damaged area.
rewind (v)	WIND (v)	WIND THE CABLE BACK ONTO ITS REEL.	Rewind the cable onto its reel.
rework (v)	💡 Refer to technical verbs, manufacturing process	DO AN INSPECTION FOR SCRATCHES. THEN, LIGHTLY POLISH ALL DAMAGED AREAS.	Do an inspection for scratches and rework all damage areas.
rig (v)	ADJUST (v)	ADJUST THE SYSTEM.	Rig the system.
RIGHT (adj)	On the east side when you look north	DO A FLOW CHECK OF THE PUMP IN THE RIGHT WING TANK.	
right-hand (adj)	RIGHT (adj)	THE FUEL CONNECTOR IS IN THE RIGHT WING.	The fuel connector is in the right-hand wing.
RIGID (adj)	That cannot easily bend or change shape	REMOVE THE SCREWS FROM THE RIGID COVER.	

Word (part of speech)	Approved meaning / ALTERNATIVES	APPROVED EXAMPLE	Not approved example
rinse (v)	FLUSH (v)	FLUSH THE FILTER WITH HOT WATER.	Rinse the filter in hot running water.
	REMOVE (v)	REMOVE THE CLEANING AGENT FROM THE SURFACE.	Rinse the cleaning agent from the surface.
	CLEAN (v)	CLEAN THE WINDOW PANE WITH A LARGE QUANTITY OF WATER.	Rinse the window pane with a large quantity of water.
ripped (adj)	DAMAGED (adj)	IF THE SEAT COVER IS DAMAGED, REPLACE IT.	If the seat cover is ripped, replace it.
rise (n)	INCREASE (v)	WHEN A FIRE STARTS, THE TEMPERATURE INCREASES AND CAUSES THE DETECTOR TO OPERATE.	When a fire starts, the temperature rise causes the detector to operate.
RISK (n)	The possibility that something that is dangerous occurs	USE A PUMP TO FILL THE STRUT WITH FLUID UNTIL THE PRESSURE INCREASES.	Pump fluid into the strut until the pressure rises.
rope off (v)	ROPE (TN)	PUT ROPES AROUND THE AREA.	Rope off the area.
rotary (adj)	TURN (v)	TURN THE GEARS TO ALIGN THEM.	Use a rotary movement to align the gears.
rotate (v)	TURN (v)	SLOWLY TURN THE VANE.	Slowly rotate the vane.
rotation (n)	TURN (v)	MAKE SURE THAT THE FAN TURNS FREELY.	Ensure the free rotation of the fan.
rotational (adj)	TURN (v)	TURN THE GEARS TO ALIGN THEM.	Use a rotational movement to align the gears.
ROUGH (adj) (ROUGHER, ROUGHEST)	Not smooth	CLEAN THE ROUGH SURFACES CAREFULLY.	
roughen (v)	ROUGH (adj)	MAKE THE FAYING SURFACES ROUGH.	Roughen the faying surfaces.

ASD STE 100

Word (part of speech)	Approved meaning / ALTERNATIVES	APPROVED EXAMPLE	Not approved example
roughness (n)	ROUGH (adj)	MAKE SURE THAT THE AREA OF THE BOND IS SUFFICIENTLY ROUGH.	Make sure the area of the bond has sufficient roughness.
round (adj)	CIRCULAR (adj)	REPAIR THE DAMAGE WITH A CIRCULAR PATCH.	Repair the damage with a round patch.
ROUNDED (adj)	Not angular	WHEN YOU INSTALL THE PART, MAKE SURE THAT THE ROUNDED EDGE IS AGAINST THE STRUCTURE.	
route (n)	ROUTING (n)	MAKE SURE THAT YOU DO NOT CHANGE THE WIRE ROUTING.	Make sure you do not change the wire routes.
route (v)	PUT (v)	PUT THE FUELING HOSE ALONG THE GROUND.	Route the fueling hose along the ground.
	ROUTING (n)	MAKE SURE THAT THE ROUTING OF THE WIRE IS CORRECT.	Make sure that the wiring is correctly routed.
ROUTING (n)	The specified direction that cables, pipes, wires, and other parts of a system must go along	DO NOT CHANGE THE ROUTING OF THE PIPE.	
ROW (n)	number of objects in a line	THE PANELS ARE INSTALLED IN ROWS.	
RUB (v), RUBS, RUBBED, RUBBED	To move or cause something to move with pressure and friction along a surface	RUB THE SURFACE WITH A CLEAN CLOTH. MAKE SURE THAT THE COILS OF THE OXYGEN HOSE DO NOT RUB TOGETHER.	
run (v)	OPERATE (v)	OPERATE THE ENGINE AT 100% THRUST.	Run the engine at 100% thrust.
running (adj)	FLUSH (v)	FLUSH THE PIPES WITH WATER.	Clean the pipes with running water.

Word (part of speech)	Approved meaning / ALTERNATIVES	APPROVED EXAMPLE	Not approved example
SAFE (adj) (SAFER, SAFEST)	Not dangerous, disarmed	MAKE THE AREA SAFE BEFORE YOU CONTINUE THE WORK.	
SAFELY (adv)	In a safe manner	MAKE SURE THAT THE LADDER IS SAFELY ATTACHED.	
SAFETY (n)	A condition that is safe	FOR YOUR SAFETY, ALWAYS USE A PROTECTIVE MASK.	
SAFETY (v), SAFETIES, SAFETIED, SAFETIED	1. To prevent accidental operation	OPEN, TAG, AND SAFETY THE CIRCUIT BREAKERS.	
	2. To make sure that something does not become loose	SAFETY THE NUT WITH LOCKWIRE.	
safety-clip (v)	LOCK (v) (WITH A CLIP [TN] OR CLIPS [TN])	LOCK THE TURNBUCKLE ON THE CONTROL ROD WITH A CLIP.	Safety-clip the turnbuckle on the control rod.
	SAFETY (v) (WITH A CLIP [TN] OR CLIPS [TN])	OPEN, TAG, AND SAFETY THE CIRCUIT BREAKER WITH A CLIP.	Open, tag, and safety -clip the circuit breaker.
safety-wire (v)	LOCK (v) (WITH LOCKWIRE [TN])	LOCK THE COVER TO THE FIRE EXTINGUISHER SWITCH WITH LOCKWIRE.	Safety-wire the cover to the fire extinguisher switch.
	SAFETY (v) (WITH SAFETY WIRE [TN])	SAFETY THE NUT WITH SAFETY WIRE.	Safety-wire the nut.
SAME (adj)	Agrees in all details	THE SAME PROCEDURE IS APPLICABLE TO THE TWO UNITS.	

Word (part of speech)	Approved meaning / ALTERNATIVES	APPROVED EXAMPLE	Not approved example
SAME (pron)	Agrees in all details	THE ADJUSTMENT OF THE LEFT AND RIGHT ACTUATORS MUST BE THE SAME.	
SAMPLE (n)	A piece or quantity of something that you use for an inspection or test procedure to show that it has specified qualities	GET A SAMPLE OF THE FUEL AND MEASURE ITS SPECIFIC GRAVITY.	
sample (v)	SAMPLE (n)	GET A SAMPLE OF FUEL AND DO A TEST FOR WATER CONTAMINATION.	Sample and test the fuel for water contamination.
SATISFACTORILY (adv)	In a satisfactory manner	MAKE SURE THAT THE MICROSWITCHES OPERATE SATISFACTORILY.	
SATISFACTORY (adj)	Agrees with all that is necessary	A CLEARANCE OF 3 mm IS SATISFACTORY.	
saturate (v)	SOAK (v)	SOAK THE ELEMENT FOR FOUR HOURS.	Saturate the element for four hours.
save (v)	KEEP (v)	KEEP THE O-RINGS FOR THE SUBSEQUENT PROCEDURES.	Save the O-rings for the subsequent procedures.
scan (v)	EXAMINE (v)	EXAMINE THE SURFACE ALONG THE TRAILING EDGE.	Scan the surface along the trailing edge.
	SCAN (TN)	THE ANTENNA DOES A SCAN THROUGH 80 DEG.	Antenna scans through 80 deg.
SCHEDULE (v), SCHEDULES, SCHEDULED, SCHEDULED	To plan something in a time or a sequence	SCHEDULE THE CHECKS OF THE TIRES AT REGULAR INTERVALS.	
scored (adj)	SCORE (TN)	IF THE BEARING RACE HAS SCORES, REPLACE IT.	If the bearing race is scored, replace it.
scrap (v)	DISCARD (v)	DISCARD THE REMOVED SEAL.	Scrap the removed seal.

Word (part of speech)	Approved meaning / ALTERNATIVES	APPROVED EXAMPLE	Not approved example
scrape (v)	REMOVE (v) (WITH A SCRAPER [TN])	USE A SCRAPER TO REMOVE THE REMAINING SEALANT	Scrape off the old sealant.
scratched (adj)	SCRATCH (TN)	REPAIR THE SURFACES THAT HAVE SCRATCHES.	Repair the scratched surfaces.
screw (v)	TURN (v)	CONTINUE TO TURN THE END FITTING UNTIL IT IS IN THE CORRECT POSITION.	Continue screwing the end fitting until it is in the correct position.
	ATTACH (v) (WITH A SCREW [TN] OR SCREWS [TN])	ATTACH THE STRAPS TO THE PANELS WITH SCREWS.	Screw the straps to the panels.
scrub (v)	CLEAN (v) (WITH A BRUSH [TN])	CLEAN THE METAL PARTS WITH A BRUSH.	Scrub all metal parts.
SEAL (n)	Something that prevents access or leaks	APPLY SEALANT TO THE FILLET SEALS.	
SEAL (v), SEALS, SEALED, SEALED	To prevent access or leaks	SEAL THE OPENINGS WITH POLYETHYLENE.	
search (v)	EXAMINE (v)	EXAMINE THE SURFACE FOR CRACKS.	Search the surface for cracks.
seat (v)	INSTALL (v)	INSTALL THE O-RING IN ITS GROOVE ON THE PISTON.	Seat the O-ring in its groove on the piston.
	AGAINST (prep)	MAKE SURE THAT THE VALVE IS IN ITS CORRECT POSITION AGAINST THE FRAME.	Make sure that the valve is seated on the frame.
SECONDARY (adj)	Second in importance	DO AN OPERATIONAL CHECK OF THE SECONDARY FLIGHT CONTROLS.	

Word (part of speech)	Approved meaning / ALTERNATIVES	APPROVED EXAMPLE	Not approved example
secure (adj)	TIGHT (adj)	MAKE SURE THAT THE BOLTS ARE TIGHT.	Make sure that the bolts are secure.
	SAFE (adj)	BEFORE YOU LIFT THE PLATFORM, MAKE SURE THAT IT IS SAFE.	Make sure that the platform is secure before you lift it.
	CORRECTLY (adv)	MAKE SURE THAT THE BRACKETS ARE CORRECTLY ATTACHED.	Check the brackets for secure attachment.
secure (v)	ATTACH (v)	REMOVE THE BOLTS THAT ATTACH THE UNIT.	Remove the bolts that secure the unit.
	SAFETY (v)	SAFETY THE PULLEY GUARD PINS WITH SPLIT PINS.	Secure the pulley guard pins with split pins.
securely (adv)	CORRECTLY (adv)	MAKE SURE THAT THE BRACKETS ARE CORRECTLY ATTACHED.	Make sure that the brackets are securely attached.
	SAFELY (adv)	MAKE SURE THAT THE LADDER IS SAFELY ATTACHED.	Make sure the ladder is securely attached.
	TIGHT (adj)	MAKE SURE THAT THE BOLTS ARE TIGHT.	Make sure that the bolts are securely installed.
security (n)	CORRECTLY (adv)	MAKE SURE THAT THE COMPONENTS ARE CORRECTLY ATTACHED.	Check the security of the components.

Word (part of speech)	Approved meaning / ALTERNATIVES	APPROVED EXAMPLE	Not approved example
SEE (v), SEES, SAW, SEEN	To know with the eyes	MAKE SURE THAT YOU CAN SEE THE CABLE THROUGH THE INSPECTION HOLE.	
	For other meanings, use: REFER (v)	REFER TO TABLE 8001 FOR THE APPLICABLE TORQUE VALUES.	See Table 8001 for the applicable torque value.
	EXAMINE (v)	EXAMINE THE MEMBRANE FOR HOLES.	Check the membrane to see if there are holes.
	MAKE SURE (v)	MOVE THE TUBE TO MAKE SURE THAT ITS INNER CONNECTION IS TIGHT.	Move the tube to see if its inner connection is tight.
seek (v)	GET (v)	GET MEDICAL AID IMMEDIATELY.	Seek medical attention immediately.
seepage (n)	LEAKAGE (n)	CLEAN THE AREAS WHERE THERE IS HYDRAULIC FLUID LEAKAGE.	Clean the areas where there is hydraulic fluid seepage.
seized (adj)	CATCH (v)	IF THE CONTROL CABLE IS CAUGHT IN THE PULLEY, RELEASE THE CABLE TENSION.	If the control cable is seized in the pulley, release the cable tension.
	MOVE (v)	IF YOU CANNOT MOVE THE BOLTS, APPLY SOME PENETRATING OIL.	If the bolts are seized, apply some penetrating oil.
	TURN (v)	IF THE FLAP CONTROL MOTOR CANNOT TURN, USE THE ALTERNATIVE MODE.	If the flap control motor is seized, use the alternate mode.

ASD STE 100

Word (part of speech)	Approved meaning / ALTERNATIVES	APPROVED EXAMPLE	Not approved example
SELECT (v), SELECTS, SELECTED, SELECTED	To make a choice	SELECT THE HYDRAULIC SYSTEM THAT YOU WILL PRESSURIZE.	
		SELECT A LANGUAGE FROM THE MENU.	
	Do not use this word as a synonym for SET (v).	SET THE SWITCH TO "TEST".	Select the switch to TEST.
SELECTION (n)	The action or result of choosing	THE OPERATION OF THE INDICATOR DOES NOT PREVENT THE SELECTION OF SYSTEM 1.	
SEMICIRCULAR (adj)	That has the shape of half a circle	THE VALVE FLAPS ARE SEMICIRCULAR.	
SEND (v), SENDS, SENT, SENT	To cause to go	SEND THE FILTER ELEMENT TO THE MAINTENANCE SHOP FOR THE NECESSARY INSPECTION.	
SENSE (v), SENSES, SENSED, SENSED	To get an input automatically	THE TEMPERATURE BULB SENSES THE EXTERNAL AIR TEMPERATURE.	
SENSITIVE (adj)	That can sense small changes	THE CAPSULE IS SENSITIVE TO PRESSURE CHANGES.	
separable (adj)	DISASSEMBLE (v)	YOU CAN DISASSEMBLE THIS UNIT INTO TWO PARTS.	This unit is separable into two parts.
	DISCONNECT (v)	YOU CAN DISCONNECT THESE LINE FITTINGS.	These line fittings are separable.

Word (part of speech)	Approved meaning / ALTERNATIVES	APPROVED EXAMPLE	Not approved example
separate (adj)	NOT CONNECTED	THESE TWO TRACKS ARE NOT CONNECTED TO THE OTHER TWO.	These two tracks are separate from the other two.
	ISOLATED (v)	EACH HYDRAULIC SYSTEM IS FULLY ISOLATED.	All hydraulic systems are completely separate.
	NOT ATTACHED	THE CAP IS NOT ATTACHED TO THE COUPLING.	The cap is separate from the coupling.
separate (v)	DISCONNECT (v)	DISCONNECT THE LINE FITTINGS.	Separate the line fittings.
	DIVIDE (v)	YOU CAN DIVIDE THE DRAINS INTO THREE GROUPS.	You can separate the drains into three groups.
SEPARATION (n)	The action or result of separating	SEPARATION OF THESE PARTS IS NOT EASY.	
SEQUENCE (n)	The relation of items that follow one after the other in a list or the relation of steps or events that occur one after the other in time	TIGHTEN THE BOLTS IN THE SEQUENCE THAT IS GIVEN IN FIGURE 3.	
serious (adj)	IMPORTANT (adj)	VIRUS CONTAMINATION IS AN IMPORTANT PROBLEM.	Virus contamination is a serious problem.
	DANGEROUS (adj)	HYDRAULIC FLUID IS DANGEROUS FOR YOUR EYES.	Hydraulic fluid can cause serious eye injury.
serrated (adj)	SERRATION (n)	USE GLOVES WHEN YOU TOUCH PARTS WITH EDGE SERRATIONS.	Use gloves when handling parts with serrated edges.
SERRATION (n)	One or more notches or teeth as in a saw	MAKE MARKS THAT SHOW THE LOCATION OF THE SERRATIONS ON THE PLATES.	
serve (v)	💡 Use an action verb.	THE RADIO MASTER SWITCH CONTROLS THE BUS BAR.	The radio master switch serves to control the bus bar.

ASD STE 100

Word (part of speech)	Approved meaning / ALTERNATIVES	APPROVED EXAMPLE	Not approved example
service (v)	SERVICING (n)	DO THE SERVICING OF THE FIRE EXTINGUISHERS.	Service the fire extinguishers.
serviceability (n)	SERVICEABLE (adj)	THE TIRE IS SERVICEABLE IF THE CUTS ARE SMALLER THAN 10 mm.	The serviceability of the tire is not affected by any cut smaller than 10 mm.
SERVICEABLE (adj)	Correct or satisfactory	DO A VISUAL INSPECTION OF THE ADAPTER TO MAKE SURE THAT IT IS SERVICEABLE.	
SERVICING (n)	The steps necessary to prepare something for operation	BEFORE YOU DO SERVICING OF THE HYDRAULIC SYSTEM, ISOLATE IT.	
SET (n)	A group of related items that you (can) use for the same purpose	USE THE SET OF TOOLS THAT IS SUPPLIED WITH THE UNIT.	
SET (v), SETS, SET, SET	To put something into a given adjustment, condition, or mode	SET THE ALTIMETER SCALE TO 1013 mbar.	
setting (n)	ADJUSTMENT (n)	DO NOT CHANGE THE ADJUSTMENT OF THE SWITCHES.	Do not change the setting of the switches.
	POSITION (n)	MAKE SURE THAT THE POSITION OF THE FLAPS IS EIGHT DEG.	Check flaps for eight deg. setting.
	SET (v)	THE MANUFACTURER SETS THE LENGTH OF THE ROD IN THE FACTORY.	Setting of the rod length is achieved in the factory.
settle (v)	COLLECT (v)	LET THE SEDIMENT COLLECT AT THE BOTTOM OF THE TANK.	Let the sediment settle at the bottom of the tank.
	STABLE (adj)	LET THE INDICATIONS BECOME STABLE.	Let the indications settle.
sever (v)	CUT (v)	MAKE SURE THAT YOU DO NOT CUT THE CONTROL CABLE.	Make sure you do not sever the control cable.

Word (part of speech)	Approved meaning / ALTERNATIVES	APPROVED EXAMPLE	Not approved example
several (adj)	SOME (adj)	SOME FUNCTIONS ARE NOT AVAILABLE.	Several functions are not available.
	If this alternative is not sufficient, give the range, quantity, number, or minimum value.	SOAK THE FILLER CAPS IN DISTILLED WATER FOR A MINIMUM OF EIGHT HOURS.	Soak the filler caps in distilled water for several hours.
severe (adj)	DANGEROUS (adj)	HYDRAULIC FLUID IS DANGEROUS FOR YOUR SKIN.	Hydraulic fluid can cause severe skin problems.
SHAKE (v), SHAKES, SHOOK, SHAKEN	To move or cause to move quickly up and down or from side to side	SHAKE THE CONTAINER.	
		THE CONTROL COLUMN STARTS TO SHAKE BEFORE A STALL OCCURS.	
shall (v)	MUST (v)	HOLES MUST NOT HAVE SHARP EDGES.	Holes shall not have sharp edges.
SHAPE (n)	The contour of an object	THE PATCH MUST BE THE SAME SHAPE AS THE CUTOUT.	
shape (v)	SHAPE (n)	MAKE THE PATCH THE SAME SHAPE AS THE CUTOUT.	Shape the patch to suit the cutout.
SHARP (adj) (SHARPER, SHARPEST)	That can cut or make a hole	MAKE A HOLE WITH A SHARP TOOL.	
sharply (adv)	QUICKLY (adv)	QUICKLY PULL ON THE CABLES TO DISENGAGE THEM.	Sharply pull on the cables to disengage them.
	SUDDENLY (adv)	MOVE THE CONTROL COLUMN FORWARD SUDDENLY.	Move the control column forward sharply.
shear (v)	BREAK (v)	TIGHTEN THE NUT. CONTINUE UNTIL THE NUT BREAKS.	Tighten the nut until it shears.
	CUT (v)	DO NOT CUT THE WIRES.	Do not shear the wires.

Word (part of speech)	Approved meaning / ALTERNATIVES	APPROVED EXAMPLE	Not approved example
SHEET (n)	A piece of material that is thin in relation to its length and width	IF THE SHEETS HAVE DENTS WITH A DEPTH OF MORE THAN 0.5 mm, REMOVE THESE DENTS.	
shield (v)	PREVENT (v)	PUT ON GOGGLES TO PREVENT INJURY TO YOUR EYES.	Shield your eyes.
	PROTECTION (n)	GIVE THE CONTROL UNIT PROTECTION FROM DAMAGE.	Shield the control unit from damage.
shift (v)	MOVE (v)	MOVE THE LEVER FORWARD.	Shift the lever forward.
SHINY (adj) (SHINIER, SHINIEST)	That can cause a reflection of light	CLEAN THE SHINY AREA OF THE OLEO STRUT.	
SHOCK (n)	The sudden effect of energy on a person or object	SHOCKS CAN CAUSE DAMAGE TO THE GYROSCOPE.	
SHORT (adj) (SHORTER, SHORTEST)	That has small length or duration	ATTACH THE SHORT ARM OF THE BELLCRANK TO THE ROD.	
	💡 Be specific if possible	AFTER YOU STOP THE POWER SUPPLY, THE TEMPERATURE DECREASES IN A SHORT TIME. THIS TIME MUST NOT BE MORE THAN 30 SECONDS.	
shorten (v)	DECREASE (v)	DO NOT DECREASE THE TEST TIME.	Do not shorten the test time.
should (v)	MUST (v)	PERSONNEL MUST USE PROTECTIVE CLOTHING.	Personnel should wear protective clothing.
	IF (conj)	IF A FAILURE OCCURS, STOP THE TEST.	Should a failure occur, stop the test.

Word (part of speech)	Approved meaning / ALTERNATIVES	APPROVED EXAMPLE	Not approved example
SHOW (v), SHOWS, SHOWED, SHOWN	1. To cause to be seen	THE INDICATOR SHOWS THE LEVEL OF HYDRAULIC FLUID IN THE RESERVOIR.	
	2. To be in view or come into view	THE SYMBOL SHOWS ON THE SCREEN.	
shut down (v)	STOP (v)	STOP THE ENGINE.	Shut down the engine.
SIDE (n)	1. The specified surface or area of an object	LUBRICATE ONE SIDE OF THE WASHER.	
	2. A location or direction that has a relationship to a center or a line of division	PUSH THE UNIT OUT AND THEN MOVE IT TO THE LEFT SIDE.	
sideways (adv)	SIDE (n)	PUSH THE UNIT OUT AND THEN MOVE IT TO THE LEFT SIDE.	Push the unit out and then move it sideways.
sight (n)	VIEW (n)	TURN THE KNOB TO MAKE THE DISPLAY GO OUT OF VIEW.	Turn the knob to make the display go out of sight.
sight (v)	LOOK (v)	LOOK ALONG THE SKIN.	Sight along the skin.
SIGN (n)	The indication of a possible condition	EXAMINE THE SURFACE FOR SIGNS OF INTERNAL DAMAGE.	
significant (adj)	IMPORTANT (adj)	THIS PROCEDURE IS IMPORTANT FOR THE CORRECT OPERATION OF THE UNIT.	This procedure is significant for the correct operation of the unit.
silence (v)	STOP (v)	STOP THE ALARM BELL	Silence the alarm bell.
similar (adj)	EQUIVALENT (adj)	USE MATERIAL 11-001 OR AN EQUIVALENT MATERIAL	Use material 11-001 or a similar material.
	ALMOST THE SAME	THE TWO ITEMS HAVE ALMOST THE SAME SHAPE.	The two items are similar in shape.

Word (part of speech)	Approved meaning / ALTERNATIVES	APPROVED EXAMPLE	Not approved example
SIMULATE (v), SIMULATES, SIMULATED, SIMULATED	To make a condition that is the same as one that can occur in operation	SIMULATE A WHEEL SPEED OF 80 KNOTS.	
simultaneous (adj)	AT THE SAME TIME	YOU MUST REMOVE THE FILTER ELEMENT AND THE FILTER HOUSING AT THE SAME TIME.	Simultaneous removal of the filter element and the filter housing is mandatory.
simultaneously (adv)	AT THE SAME TIME	DO THESE TWO STEPS AT THE SAME TIME.	Do these two steps simultaneously.
SINCE (conj)	Function word that shows: "from some time in the past until a later time or now"	IF IT IS MORE THAN TWO HOURS SINCE YOU MIXED THE COMPOUND, DO NOT USE IT	
	💡 For other meanings, use: BECAUSE (conj)	BE CAREFUL WHEN YOU USE ALODINE, BECAUSE IT IS A DANGEROUS MATERIAL.	Since Alodine is a dangerous material, be careful when you use it.
single (adj)	ONE (TN)	ONE CRACK, 0.50 INCH LONG, IS PERMITTED.	A single crack, 0.50 inch long, is allowed.
situated (adj)	INSTALL (v)	THE TRIM CONTROL KNOB IS INSTALLED ON THE CONTROL PEDESTAL	The trim control knob is situated on the control pedestal.
	BE (v)	THE TRIM CONTROL KNOB IS ON THE CONTROL PEDESTAL.	The trim control knob is situated on the control pedestal.
size (n)	DIMENSION (n)	THESE CASES HAVE DIFFERENT DIMENSIONS.	These cases are of different sizes.
skid (v)	SKID (TN)	THIS SHOWS THAT THE AIRCRAFT IS IN A SKID.	This indicates that the aircraft is skidding.

Word (part of speech)	Approved meaning / ALTERNATIVES	APPROVED EXAMPLE	Not approved example
slack (adj)	TENSION (TN)	MAKE SURE THAT THE TENSION IN THE CONTROL CABLES IS CORRECT	Check for slack control cables.
slack (n)	TENSION (TN)	MAKE SURE THAT THE TENSION IN THE CONTROL CABLES IS CORRECT.	Check for slack in the control cables.
slacken (v)	TENSION (TN)	RELEASE THE TENSION IN THE CONTROL CABLES.	Slacken the control cables.
slackness (n)	TENSION (TN)	MAKE SURE THAT THE TENSION IN THE CABLES IS CORRECT.	Make sure there is no slackness in the cables.
slave (v)	CONTROL (v)	THE PILOT'S INDICATORS CONTROL THE COPILOT'S INDICATORS.	The copilot's indicators are slaved to the pilot's indicators.
slide (v)	MOVE (v)	MOVE THE COMPUTER HORIZONTALLY TO PREVENT DAMAGE.	Slide the computer horizontally to avoid damage.
slight (adj)	SMALL (adj)	IF THE LEAKAGE IS SMALL, TORQUE THE CONNECTION TO 4.0 Nm. THEN, DO THE TEST AGAIN.	If slight leakage is found, torque the connection to 4.0 Nm. Then repeat the test.
	LIGHT (adj)	APPLY A LIGHT FORCE TO COMPRESS THE SPRING.	Apply a slight force to compress the spring.
slightly (adv)	SMALL (adj)	MOVE THE ADAPTER A SMALL DISTANCE FORWARD.	Move the adapter slightly forward.

ASD STE 100

Word (part of speech)	Approved meaning / ALTERNATIVES	APPROVED EXAMPLE	Not approved example
slip (v)	MOVE (v)	MOVE THE CARRIAGE ALONG THE FLAP TRACK.	Slip the carriage along the flap track.
	REMOVE (v)	REMOVE THE CLAMP FROM THE CABLE.	Slip the clamp from the cable.
	CAUSE TO FALL	IF FUEL OR LUBRICATING OIL SPILLS, CLEAN THE AREA IMMEDIATELY. A WET SURFACE IS DANGEROUS AND CAN CAUSE YOU TO FALL.	If fuel or lubricating oil spills, clean the area immediately. You can slip and fall.
	MOVE ACCIDENTALLY	MAKE SURE THAT THE CLUTCH DOES NOT MOVE ACCIDENTALLY.	Make sure that the clutch does not slip.
SLOPE (n)	A surface that is not level	IF THE AIRCRAFT IS PARKED ON A SLOPE, MAKE SURE THAT WHEEL CHOCKS ARE IN POSITION.	
SLOT (n)	A long opening that is not wide	PUSH THE CABLES THROUGH THE SLOT IN FRAME 8 AND ATTACH THEM TO THE CLIPS.	
SLOW (adj) (SLOWER, SLOWEST)	At low speed	MAKE SURE THAT THE MOVEMENT OF THE ELEVATORS IS SLOW.	
slow down (v)	DECREASE (v)	DECREASE THE SPEED OF THE SCREWING MACHINE TO PREVENT DAMAGE TO FASTENERS.	Slow down the screwing machine to prevent damage to fasteners.
SLOWLY (adv)	In a slow manner	TURN THE KNOB SLOWLY.	
sluggish (adj)	SLOW (adj)	IF THE MOVEMENT OF THE NEEDLE IS TOO SLOW, REPLACE THE SENSOR	If the movement of the needle is sluggish, replace the sensor.

Word (part of speech)	Approved meaning / ALTERNATIVES	APPROVED EXAMPLE	Not approved example
SMALL (adj) (SMALLER, SMALLEST)	Less than average in dimension, quantity, quality, or capacity	WHEN YOU REFUEL THE AIRCRAFT, A SMALL QUANTITY OF FUEL COMES OUT OF THE VENT LINE.	
smear (v)	APPLY (v)	APPLY GREASE TO THE TAPER SLEEVE.	Smear grease on the taper sleeve.
SMELL (v), SMELLS, SMELLED, SMELLED	To sense with the nose	IF YOU SMELL OIL IN THE COMPARTMENT, REPLACE THE RECIRCULATION FILTERS.	
SMOKE (n)	A gas that has particles of burned material and that you can see	WHEN THE CONCENTRATION OF SMOKE IS MORE THAN THE LIMIT, AN ALARM OPERATES.	
SMOKE (v), SMOKES, SMOKED, SMOKED	To breathe the fumes of burning material and especially tobacco	DO NOT SMOKE IN THE WORK AREA.	
SMOOTH (adj) (SMOOTHER, SMOOTHEST)	1. That has a continuous uniform surface	MAKE SURE THAT THE PAINTED SURFACE IS SMOOTH.	
	2. That has a constant rate of movement	EXAMINE THE LINKAGE FOR SMOOTH MOVEMENT.	
smooth (v)	SMOOTH (adj)	MAKE THE TAPE SMOOTH.	Smooth the tape out.
SMOOTHLY (adv)	In a smooth manner	MAKE SURE THAT THE REDUCTION GEAR MOVES SMOOTHLY.	
snag (v)	CATCH (v)	THE CLOTH WILL CATCH ON BROKEN WIRES.	The cloth will snag on broken wires.
snap (n)	CLICK (n)	WHEN YOU ATTACH THE SPRING CLIP, MAKE SURE THAT YOU HEAR A CLICK.	Ensure that there is a snap when you fit the spring clip.

Word (part of speech)	Approved meaning / ALTERNATIVES	APPROVED EXAMPLE	Not approved example
snap (v)	MOVE QUICKLY	THE RETAINING CLIP MUST MOVE QUICKLY INTO ITS POSITION.	The retaining clip must snap into its position.
	BREAK (v)	IF YOU BEND THIS PART TOO FAR, IT WILL BREAK.	If you bend this part too far, it will snap.
so (that) (conj)	UNTIL (prep)	ADJUST THE LENGTH OF THE ROD UNTIL YOU GET A MINIMUM CLEARANCE OF 0.1 in.	Adjust the length of rod so that a minimum gap of 0.1 in. is obtained.
	PREVENT (v)	LOCK THE WHEEL TO PREVENT MOVEMENT.	Lock the wheel so that it does not move.
SOAK (v), SOAKS, SOAKED, SOAKED	1. To put something into a liquid and keep it there until it is fully wet or soft	SOAK THE FILTER IN THE CLEANING SOLUTION FOR 4 HOURS.	
	2. To stay in liquid until fully wet or soft.	THE COMPONENT MUST SOAK IN THE SOLUTION FOR A MINIMUM OF 2 HOURS.	
soapy (adj)	SOAP (TN)	CLEAN THE SURFACE WITH A SOLUTION OF SOAP AND WATER.	Clean the surface using soapy water.
SOFT (adj) (SOFTER, SOFTEST)	Flexible, not hard	RUB THE SURFACE WITH A SOFT, DRY CLOTH.	
soften (v)	MAKE···SOFT	PUT THE TOOLS IN SOLVENT TO MAKE THE COMPOUND SOFT.	Put the tools in solvent to soften the compound.
soiled (adj)	DIRTY (adj)	DISCARD THE DIRTY RAGS.	Scrap the soiled rags.
SOLID (adj)	That has theproperties of a solid	THE RAILS ARE MADE FROM SOLID BARS.	
SOLID (n)	Material that is not a gas or a liquid	EXAMINE THE OIL FOR SOLIDS.	
solidify (v)	SOLID (adj)	DO NOT LET THE FOAM BECOME SOLID.	Do not allow the foam to solidify.

Word (part of speech)	Approved meaning / ALTERNATIVES	APPROVED EXAMPLE	Not approved example
SOLUTION (n)	1. A liquid that includes a dissolved material	PREPARE THE SOLUTION IN A CONTAINER MADE OF CERAMIC MATERIAL.	
	2. The answer to a problem	A BITE TEST WILL GIVE THE SOLUTION.	
solve (v)	SOLUTION (n)	IF THE REMOVAL OF THE VALVE WAS NOT THE SOLUTION TO THE PROBLEM, REPLACE THE UNIT.	If the removal of the valve did not solve the problem, replace the unit.
SOME (adj)	Related to a quantity not specified	SOME MODELS DO NOT HAVE THIS FUNCTION.	
SOME (pron)	Related to a quantity not specified	SOME MODELS HAVE THIS FUNCTION, BUT SOME DO NOT.	
SOMETHING (pron)	A thing that is not determined or specified	IF SOMETHING UNUSUAL OCCURS, DO A BITE TEST.	
soon (adv)	TIME (n)	WHEN YOU STOP THE POWER SUPPLY, THE TEMPERATURE WILL DECREASE IN A SHORT TIME.	When you stop the power supply, the temperature will decrease soon.
	Give the time if possible.	WHEN YOU STOP THE POWER SUPPLY, THE TEMPERATURE WILL DECREASE IN APPROXIMATELY 1 MINUTE.	When you stop the power supply, the temperature will decrease soon.
SOUND (n)	Something that you can hear	INCREASE THE VOLUME OF THE SOUND.	
sound (v)	OPERATE (v)	THE ALARM BELL OPERATES.	The alarm bell sounds.

ASD STE 100

Word (part of speech)	Approved meaning / ALTERNATIVES	APPROVED EXAMPLE	Not approved example
SOURCE (n)	1. Something that supplies energy or data	USE A HYDRAULIC SOURCE TO OPERATE THE SWAGING TOOL.	
	2. The point where something starts	WHEN YOU FIND THE SOURCE OF THE LEAKAGE, CLEAN THE SURFACE WITH SOLVENT.	
SPACE (n)	A distance, area, or volume	PUT THE SEALANT INTO THE SPACE BEHIND THE FLANGE OF THE WATER INJECTOR.	
space (v)	DISTANCE (n)	MAKE SURE THAT THERE IS AN EQUAL DISTANCE BETWEEN THE HOLES.	Make sure you space the holes equally.
spacing (n)	DISTANCE (n)	REFER TO FIG. 401 FOR THE DISTANCE BETWEEN RIVETS.	The rivet spacing is given in Fig. 401.
spanwise (adj)	SPAN (TN)	MAKE SURE THAT THERE ARE NO SIGNS OF MOVEMENT ALONG THE SPAN.	Check for signs of spanwise movement.
sparingly (adv)	QUANTITY (n)	APPLY A SMALL QUANTITY OF GREASE.	Apply grease sparingly.
SPARK (n)	hot, bright particle of a material that burns	DO NOT USE TEST EQUIPMENT THAT CAN CAUSE SPARKS.	
spark (v)	SPARK (n)	PUT ON GOGGLES WHEN YOU USE ELECTRICAL EQUIPMENT WHICH MAKES SPARKS.	Wear goggles when using electrical equipment that sparks.
SPEAK (v), SPEAKS, SPOKE, SPOKEN	To use a voice to make words	SPEAK INTO THE MICROPHONE.	
SPECIAL (adj)	For a specified function	TIGHTEN THE SPECIAL NUT.	

Word (part of speech)	Approved meaning / ALTERNATIVES	APPROVED EXAMPLE	Not approved example
SPECIALLY (adv)	In a special manner	THIS EXTRACTOR IS SPECIALLY MADE TO REMOVE THESE PINS.	
specific (adj)	SPECIAL (adj)	USE SPECIAL TOOLS TO PREVENT POSSIBLE DAMAGE.	Use specific tools to preclude the possibility of damage.
	SPECIFIED (adj)	THESE AREAS HAVE SPECIFIED DAMAGE LIMITS.	These areas have specific damage limits.
specifically (adv)	SPECIALLY (adv)	THESE MATERIALS ARE SPECIALLY MADE FOR PLASTIC SURFACES.	These materials are specifically designed for plastic surfaces.
SPECIFIED (adj)	Given in, identified in, or related to a specification, regulation, or procedure	INFLATE THE TIRE WITH NITROGEN TO THE SPECIFIED PRESSURE.	
speck (n)	PARTICLE (n)	REMOVE ALL PARTICLES OF DUST FROM THE LENS.	Remove all specks of dust from the lens.
speech (n)	VOICE (n)	IF YOU CANNOT HEAR THE VOICE, REPLACE THE UNIT.	If the speech is not audible, replace the unit.
SPEED (n)	The rate of movement	IF THE WIND SPEED IS MORE THAN 20 KNOTS, DO NOT OPEN THE RADOME.	
SPHERICAL (adj)	That has the shape of a sphere	THE ACCUMULATORS ARE SPHERICAL AND HAVE BLADDERS.	
SPILL (v), SPILLS, SPILLED, SPILLED	To accidentally flow, or cause to flow, out of a container	IF THE ELECTROLYTE SPILLS, REMOVE IT IMMEDIATELY.	
		IF YOU SPILL THE ELECTROLYTE, REMOVE IT IMMEDIATELY.	

Word (part of speech)	Approved meaning / ALTERNATIVES	APPROVED EXAMPLE	Not approved example
spillage (n)	CONTAMINATION (n)	FIND THE AREA WHERE THERE IS MERCURY CONTAMINATION.	Find the area of the mercury spillage.
	SPILL (v)	IF ACID SPILLS, CLEAN THE AREA.	After acid spillage, clean the area.
spin (v)	TURN ⋯ QUICKLY	TURN THE WHEEL QUICKLY WITH YOUR HAND.	Spin the wheel by hand.
splash (v)	GET (v)	IF YOU GET FLUID IN YOUR EYES, GET MEDICAL AID.	If fluid splashes into eyes, get medical aid.
splined (adj)	SPLINE (TN)	THE DRIVE SHAFT HAS SPLINES.	The drive shaft is splined.
split (adj)	DAMAGED (adj)	REPLACE DAMAGED CASINGS.	Split casings must be replaced.
split (v)	DIVIDE (v)	DIVIDE THE ELECTRICAL LOAD BETWEEN THE TWO BUS BARS.	Split the electrical load between the two bus bars.
	BREAK (v)	MAKE SURE THAT THE CASING DOES NOT BREAK WHEN YOU APPLY THE MAXIMUM TEST PRESSURE.	Make sure that the casing does not split when you apply the maximum test pressure.
spot (n)	MARK (n)	A RED MARK ON THE PIN IDENTIFIES THE LUBRICATION POINT.	A red spot on the pin identifies the lubrication point.
	STAIN (TN)	REMOVE ALL STAINS FROM THE CARPET WITH SOAP AND WARM WATER.	Remove any spots from the carpet with soap and warm water.
spot (v)	FIND (v)	IF YOU FIND CORROSION IN THIS AREA, USE REPAIR SCHEME No. 3.	If you spot corrosion in this area, use repair scheme No. 3.
SPRAY (n)	A jet of very small drops of liquid	THE SEALANT IS RESISTANT TO SALT SPRAY.	

Word (part of speech)	Approved meaning / ALTERNATIVES	APPROVED EXAMPLE	Not approved example
SPRAY (v) SPRAYS, SPRAYED, SPRAYED	To apply as a spray	DO NOT SPRAY DISINFECTANTS DIRECTLY ONTO THE CARPETS OR INSTRUMENT PANELS.	
spread (v)	APPLY (v)	APPLY THE COMPOUND EQUALLY.	Spread compound evenly.
spring (v)	MOVE (v)	MAKE SURE THAT THE PINS DO NOT MOVE OUT OF THE NOTCH.	Make certain that the pins do not spring out of the notch.
spurious (adj)	UNWANTED (adj)	IF THERE ARE UNWANTED INDICATIONS, DO A TEST.	In the event of spurious indications, do a test.
stability (n)	STABLE (adj)	MAKE SURE THAT THE AIRCRAFT IS STABLE BEFORE YOU LIFT IT WITH JACKS.	Before jacking up aircraft make sure that aircraft stability is ensured.
stabilization (n)	STABLE (adj)	MAKE SURE THAT THE OIL PRESSURE DECREASES WHEN THE TEMPERATURE IS STABLE.	Check that oil pressure drops after stabilization of temperature.
stabilize (v)	STABLE (adj)	LET THE V-BARS BECOME STABLE.	Allow V-bars to stabilize.
STABLE (adj)	That does not change or move	MAKE SURE THAT THE PRESSUREINDICATION S ARE STABLE.	
stage (n)	STEP (n)	DO NOT REMOVE THE PIN DURING THIS STEP.	Do not remove the pin at this stage.
stained (adj)	DIRTY (adj)	IF THE CARPET IS DIRTY, CLEAN IT WITH MATERIAL NO. 8.	If the carpet is stained, clean it with the Material No. 8.
	STAIN (TN)	IF THERE ARE HYDRAULIC FLUID STAINS ON THE COVER, EXAMINE THE LINE COUPLINGS.	If the cover is stained by hydraulic fluid, check line couplings.

Word (part of speech)	Approved meaning / ALTERNATIVES	APPROVED EXAMPLE	Not approved example
stamp (v)	STAMP (TN)	PUT THE TEST DATE ON THE CYLINDER NECK WITH THE APPLICABLE STAMP.	Stamp the test date on the cylinder neck.
stand (v)	STAY (v)	STAY AWAY FROM SURFACES THAT MOVE.	Do not stand near moving surfaces.
STANDARD (adj)	Related to equipment and procedures that are normally used	IN THIS PROCEDURE, USE STANDARD TOOLS.	
starboard (adj)	RIGHT (adj)	ON THE RIGHT WING, MOVE THE AILERONS UP.	On the starboard wing, move the ailerons up.
START (n)	The beginning of a movement or operation	MOVEMENT CAN BE SLOW AT THE START.	
START (v), STARTS, STARTED, STARTED	1. To begin a procedure, movement, or operation	START THE ENGINE.	
	2. To come into being, activity, or operation	MEASURE THE BEND RADIUS OF THE HOSE FROM THE POINT WHERE THE BEND STARTS.	
state (n)	CONDITION (n)	EXAMINE THE CONDITION OF THE UNIT.	Examine the state of the unit.
state (v)	TELL (v)	UNLESS THE MANUFACTURER'S INSTRUCTIONS TELL YOU DIFFERENTLY, DO THE PROCEDURE THAT FOLLOWS.	Unless otherwise stated by the manufacturer, do the following procedure.
station (v)	PUT (v)	PUT A PERSON NEAR THE FUEL TANK.	Station a person near the fuel tank.
stationary (adj)	STABLE (adj)	WHEN THE PRESSURE IS STABLE, CLOSE THE VALVE.	When the pressure is stationary, close the valve.
	STOP (v)	WHEN THE FLYWEIGHTS STOP, DO THE TEST.	When the flyweights are stationary, do the test.

Word (part of speech)	Approved meaning / ALTERNATIVES	APPROVED EXAMPLE	Not approved example
STAY (v), STAYS, STAYED, STAYED	To continue to be in a location or condition	IF THE AIRCRAFT MUST STAY IN THE HANGAR, MAKE SURE THAT THE EXIT IS CLEAR.	
steadily (adv)	CONTINUOUSLY (adv)	IF THE TEMPERATURE INCREASES CONTINUOUSLY, STOP THE ENGINE.	If the temperature increases steadily, stop the engine.
steady (adj)	STABLE (adj)	MAKE SURE THAT THE SYSTEM PRESSURE IS STABLE.	Make sure that the system pressure is steady.
STEP (n)	A specified part of a procedure	DO STEPS 13 THRU 16 A MINIMUM OF THREE TIMES.	
stick (v)	ATTACH (v)	ATTACH THE LABEL TO THE SURFACE.	Stick the label to the surface.
	FREELY (adv)	MAKE SURE THAT THE FAN BLADES MOVE FREELY.	Check that the fan blades do not stick.
	CATCH (v)	REMOVE ALL JEWELRY THAT CAN CATCH IN THE MACHINE.	Remove all jewelry that can get stuck in the machine.
sticky (adj)	TACKY (adj)	PUT THE PATCH ON THE SURFACE WHEN THE CEMENT IS TACKY	Put the patch on the surface when the cement is sticky.
stiff (adj)	MOVE (v)	IF THE PISTON DOES NOT MOVE EASILY IN THE SLEEVE, DO A DIMENSIONAL INSPECTION OF THE PARTS.	If the piston is stiff, check the dimensions of the piston and sleeve.
still (adv)	STAY (v)	MAKE SURE THAT THE "OVHT" LIGHT STAYS ON.	Make sure that the "OVHT" light is still illuminated.
	CONTINUE (v)	MAKE SURE THAT THE ROTOR CONTINUES TO TURN.	Make sure that the rotor still turns.

ASD STE 100

Word (part of speech)	Approved meaning / ALTERNATIVES	APPROVED EXAMPLE	Not approved example
stimulate (v)	INCREASE (v)	INCREASE THE AIRFLOW.	Stimulate the airflow.
stir (v)	MIX (v)	MIX THE BONDING MATERIAL WITH A SPATULA.	Stir the bonding material with a spatula.
STOP (v), STOPS, STOPPED, STOPPED	To cause the end of a procedure, movement, or an operation	STOP THE ENGINE.	
	To come to an end	WHEN THE FLOW STOPS, REMOVE THE DRAIN HOSE.	
store (v)	KEEP (v)	KEEP THE CARTRIDGES IN A SAFETY AREA.	Cartridges should be stored in a safety area.
	CONTAIN (v)	THE FIRE EXTINGUISHER BOTTLES CONTAIN THE AGENT HALON 1301 IN LIQUID CONDITION.	The fire extinguisher bottles store the agent Halon 1301 in liquid condition.
	STORAGE (TN)	WHEN YOU PUT THE UNIT INTO STORAGE, OBEY THE APPLICABLE STORAGE INSTRUCTIONS.	When you store the unit, obey the applicable storage instructions.
STOW (v), STOWS, STOWED, STOWED	To move or cause to move into a specified position of storage.	STOW THE LIFE VEST SAFELY BELOW THE PASSENGER SEAT.	
		MAKE SURE THAT THE THRUST REVERSER STOWS WHEN YOU PUSH THE QUADRANT CONTROL FORWARD.	
STRAIGHT (adj) (STRAIGHTER, STRAIGHTEST)	Without curves or bends	MAKE SURE THAT THE STRAIGHT PART OF THE RIGGING PIN IS SMOOTH.	
straighten (v)	STRAIGHT (adj)	DO NOT TRY TO MAKE THE BENDS IN THE CABLE STRAIGHT.	Do not try to straighten the bends in the cable.

Word (part of speech)	Approved meaning / ALTERNATIVES	APPROVED EXAMPLE	Not approved example
strain (v)	FILTER (TN)	PUT THE OIL THROUGH A FILTER BEFORE YOU USE IT.	Strain the oil before use.
	STRAIN (TN)	DO NOT PUT STRAIN ON THE BELLOWS.	Do not strain bellows.
strap (v)	ATTACH (v) (WITH STRAPS [TN])	USE A STRAP TO ATTACH THE CABLES TO THE STRUCTURE.	Strap the cables to the structure.
stress (v)	FORCE (TN)	DO NOT PUT TOO MUCH FORCE ON THE DUCTING.	Do not stress the ducting unnecessarily.
strictly (adv)	FULLY (adv)	FULLY OBEY THE SAFETY PRECAUTIONS.	Strictly obey the safety precautions.
strike (v)	HIT (v)	MAKE SURE THAT THE SLING DOES NOT HIT THE FUSELAGE SKIN.	Make certain that the sling does not strike the fuselage skin.
STRIP (n)	A piece of material that is long and thin, but not wide	PUT A STRIP OF ADHESIVE TAPE ALONG THE INSULATION BLANKET.	
strip (v)	REMOVE (v)	REMOVE THE INSULATION FROM THE WIRE.	Strip the insulation from the wire.
STRIPE (n)	A line on a surface which is a different color	THE FLAG HAS RED AND WHITE STRIPES.	
striped (adj)	STRIPE (n)	THE FLAG HAS RED AND WHITE STRIPES.	The flag is striped red and white.
stroke (n)	TRAVEL (n)	TO BLEED THE BRAKING SYSTEM, OPERATE THE HAND PUMP HANDLE THROUGH ITS FULL TRAVEL	Bleed the braking system by applying full strokes to the hand pump handle.
STRONG (adj) (STRONGER, STRONGEST)	With much strength, power, or concentration	MOOR THE AIRCRAFT CAREFULLY WHEN WINDS ARE STRONG.	
STRUCTURAL (adj)	Related to the structure	STRUCTURAL REPAIRS ARE SPECIFIED IN THE STRUCTURAL REPAIR MANUAL	

Word (part of speech)	Approved meaning / ALTERNATIVES	APPROVED EXAMPLE	Not approved example
STRUCTURALLY (adv)	Related to the structure	THE LIST GIVES YOU STRUCTURALLY IMPORTANT ITEMS.	
STRUCTURE (n)	1. A construction	ATTACH THE WIRES TO THE STRUCTURE.	
	2. The arrangement of something	THE INTRODUCTION GIVES YOU THE STRUCTURE OF THE MAINTENANCE MANUAL.	
SUBASSEMBLY (n)	An assembly that is a part of a larger assembly	DO NOT CHANGE THE POSITION OF THE SUBASSEMBLIES.	
subject (v)	APPLY (v)	APPLY SUCTION TO THE SYSTEM.	Subject the system to suction.
submerge (v)	PUT (v)	PUT THE FILTER ELEMENT FULLY INTO THE FLUID.	Submerge the filter element in the fluid.
submit (v)	SEND (v)	SEND THE METAL PARTICLES TO A LABORATORY FOR ANALYSIS.	Submit the metal particles to a laboratory for analysis.
SUBSEQUENT (adj)	Following in an unspecified time or sequence	A SUBSEQUENT REPAIR WILL BE FOR THE NEW CONFIGURATION ONLY.	
	Use NEXT (adj) for the first occurrence that follows immediately in time or sequence.	DO THE NEXT INSPECTION.	Do the immediately subsequent inspection.
SUBSEQUENTLY (adv)	After an unspecified time	MAKE SURE THAT THE TOOL IS SUBSEQUENTLY AVAILABLE FOR THE INSTALLATION PROCEDURE.	
	Use THEN (adv) for an occurrence that follows immediately in time or sequence.	LIFT THE COVER.THEN PULL THE HANDLE.	Lift the cover and subsequently pull the handle.

Word (part of speech)	Approved meaning / ALTERNATIVES	APPROVED EXAMPLE	Not approved example
subsequent to (prep)	AFTER (conj)	AFTER YOU INSTALL THE COMPONENT, REMOVE THE HANDLING TOOL.	Remove the handling tool subsequent to the installation of the component.
substance (n)	MATERIAL (n)	THE PRIMER CONTAINS A MATERIAL THAT PREVENTS CORROSION.	The primer contains a corrosion-inhibiting substance.
substitute (adj)	EQUIVALENT (adj)	USE AN EQUIVALENT MATERIAL IF THE SPECIFIED ONE IS NOT AVAILABLE.	A substitute material may be used if the specified one is not available.
	ALTERNATIVE (adj)	IF THIS SPECIAL TOOL IS NOT AVAILABLE, USE AN ALTERNATIVE METHOD.	If this special tool is not available, use a substitute method.
substitute (n)	ALTERNATIVE (n)	YOU CAN USE ALTERNATIVES FOR THESE ITEMS.	Equivalent substitutes may be used for these items.
substitute (v)	REPLACE (v)	DO NOT REPLACE THE SELF-LOCKING NUTS WITH PLAIN NUTS.	Do not substitute the self-locking nuts with plain nuts.
SUBTRACT (v), SUBTRACTS, SUBTRACTED, SUBTRACTED	To take from a number or quantity	SUBTRACT COEFFICIENT "A" FROM THE INDICATION.	
successful (adj)	CORRECT (adj)	IF THE TEST RESULTS ARE NOT CORRECT, REPLACE THE UNIT.	If the test is not successful, replace the unit.
	SATISFACTORY (adj)	IF THE TEST RESULTS ARE NOT SATISFACTORY, REPLACE THE UNIT.	If the test is not successful, replace the unit.
SUCH (adj)	Of the same group	WHEN YOU DO WORK ON SUCH SYSTEMS, USE GOGGLES.	
such as	FOR EXAMPLE	WHEN YOU REMOVE THE STUD, USE APPLICABLE TOOLS. FOR EXAMPLE, USE A PLASTIC MALLET AND A PUNCH.	When you remove the stud, use applicable tools such as a plastic mallet and a punch.

ASD STE 100

Word (part of speech)	Approved meaning / ALTERNATIVES	APPROVED EXAMPLE	Not approved example
suck (v)	SUCTION (TN)	USE SUCTION TO REMOVE THE UNWANTED MATERIAL.	Suck out the unwanted material.
SUDDEN (adj)	That occurs in a short time	SUDDEN MOVEMENT CAN CAUSE DAMAGE TO THE LIMIT STOPS.	
SUDDENLY (adv)	In a sudden manner	IF THE TEMPERATURE INCREASES SUDDENLY, STOP THE ENGINE.	
SUFFICIENT (adj)	Not less (or more) than necessary	ADJUST THE CLAMP UNTIL THERE IS SUFFICIENT FRICTION TO KEEP IT IN POSITION.	
SUFFICIENTLY (adv)	Not less (or more) than necessary	WHEN THE PAINT IS SUFFICIENTLY SOFT, REMOVE IT WITH A PLASTIC SPATULA.	
suitable (adj)	APPLICABLE (adj)	PUT THE APPLICABLE SCREWDRIVER IN THE SLOT.	Put a suitable screwdriver in the slot.
	CORRECT (adj)	PUT THE CORRECT PLUGS ON THE DISCONNECTED LINES.	Put suitable plugs on the disconnected lines.
suitably (adv)	SUFFICIENTLY (adv)	WHERE THE PAINT IS SUFFICIENTLY SOFT, REMOVE IT WITH A PLASTIC SPATULA.	Where the paint is suitably soft, remove it with a plastic spatula.
SUM (n)	The result when you add	CALCULATE THE SUM OF THE LOADS FOR EACH AREA.	
SUPPLY (n)	Something that is supplied	STOP THE ELECTRICAL POWER SUPPLY.	
SUPPLY (v), SUPPLIES, SUPPLIED, SUPPLIED	To give something that is necessary	SUPPLY ELECTRICAL POWER TO THE AUXILIARY SYSTEM.	

Word (part of speech)	Approved meaning / ALTERNATIVES	APPROVED EXAMPLE	Not approved example
support (n)	SUPPORT (TN)	PUT A SUPPORT BELOW THE ITEM BEFORE YOU DISCONNECT IT.	Make certain there is adequate support for the item before disconnecting it.
	HOLD (v)	MAKE SURE THAT A PERSON HOLDS THE COMPONENT WHILE YOU DISCONNECT IT.	Make certain that someone provides adequate support during component disconnection.
support (v)	HOLD (v)	HOLD THE SWITCH AND REMOVE THE SCREWS.	Support the switch and remove the screws.
	SUPPORT (TN)	PUT A SUPPORT BELOW THE PUMP, THEN PULL IT OFF THE DRIVE SHAFT.	Support the pump, then pull it off the drive shaft.
SURE (adj)	Certain	IF YOU ARE NOT SURE THAT A PART IS SERVICEABLE, DISCARD IT.	
SURFACE (n)	One or more of the faces of something	RUB THE SURFACE QUICKLY WITH A SOFT, DRY CLOTH.	
surplus (adj)	UNWANTED (adj)	REMOVE THE UNWANTED GREASE.	Wipe off surplus grease.
surrounding (adj)	ADJACENT (adj)	CLEAN THE MOUNTING AND THE ADJACENT AREA.	Clean the mounting and the surrounding area.
	AROUND (prep)	REMOVE ALL SEALANT THAT IS AROUND THE HOLE.	Remove all sealant surrounding the hole.
survey (v)	EXAMINE (v)	EXAMINE THE SURFACE.	Survey the surface.
	INSPECTION (n)	DO AN INSPECTION OF THE SURFACE.	Survey the surface.
suspect (adj)	THINK (v)	REMOVE THE VALVE THAT YOU THINK IS UNSERVICEABLE.	Remove the suspect valve.

ASD STE 100

Word (part of speech)	Approved meaning / ALTERNATIVES	APPROVED EXAMPLE	Not approved example
suspect (v)	THINK (v)	IF YOU THINK THAT THE HYDRAULIC PUMP DOES NOT OPERATE CORRECTLY, DO A SYSTEM CHECK.	If you suspect that the hydraulic pump does not operate correctly, do a system check.
suspend (v)	HANG (v)	HANG THE ENGINE IN A FIREPROOF BAY.	Suspend the engine in a fireproof bay.
	STOP (v)	IF THE CABLE CATCHES, STOP THE PROCEDURE.	If the cable catches, suspend all operations.
SWALLOW (v), SWALLOWS, SWALLOWED, SWALLOWED	To take through the mouth and esophagus into the stomach ⊙ Use this word for safety instructions only.	IF YOU SWALLOW NITRIC ACID, GET MEDICAL AID IMMEDIATELY.	
swap (v)	INTERCHANGE (v)	INTERCHANGE THE COMPUTERS 1 AND 2. THEN DO THE TEST AGAIN.	Swap computers 1 and 2. Then do the test again.
sweep (v)	SCAN (TN)	MAKE A SCAN OF THE FREQUENCY BAND.	Sweep the frequency band.
swing (v)	MOVE (v)	MOVE THE SHOCK ABSORBERS INTO THEIR CORRECT POSITIONS.	Swing the shock absorbers into their correct positions.
	CALIBRATE (v)	YOU CAN CALIBRATE ALL THE COMPASS SYSTEMS AT THE SAME TIME.	All compass systems may be swung simultaneously.
switch (v)	SET (v)	SET THE SELECTOR TO "SYSTEM DISPLAY".	Switch the selector to "SYSTEM DISPLAY".
switch off (v)	STOP (v)	STOP THE UNIT AFTER 5 MIN.	Switch off the unit after 5 min.
	SWITCH (TN)	SET THE NAV 1 SWITCH TO "OFF".	Switch off NAV 1.

Word (part of speech)	Approved meaning / ALTERNATIVES	APPROVED EXAMPLE	Not approved example
switch on (v)	START (v)	START THE UNIT.	Switch on the unit.
	SWITCH (TN)	SET THE NAV 1 SWITCH TO "ON".	Switch on NAV 1.
SYMBOL (n)	A written sign that identifies a quantity, operation, item, or condition	THE SPECIFICATION GIVES THE SYMBOLS FOR RELAYS, DIODES, AND OTHER PARTS OF THE SYSTEM.	
SYMMETRICAL (adj)	That has or is with symmetry	MAKE SURE THAT THE POSITION OF THE WING FLAPS IS SYMMETRICAL.	
SYMMETRICALLY (adv)	In a symmetrical manner	THE ELEVATORS MUST MOVE SYMMETRICALLY.	
SYMPTOM (n)	A sign of a condition	IF THE SYMPTOMS OCCUR AGAIN, REMOVE THE UNIT.	
synchronize (v)	ADJUST (v)	ADJUST COMPASS SYSTEM 1 UNTIL IT AGREES WITH COMPASS SYSTEM 2.	Synchronize compass system 1 with compass system 2.
SYNCHRONIZED (adj)	1. That operates at the same time	MAKE SURE THAT THE TWO ROTORS ARE SYNCHRONIZED.	
	2. That agrees with	STOP THE TEST WHEN THE TIMERS ARE SYNCHRONIZED.	
SYSTEM (n)	An assembly of related parts to do a specified operation	DO NOT FILL THE SYSTEM DIRECTLY FROM A HIGH-PRESSURE CYLINDER.	

ASD STE 100

Word (part of speech)	Approved meaning / ALTERNATIVES	APPROVED EXAMPLE	Not approved example
TACKY (adj) ⚙ No other forms of this adjective	Sticky when you touch it	WHEN THE COMPOUND IS TACKY, APPLY THE PATCH.	
TAG (v), TAGS, TAGGED, TAGGED	To put a tag on	OPEN, TAG, AND SAFETY THE CIRCUIT BREAKERS.	
take (v)	REMOVE (v)	REMOVE THE FILTER FROM THE SOLVENT.	Take the filter from the solvent.
	READ (v)	LET THE DIAL BECOME STABLE BEFORE YOU READ THE INDICATIONS.	Let the dial become stable before taking readings.
	GET (v)	GET A SAMPLE OF HYDRAULIC FLUID.	Take a sample of hydraulic fluid.
	NECESSARY (adj)	TWO HOURS ARE NECESSARY TO DO THE PROCEDURE.	The procedure takes 2 hours to complete.
take care (v)	MAKE SURE (v)	DURING THIS STEP, MAKE SURE THAT YOU DO NOT CAUSE DAMAGE TO THE SURFACE.	During this step, take care not to cause damage to the surface.
	OBEY (v)	OBEY THE SAFETY PRECAUTIONS WHEN YOU DO WORK WITH HIGH VOLTAGES.	You must take care when you work with high voltages.
	DO NOT (v)	DO NOT INTERCHANGE THE TWO UNITS.	Take care not to interchange the two units.
	CAREFUL (adj)	BE CAREFUL WHEN YOU INSTALL THE ELECTRONIC BOARD.	Take care when installing the electronic board.
talk (v)	SPEAK (v)	SPEAK INTO THE MICROPHONE.	Talk into the microphone.
TAP (v), TAPS, TAPPED, TAPPED	To hit lightly and quickly	TAP THE BOLT WITH A MALLET.	

Word (part of speech)	Approved meaning / ALTERNATIVES	APPROVED EXAMPLE	Not approved example
tape (v)	TAPE (TN)	PUT THE FOIL IN POSITION AND ATTACH IT WITH ADHESIVE TAPE.	Tape the foil in position.
taped (adj)	RECORD (v)	MAKE SURE THAT YOU CAN HEAR THE RECORDED ANNOUNCEMENTS.	Make sure that you can hear the taped announcements.
TASK (n)	Assigned work or procedure	EACH STEP OF THE TASK HAS AN IDENTIFICATION LETTER.	
taut (adj)	TENSION (TN)	MAKE SURE THAT THE TENSION IN THE CABLES IS CORRECT.	Make sure the cables are taut.
tear (v)	DAMAGE (n)	BE CAREFUL THAT YOU DO NOT CAUSE DAMAGE TO THE BELLOWS.	Take care you do not tear the bellows.
technique (n)	METHOD (n)	THIS METHOD GIVES THE BEST RESULTS.	This technique gives the best results.
TELESCOPIC (adj)	Related to items that retract into each other	INSTALL THE TELESCOPIC DUCTS IN THE WING DE-ICING SYSTEM.	
TELL (v), TELLS, TOLD, TOLD	To give an order or supply information	PUT A WARNING NOTICE IN THE COCKPIT TO TELL PERSONS NOT TO OPERATE THE FLIGHT CONTROLS.	
		THE COMPUTER TELLS THE FUEL CONTROLLER TO OPEN THE FUEL CONTROL VALVE.	
TEMPORARILY (adv)	In a temporary manner	ATTACH THE COVER TEMPORARILY.	
TEMPORARY (adj)	For a short time only, not permanent	THIS INSTALLATION IS ONLY TEMPORARY.	
tension (v)	TENSION (TN)	ADJUST THE TENSION IN THE CABLES TO THE CORRECT VALUE.	Tension cables to the correct value.

ASD STE 100

Word (part of speech)	Approved meaning / ALTERNATIVES	APPROVED EXAMPLE	Not approved example
terminate (v)	STOP (v)	STOP THE TEST AFTER 2 SECONDS.	Terminate the test after 2 seconds.
TERTIARY (adj)	Third in importance	THERE ARE THREE CLASSES OF STRUCTURE: PRIMARY, SECONDARY, AND TERTIARY.	
TEST (n)	The procedure where an object or system is operated to make sure that its performance and/or function is correct	DISCONNECT ALL THE SYSTEMS WHICH ARE NOT NECESSARY FOR THE TEST.	
test (v)	TEST (n)	DO A FUNCTIONAL TEST OF THE WARNING SYSTEM.	Functionally test warning system.
THAN (conj)	Function word that you use with comparative adjectives or adverbs	MAKE SURE THAT THE TOTAL ANGLE IS SMALLER THAN 20 DEG. CORROSION CAN OCCUR MORE EASILY IN THIS AREA THAN IN OTHER AREAS.	
THAT (conj)	Function word that starts a subordinate clause	MAKE SURE THAT THE SURFACE IS CLEAN.	
THAT (pron)	Function word that shows the person or thing referred to	EXAMINE THE UNIT TO SEE IF THAT IS THE PROBLEM.	
THE (art)	Function word: definite article	REMOVE THE SEVEN FLEXIBLE HOSES.	
THEIR (adj)	Belonging to persons or things	WRITE TO THE MANUFACTURERS FOR THEIR REPAIR SCHEMES.	
THEM (pron)	Function word that shows the persons or things referred to	IF THE CANOPIES ARE DIRTY, CLEAN THEM.	
THEN (adv)	Immediately after in time or sequence	LIFT THE COVER. THEN PULL THE HANDLE.	

Word (part of speech)	Approved meaning / ALTERNATIVES	APPROVED EXAMPLE	Not approved example
THERE (adv)	In that position	IF THE LABEL IS NOT THERE, ATTACH A NEW ONE.	
THERE (pron)	Function word that starts a sentence or a subordinate clause	THERE ARE THREE JACKING POINTS ON THE FUSELAGE.	
		MAKE SURE THAT THERE ARE NO LOOSE OBJECTS.	
therefore (adv)	THUS (adv)	THIS TORQUE SHAFT CANNOT MOVE INBOARD. THUS, BEFORE YOU REMOVE IT, REMOVE THE OUTBOARD TORQUE SHAFT.	This torque shaft cannot move inboard. Therefore, before you remove it, remove the outboard torque shaft.
	AS A RESULT	THIS TORQUE SHAFT CANNOT MOVE INBOARD. AS A RESULT, BEFORE YOU REMOVE IT, REMOVE THE OUTBOARD TORQUE SHAFT.	This torque shaft cannot move inboard. Therefore, before you remove it, remove the outboard torque shaft.
THESE (adj)	Refers to specified persons or things	REMOVE THESE PARTS.	
THESE (pron)	Function word that shows the persons or things referred to	THESE ARE SPECIAL TOOLS.	
THEY (pron)	Function word that shows the persons or things referred to	DENTS ARE NOT PERMITTED IF THEY PREVENT CORRECT OPERATION OF THE PARTS.	
THICK (adj) (THICKER, THICKEST)	That has a large thickness	APPLY A THICK LAYER OF GREASE ON THE BARE METAL.	
THICKNESS (n)	The smallest of the three dimensions of an object	THE THICKNESS OF PRIMER LAYER MUST BE BETWEEN 0.05 mm AND 0.06 mm.	

ASD STE 100

Word (part of speech)	Approved meaning / ALTERNATIVES	APPROVED EXAMPLE	Not approved example
THIN (adj) (THINNER, THINNEST)	That has a small thickness	APPLY A THIN LAYER OF SEALING COMPOUND ON THE BARE METAL.	
thin (v)	LIQUID (adj)	ADD SOLVENT TO MAKE THE PAINT MORE LIQUID.	Add solvent to thin the paint.
THINK (v), THINKS, THOUGHT, THOUGHT	To have an opinion	IF YOU THINK THAT THE WATER WILL FREEZE, ADD ANTIFREEZE.	
THIS (adj)	Refers to a specified person or thing	DO THIS TEST AT FULL VOLTAGE.	
THIS (pron)	Function word that shows the person or thing referred to	REFER TO TESTING AND FAULT ISOLATION. THIS TELLS YOU THE PARTS TO REPLACE.	
thorough (adj)	FULL (adj)	DO A FULL CHECK OF THE HYDRAULIC SYSTEM.	Do a thorough check of the hydraulic system.
thoroughly (adv)	FULLY (adv)	DRY THE SURFACE FULLY.	Dry the surface thoroughly.
THOSE (pron)	Function word that shows the persons or things referred to	WHEN YOU EXAMINE THE PARTS, DISCARD THOSE THAT ARE DAMAGED.	
thread (v)	PUT (v)	PUT TAPE ON THE ROLLER.	Thread tape on the roller.
	TURN (v)	TURN THE LOCK NUT ON THE FITTING.	Thread the lock nut on the fitting.
threaded (adj)	THREAD (TN)	PUT THE END OF THE ROD THAT HAS A THREAD IN THE FITTING.	Put the threaded end of the rod in the fitting.
THROUGH (adv)	Function word that shows movement into one end or side and out of the other	IF FUMES COME THROUGH, DO THE EMERGENCY PROCEDURE.	
THROUGH (prep)	Function word that shows movement into one end or side and out of the other	MAKE SURE THAT THE FLUID THAT GOES THROUGH THE TUBE HAS NO BUBBLES.	

Word (part of speech)	Approved meaning / ALTERNATIVES	APPROVED EXAMPLE	Not approved example
throughout (prep)	DURING (prep)	MAKE SURE THAT THE DOORS ARE CLOSED DURING THE PRESSURIZATION TEST.	Make sure that the doors are closed throughout the pressurization test.
THRU (prep)	From a point in a sequence to another	DO STEPS 4 THRU 10 AGAIN.	
THUS (adv)	For that reason	THIS BOILER CONTROLLER IS APPLICABLE TO ALL SYSTEMS. THUS, IT CAN ALSO CONTROL THERMAL OIL HEATERS.	
	For other meanings, use: FOLLOW (v)	CALCULATE THE THICKNESS OF THE SHIM AS FOLLOWS: T=X-Y.	The thickness of the shim is thus calculated: T=X-Y.
tie (v)	ATTACH (v)	ATTACH THE THREADING CORD TO THE NEW CABLE.	Tie the threading cord to the new cable.
TIGHT (adj) (TIGHTER, TIGHTEST)	Not free	MAKE SURE THAT THE NUTS ARE TIGHT.	
	For other meanings, use: SEAL (v)	MAKE SURE THAT THE FUEL TANK IS SEALED.	Make sure that the fuel tank is tight.
	TENSION (TN)	MAKE SURE THAT THERE IS TENSION IN THE LOCKWIRE.	Make sure that the lockwire is tight.
TIGHTEN (v), TIGHTENS, TIGHTENED, TIGHTENED	To cause to be tight	TIGHTEN THE SCREWS.	
TIGHTLY (adv)	In a tight manner	HOLD THE CYLINDER TIGHTLY.	
till (conj)	UNTIL (conj)	MOVE THE LEVER UNTIL IT TOUCHES THE STOP.	Move the lever till it hits the stop.

ASD STE 100

Word (part of speech)	Approved meaning / ALTERNATIVES	APPROVED EXAMPLE	Not approved example
TILT (v), TILTS, TILTED, TILTED	To move at an angle or to put something at an angle between the vertical and the horizontal	TO ALIGN THE BOLT, TILT IT TO THE LEFT SIDE.	
		IF THE SHAFT TILTS, STOP THE TEST PROCEDURE.	
TIME (n)	1. A duration that you can measure	THE TIME BETWEEN CLICKS MUST BE 20 SECONDS.	
	2. An occurrence	DO STEP 2 THREE TIMES. DO NOT TIGHTEN THE NUTS AT THIS TIME.	
time (v)	TIME (n)	MEASURE THE TIME THAT IS NECESSARY FOR THE PRESSURE TO DECREASE.	Time the pressure decay.
tip (n)	POINT (n)	BEFORE YOU MAKE THE HOLE, MAKE SURE THAT THE POINT OF THE DRILL BIT IS SHARP.	Before you make the hole, make sure the tip of the drill bit is sharp.
tip (v)	TILT (v)	TO INSTALL THE INDICATOR, TILT IT REARWARD.	To install the indicator, tip it rearward.
TO (prep)	Function word that shows: "OFF". - The direction of, point of arrival or time, connection, result, cause - That the word that follows is an infinitive	SET THE SWITCH TO THIS VALUE IS EQUIVALENT TO THE MAXIMUM. ATTACH THE UNIONS TO THE VALVE. GET ACCESS TO THE SELECTOR VALVES. TRY TO LIFT THE COVER MANUALLY.	

Word (part of speech)	Approved meaning / ALTERNATIVES	APPROVED EXAMPLE	Not approved example
TOGETHER (adv)	In one group or position	USE TAPE TO ATTACH THE CABLES TOGETHER.	
	For other meanings, use: AT THE SAME TIME	DISASSEMBLE THE BYPASS VALVE AND THE DUMP VALVE AT THE SAME TIME.	Disassemble the bypass valve and the dump valve together.
TOLERANCE (n)	A permitted difference from a standard	THE TOLERANCE IS PLUS OR MINUS 0.2 mm.	
TOO (adv)	More than is necessary or correct	MAKE SURE THAT THE TEMPERATURE IS NOT TOO HIGH.	
TOOL (n)	An object used to make or do something	REMOVE ALL TOOLS AND EQUIPMENT.	
TOP (adj)	That is uppermost	A NUMBER IN THE TOP LEFT CORNER OF THE DISPLAY REFERS TO A RELATED PAGE.	
TOP (n)	The uppermost position	THE VERTICAL STABILIZER IS INSTALLED ON THE TOP OF THE FUSELAGE TAIL SECTION.	
top off (v)	FILL (v)	FILL THE HYDRAULIC SYSTEM AS NECESSARY.	Top off the hydraulic system as necessary.
	ADD (v)	ADD FLUID TO THE HYDRAULIC RESERVOIR AS NECESSARY.	Top off the hydraulic reservoir as necessary.
TORQUE (v), TORQUES, TORQUED, TORQUED	To tighten to a specified torque	TORQUE THE PLUG TO 6 Nm.	
TOTAL (adj)	All of	THE TOTAL QUANTITY OF FUEL IN THE CENTER TANK IS 5000 LB.	

ASD STE 100

Word (part of speech)	Approved meaning / ALTERNATIVES	APPROVED EXAMPLE	Not approved example
TOTAL (n)	The full quantity	ADD THE VALUES. THE TOTAL MUST NOT BE MORE THAN 15 mm.	
TOUCH (v), TOUCHES, TOUCHED, TOUCHED	To be in contact	MAKE SURE THAT THE LOCK NUT TOUCHES THE SPRING.	
TOW (v), TOWS, TOWED, TOWED	To pull something along	MAKE SURE THAT YOU COMPLETE THE PROCEDURE BEFORE YOU TOW THE VEHICLE BACK TO ITS INITIAL POSITION.	
toward (prep)	TO (prep)	THE ARROW MUST POINT TO THE REAR.	The arrow must point toward the rear.
	DIRECTION (n)	MANUALLY PUSH THE RAM AIR TURBINE IN THE DIRECTION OF THE RETRACTED POSITION.	Manually push the Ram Air Turbine toward the retracted position.
toxic (adj)	POISONOUS (adj)	THIS COMPOUND IS POISONOUS.	This compound is toxic.
trace (n)	SIGN (n)	EXAMINE THE AREA AROUND THE DRAIN HOLES FOR SIGNS OF CORROSION.	Check the area surrounding the drain holes for traces of corrosion.
trace (v)	FIND (v)	FIND THE BROKEN WIRE.	Trace the broken wire.
track (v)	MONITOR (v)	MONITOR THE TEMPERATURE.	Track the temperature.
trained (adj)	APPROVED (adj)	ONLY APPROVED PERSONNEL CAN OPERATE THE BRAKES.	Only trained personnel can operate the brakes.

Word (part of speech)	Approved meaning / ALTERNATIVES	APPROVED EXAMPLE	Not approved example
transfer (n)	MOVEMENT (n)	MAKE SURE THAT THE RATE OF MOVEMENT OF FUEL FROM THE WING TANKS TO THE CENTER TANK IS EQUAL	Make sure the rate of fuel transfer from the wing tanks to the center tank is equal.
	SUPPLY (n)	MAKE SURE THAT THE RATE OF SUPPLY OF FUEL FROM THE WING TANKS TO THE CENTER TANK IS EQUAL	Make sure the rate of fuel transfer from the wing tanks to the center tank is equal.
transfer (v)	MOVE (v)	MOVE THE COUPLINGS TO THE NEW UNIT.	The couplings must be transferred to the new unit.
	INSTALL (v)	INSTALL THE COUPLINGS ON THE NEW UNIT.	Transfer the couplings to the new unit.
transition (n)	CHANGE (n)	THE CHANGE FROM FULL-RATE OPERATION TO HALF-RATE OPERATION MUST OCCUR IMMEDIATELY.	The transition from fullrate operation to halfrate operation must occur immediately.
TRANSMIT (v), TRANSMITS, TRANSMITTED, TRANSMITTED	To send energy or a signal	MAKE SURE THAT THE TRANSPONDER TRANSMITS THE SIGNAL CORRECTLY.	
TRANSPARENT (adj)	Easy to see through	PUT A TRANSPARENT SHEET OF PLASTIC ON THE SURFACE.	
transport (v)	SEND (v)	SEND THE PART TO THE OVERHAUL SHOP.	Transport the part to the overhaul shop.
trapped (adj)	CAUGHT (adj)	MAKE SURE THAT THE CABLE IS NOT CAUGHT.	Make sure that the cable is not trapped.
TRAVEL (n)	The movement of an item	MAKE SURE THAT THE RANGE OF TRAVEL OF THE CONTROL SURFACES IS CLEAR.	

Word (part of speech)	Approved meaning / ALTERNATIVES	APPROVED EXAMPLE	Not approved example
travel (v)	GO (v)	THE TURNBUCKLE GOES THROUGH A HOLE IN THE BULKHEAD.	The turnbuckle travels through a hole in the bulkhead.
	MOVE (v)	THE LEVER MOVES THROUGH A 30-DEG. ARC.	The lever travels through a 30-deg. arc.
treat (v)	APPLY (v)	APPLY WAX TO THE SURFACE.	Treat the surface with wax.
	TOUCH (v)	BE CAREFUL WHEN YOU TOUCH PRINTED CIRCUIT BOARDS.	Be careful when you treat printed circuit boards.
trigger (v)	CAUSE (v)	HEAT CAUSES THE PRESSURE TO INCREASE.	Heat triggers a pressure increase.
	START (v)	THIS SIGNAL STARTS THE OPERATION OF THE TEST SET.	This signal triggers test set operation.
trim (v)	CUT (v)	CUT THE PATCH TO THE CORRECT DIMENSION.	Trim the patch to fit.
trip (v)	OPEN (v)	OPEN THE CIRCUIT BREAKER.	Trip the circuit breaker.
	RELEASE (v)	THE HOLD-ON SWITCH RELEASES.	Hold-on switch trips.
	CAUSE TO FALL	AN IRREGULAR SURFACE CAN CAUSE YOU TO FALL.	You can trip and fall on an irregular surface.
triple (adj)	THREE (TN)	APPLY THREE LAYERS OF PRIMER.	Apply a triple coat of primer.
troubleshoot (v)	TROUBLESHOOTING (TN)	DO THE TROUBLESHOOTING PROCEDURE ON THE VHF NAVIGATION SYSTEM.	Troubleshoot the VHF navigation system.
true (adj)	CORRECT (adj)	MAKE SURE THAT THE VALUE SHOWN ON THE INDICATOR IS CORRECT.	Make sure that the indicator reading is true.
	AGREE (v)	MAKE SURE THAT THE INDICATION ON THE GAUGE AGREES WITH THE QUANTITY THAT IS IN THE TANK.	Make sure that the gauge shows the true quantity that is in the tank.

Word (part of speech)	Approved meaning / ALTERNATIVES	APPROVED EXAMPLE	Not approved example
TRY (v), TRIES, TRIED, TRIED	To make an effort to do something	TRY TO MOVE THE CONTROL COLUMN.	
tuck (v)	PUT (v)	PUT THE HEADSTRAP INTO THE FACE PIECE.	Tuck the headstrap into the face piece.
TUNE (v), TUNES, TUNED, TUNED	To adjust equipment to the best performance	TUNE ADF 1 TO A KNOWN FREQUENCY.	
TURN (n)	One full cycle of movement around an axis	LET THE PRESSURE BECOME STABLE AFTER EACH TURN OF THE ADJUSTMENT SCREW.	
TURN (v), TURNS, TURNED, TURNED	To move or cause to move around an axis or a point	TURN THE CONTROL CLOCKWISE. THE BEARING TURNS AT 1500 RPM.	
twice (adv)	TWO (TN)	DO THIS PROCEDURE TWO TIMES.	Do this procedure twice.
TWIST (v), TWISTS, TWISTED, TWISTED	1. To use a force that turns something and causes a distortion	DO NOT TWIST THE CABLES.	
	2. To turn or change shape as a result of torsion	IF THE CABLE TWISTS, DISCONNECT THE TWO CONNECTORS.	
TYPE (n)	A specified group	FIND THE TYPE AND DIMENSIONS OF THE DAMAGE.	
TYPICAL (adj)	That has the important qualities of a group	THIS INSTALLATION PROCEDURE IS TYPICAL FOR THIS TYPE OF FASTENER.	

Word (part of speech)	Approved meaning / ALTERNATIVES	APPROVED EXAMPLE	Not approved example
unable (adj)	CANNOT (v)	IF YOU CANNOT TURN THE PULLEY, MAKE SURE THAT THE PIN IS REMOVED.	If you are unable to turn the pulley, make sure that the pin is removed.
unauthorized (adj)	NOT APPROVED	IF YOU ARE NOT APPROVED TO DO THIS WORK, DO NOT DO THIS ENGINE TEST.	If you are unauthorized, do not do this engine test.
uncap (v)	REMOVE (v) (A CAP [TN] OR CAPS [TN])	REMOVE THE CAPS FROM THE HOSES.	Uncap the hoses.
unclip (v)	REMOVE (v) (FROM A CLIP [TN] OR CLIPS [TN])	REMOVE THE VISOR FROM THE CLIP.	Unclip the visor.
uncoil (v)	UNWIND (v)	UNWIND THE CABLES CAREFULLY.	Uncoil the cables carefully.
uncontaminated (adj)	CLEAN (adj)	MAKE SURE THAT THE HYDRAULIC FLUID IS CLEAN.	Make sure that the hydraulic fluid is uncontaminated.
	CONTAMINATION (n)	MAKE SURE THAT THERE IS NO CONTAMINATION IN THE FUEL TANKS.	Make sure that the fuel tanks are uncontaminated.
uncouple (v)	DISCONNECT (v)	DISCONNECT THE TOW BAR FROM THE VEHICLE.	Uncouple the tow bar from the vehicle.
uncovered (adj)	COVER (TN)	DO NOT PUT A COVER ON THE CONTAINER.	Leave the container uncovered.
undamaged (adj)	NOT DAMAGED	MAKE SURE THAT THE SKIN IS NOT DAMAGED.	Make sure that the skin is undamaged.
UNDEMANDED (adj)	That occurs without an apparent cause	IF YOU GET AN UNDEMANDED MOVEMENT, DO A TEST OF THE SYSTEM.	

Word (part of speech)	Approved meaning / ALTERNATIVES	APPROVED EXAMPLE	Not approved example
under (prep)	BELOW (prep)	INSTALL THE CABLE THROUGH THE GUIDE TUBE BELOW THE CABIN FLOOR.	Install the cable through the guide tube under the cabin floor.
	IN (prep)	THIS CAN OCCUR IN DIFFERENT CONDITIONS.	This can occur under different conditions.
	LESS THAN	MAKE SURE THAT THE PRESSURE IS LESS THAN 30 PSI.	Make sure the pressure is under 30 psi.
underneath (prep)	BELOW (prep)	PUT THE CONTAINER BELOW THE DRAIN VALVE.	Place the container underneath the drain valve.
underside (n)	BOTTOM (n)	EXAMINE THE FOUR ATTACHING HOLES ON THE BOTTOM.	Examine the four attaching holes on the underside.
undertake (v)	DO (v)	DO THIS TASK IN AN AREA THAT HAS GOOD AIRFLOW.	Undertake this task in an area that has good airflow.
	Use a specific action verb.	DO NOT START THE TEST WITHOUT PRECAUTIONS.	Do not undertake the test without precautions.
undo (v)	LOOSEN (v)	LOOSEN THE BOLTS THAT ATTACH THE UNIT.	Undo the bolts that attach the unit.
undue (adj)	UNWANTED (adj)	TO PREVENT UNWANTED FRICTION, POLISH THE SURFACE.	To prevent undue friction, polish the surface.
uneven (adj)	EQUAL (adj)	MAKE SURE THAT THE FUEL LOAD IS EQUAL ON EACH SIDE OF THE AIRCRAFT CENTERLINE.	Avoid uneven fuel load about the aircraft centerline.
	ROUGH (adj)	REPLACE THE SLIDE VALVE IF ITS SURFACE IS ROUGH.	Replace the slide valve if its surface is uneven.

ASD STE 100

Word (part of speech)	Approved meaning / ALTERNATIVES	APPROVED EXAMPLE	Not approved example
UNFOLD (v), UNFOLDS, UNFOLDED, UNFOLDED	To open or to straighten or to cause to open or to straighten from a folded position or condition	UNFOLD THE SHEETING CAREFULLY.	
		MAKE SURE THAT THE INDICATOR LIGHT COMES ON WHEN THE BLADES UNFOLD.	
uniform (adj)	CONSTANT (adj)	CURE THE SEALANT AT A CONSTANT TEMPERATURE.	Cure the sealant at a uniform temperature.
	EQUAL (adj)	THE FUEL LOAD MUST BE EQUAL ON EACH SIDE OF THE AIRCRAFT CENTERLINE.	The fuel load must be uniform on each side of the aircraft centerline.
uniformly (adv)	EQUALLY (adv)	MAKE SURE THAT THE TWO PISTONS EXTEND EQUALLY.	Make sure that the two pistons extend uniformly.
unintentional (adj)	ACCIDENTAL (adj)	A GUARD ON THE CONTROL SWITCH OF THE PUMP PREVENTS ACCIDENTAL OPERATION.	A guard on the control switch of the pump prevents unintentional operation.
unintentionally (adv)	ACCIDENTALLY (adv)	IF YOU ACCIDENTALLY SPRAY RAIN REPELLENT FLUID ONTO A DRY WINDSHIELD, REMOVE THE FLUID WITH SOLVENT.	If rain repellent fluid is unintentionally sprayed onto a dry windshield, remove the fluid with solvent.
UNIT (n)	1. Equipment that does a function	YOU CAN REPLACE A LARGE NUMBER OF UNITS DURING ENGINE INSTALLATION.	
	2. A quantity that is a standard of measurement	THIS MANUAL USES SI UNITS.	
UNKNOWN (adj)	Not known	DO NOT USE FUEL WITH UNKNOWN PROPERTIES.	

Word (part of speech)	Approved meaning / ALTERNATIVES	APPROVED EXAMPLE	Not approved example
unlatch (v)	RELEASE (v)	THE SWITCH MUST RELEASE.	Switch must unlatch.
	OPEN (v)	THE SWITCH MUST OPEN.	Switch must unlatch.
UNLESS (conj)	Except if	DO NOT REMOVE THE ADAPTER FROM THE STABILIZER UNLESS A REPAIR IS NECESSARY.	
unload (v)	RELEASE (v)	RELEASE THE SPRING TENSION.	Unload the spring tension.
	LOAD (TN)	REMOVE THE LOAD FROM THE SPRING BALANCE.	Unload the spring balance.
UNLOCK (v), UNLOCKS, UNLOCKED, UNLOCKED	To release or become released from a locked condition	MAKE SURE THAT THE CABIN DIFFERENTIAL PRESSURE IS ZERO BEFORE YOU UNLOCK THE DOOR.	
		IF THE LEVER UNLOCKS DURING THE TEST, SET THE LEVER TO THE LOCKED POSITION AGAIN.	
unnecessary (adj)	NOT NECESSARY	REMOVE THE GROUND EQUIPMENT THAT IS NOT NECESSARY.	Remove the unnecessary ground equipment.
unobstructed (adj)	CLOGGED (adj)	MAKE SURE THAT THE DRAIN OPENINGS ARF NOT CLOGGED.	Make sure that the drain openings are unobstructed.
	CLEAR (adj)	AN ATTENDANT MUST HAVE A CLEAR VIEW OF THE PERSON IN THE TANK.	An attendant must have an unobstructed view of the person in the tank.
unpack (v)	REMOVE (v)	REMOVE THE PARTS FROM THE SHIPPING CONTAINER.	Unpack the shipping container.
unpainted (adj)	BARE (adj)	APPLY PROTECTIVE TREATMENT ON THE BARE SURFACES.	Protect the unpainted surfaces.

ASD STE 100

Word (part of speech)	Approved meaning / ALTERNATIVES	APPROVED EXAMPLE	Not approved example
unplug (v)	DISCONNECT (v)	DISCONNECT THE SOLDERING IRON.	Unplug the soldering iron.
	PLUG (TN)	REMOVE THE PLUG FROM THE FUEL LINE.	Unplug the fuel line.
unprotected (adj)	PROTECTION (n)	WHEN YOU REMOVE THE COVER, THE CONTACTS HAVE NO PROTECTION.	When you remove the cover, the contacts are unprotected.
unreel (v)	UNWIND (v)	UNWIND THE HOSE.	Unreel the hose.
unrestricted (adj)	FREE (adj)	THE BUSHINGS MUST BE FREE TO TURN.	Bushing rotation must be unrestricted.
unsafe (adj)	DANGEROUS (adj)	IN THESE CONDITIONS, IT IS DANGEROUS TO REMOVE THE CARTRIDGES FROM THE FIRE EXTINGUISHER BOTTLE.	In these conditions, it is unsafe to remove the cartridges from the fire extinguisher bottle.
UNSATISFAC-TORILY (adv)	In an unsatisfactory manner	IF THE ELEVATORS OPERATE UNSATISFACTORILY, MOVE THE CONTROL COLUMN.	
UNSATISFAC-TORY (adj)	Not satisfactory	IF THE CONDITION OF THE FILTERS IS UNSATISFACTORY, REPLACE THEM.	
unscrew (v)	REMOVE (v)	REMOVE THE SPACERS.	Unscrew the spacers.
	LOOSEN (v)	LOOSEN THE CAPTIVE BOLTS.	Unscrew the captive bolts.
	TURN (v)	TURN THE END FITTING TO ALIGN THE RIGGING HOLES.	Unscrew the end fitting to align the rigging holes.
UNSERVICEABLE (adj)	Not fit for its purpose	REPLACE THE UNSERVICEABLE BUSHINGS.	
unstable (adj)	NOT STABLE	IF THE SURFACE IS NOT STABLE, AN ACCIDENT CAN OCCUR.	If the surface is unstable, an accident can occur.

Word (part of speech)	Approved meaning / ALTERNATIVES	APPROVED EXAMPLE	Not approved example
UNTIL (conj)	Up to the time that	MOVE THE LEVER UNTIL THE END OF THE LINK TOUCHES THE LOCK BAR.	
UNTIL (prep)	Up to the time of	KEEP THE FIRE BOTTLE ARMED UNTIL THE END OF THE TEST.	
unused (adj)	NEW (adj)	FILL THE TANK WITH NEW OIL.	Fill the tank with unused oil.
UNUSUAL (adj)	Not usual	UNUSUAL LOADS CAN CAUSE TREAD SEPARATION IN THE TIRES.	
UNUSUALLY (adv)	In an unusual manner	THE VALVE OPERATES WHEN THERE IS AN UNUSUALLY LARGE FLOW OF FLUID.	
UNWANTED (adj)	That must not be there	UNWANTED AIR GOES OUT THROUGH THE OVERFLOW PORT. IF THE DRAIN HOLE IS BLOCKED, REMOVE THE UNWANTED MATERIAL.	
UNWIND (v), UNWINDS, UNWOUND, UNWOUND	To remove or become removed from around an object	UNWIND THE CABLE. IF THE HOSE UNWINDS TOO QUICKLY FROM THE REEL, STOP THE TEST.	
UP (adj)	In a position above	MAKE SURE THAT THE ANCHOR IS UP.	
UP (adv)	To a position above	IF THE POINTER MOVES UP, DECREASE THE POWER.	
UP (prep)	To a position above	LET THE SLEEVE MOVE UP THE GUIDE TUBE.	

ASD STE 100

Word (part of speech)	Approved meaning / ALTERNATIVES	APPROVED EXAMPLE	Not approved example
upon (prep)	ON (prep)	PUT THE OHMMETER ON A FLAT SURFACE.	Put the ohmmeter upon a flat surface.
	WHEN (conj)	WHEN YOU SET THE LEVER TO "UP", THE HYDRAULIC PRESSURE MUST DECREASE.	Upon UP selection, the hydraulic pressure must decrease.
upper (adj)	MAXIMUM (adj)	FILL THE CONTAINER TO THE MAXIMUM LEVEL.	Fill the container to the upper level.
	TOP (adj)	THE AIRFLOW THEN GOES ALONG THE TOP AND BOTTOM SURFACES OF THE SLATS.	The airflow then passes over the upper and lower surfaces of the slats.
uppermost (adj)	UP (adv)	INSTALL THE BOLTS WITH THEIR HEADS UP.	Install the bolts with their heads in uppermost position.
uppermost (adv)	UP (adv)	INSTALL THE BOLTS WITH THEIR HEADS UP.	Install the bolts with their heads uppermost.
UPSTREAM (adj)	In a direction opposite to the flow	DISCONNECT THE UPSTREAM CONNECTION OF THE VALVE.	
UPSTREAM (adv)	In a direction opposite to the flow	MOVE THE PROBE UPSTREAM AND MONITOR THE TEMPERATURE AGAIN.	
UPSTREAM OF (prep)	In a direction opposite to the flow	DISCONNECT THE CONNECTION UPSTREAM OF THE VALVE.	
up to (prep)	UNTIL (prep)	UNTIL THIS STEP, THE UNIT IGNORES ALL OUTPUT SIGNALS.	Up to this step the unit ignores all output signals.
	THRU (prep)	DO STEPS 1 THRU 4.	Do all steps up to and including step 4.
	MAXIMUM (n)	YOU CAN INSTALL A MAXIMUM OF TEN WASHERS.	You can install up to ten washers.

Word (part of speech)	Approved meaning / ALTERNATIVES	APPROVED EXAMPLE	Not approved example
upward (adv)	UP (adv)	MOVE THE LEVER UP.	Move the lever upward.
urgently (adv)	IMMEDIATELY (adv)	GET MEDICAL AID IMMEDIATELY.	Seek medical aid urgently.
usage (n)	USE (v)	DO NOT USE INCORRECT THINNERS. THIS CAN CAUSE PROBLEMS.	The usage of incorrect thinners can cause problems.
use (n)	OPERATION (n)	WHEN THE MOTOR IS IN OPERATION, KEEP YOUR HANDS AWAY FROM THE BLADE.	Keep your hands away from the blade when the motor is in use.
	USE (v)	USE PROTECTIVE GLOVES DURING THIS TASK.	The use of protective gloves is mandatory during this task.
USE (v), USES, USED, USED	To make something do its specified function	USE THE TEST BOX TO DO A TEST ON THE SYSTEM. USE A SPECIAL CONTAINER FOR STORAGE. DO NOT USE HIGH PRESSURE DURING THE CLEANING PROCEDURE.	
using (v)	USE (v)	USE A 1/2 INCH WRENCH TO REMOVE THE COVER.	Remove the cover using a 1/2 inch wrench.
	WITH (prep)	REMOVE THE COVER WITH A 1/2 INCH WRENCH.	Remove the cover using a 1/2 inch wrench.
USUAL (adj)	That you use or that occurs most frequently	IF YOU DO NOT GET THE USUAL RESULTS, DO A SYSTEM TEST.	
USUALLY (adv)	In a usual manner	USUALLY, THE HYDRAULIC FLUID FLOWS INTO THE VALVE THROUGH PORT A AND OUT THROUGH PORT B.	

ASD STE 100

Word (part of speech)	Approved meaning / ALTERNATIVES	APPROVED EXAMPLE	Not approved example
utilization (n)	USE (v)	READ THE INSTRUCTIONS THAT TELL YOU HOW TO USE THE OXYGEN MASK.	Read the oxygen mask instructions for its utilization.
utilize (v)	USE (v)	USE AN OIL CAN TO LUBRICATE THE TURNBUCKLE.	Utilize an oil can for turnbuckle lubrication.

Word (part of speech)	Approved meaning / ALTERNATIVES	APPROVED EXAMPLE	Not approved example
valid (adj)	CORRECT (adj)	MAKE SURE THAT THE TEST RESULTS ARE CORRECT.	Make sure that the test results are valid.
	APPLICABLE (adj)	THIS PROCEDURE IS APPLICABLE ONLY IN DIGITAL MODE.	This procedure is only valid in digital mode.
	This word becomes part of a technical name when associated to an official document.	NDT PERSONNEL MUST HOLD A VALID CERTIFICATE OF COMPETENCE AT LEVEL 1, 2 OR 3.	
validity (n)	CORRECT (adj)	MAKE SURE THAT THE TEST RESULTS ARE CORRECT.	Check the validity of the test results.
	APPLICABLE (adj)	THIS STEP IS APPLICABLE ONLY WHEN YOU APPLY THE TOP LAYER OF PAINT.	The validity of this step is restricted to the application of the paint topcoat.
VALUE (n)	A quantity that is calculated or given	MAKE SURE THAT THE VALUES AGREE WITH THE TOLERANCES.	
variable (adj)	CHANGE (v)	IF THE HUMIDITY CHANGES FREQUENTLY, PUT A COVER ON THE UNIT.	If the humidity is variable, put a cover on the unit.
various (adj)	DIFFERENT (adj)	REFER TO TABLE 5 FOR THE DIFFERENT TORQUE VALUES THAT ARE APPLICABLE TO THE UNIT.	Refer to Table 5 for the various torque values that are applicable to the unit.

Word (part of speech)	Approved meaning / ALTERNATIVES	APPROVED EXAMPLE	Not approved example
vary (v)	CHANGE (v)	CHANGE THE FREQUENCY AND RECORD THE RESULTS.	Vary the frequency and record the results.
vent (v)	RELEASE (v)	RELEASE THE PRESSURE.	Vent the pressure.
	FLOW (v)	LET THE FUEL FLOW FREELY OVERBOARD.	Let the fuel vent freely overboard.
	OPEN (adj)	MAKE SURE THAT THE TANK IS IN AN OPEN AREA THAT HAS A GOOD AIRFLOW.	Make sure that the tank is in an area that is vented to the atmosphere.
ventilate (v)	AIRFLOW (n)	MAKE SURE THAT THE AREA WHERE YOU WILL USE THIS SOLVENT HAS GOOD AIRFLOW.	Ventilate the area where this solvent is used.
ventilation (n)	AIRFLOW (n)	MAKE SURE THAT THE AIRFLOW IS SUFFICIENT.	Make sure that the ventilation is sufficient.
verbal (adj)	TELL (v)	TELL THE CHIEF ABOUT THE RESULTS.	Give a verbal message about the results to the chief.
	HEAR (v)	MAKE SURE THAT A PERSON WHO IS NOT IN THE TANK CAN ALWAYS HEAR YOU.	Make sure that you maintain verbal contact with an operator outside the tank.
verify (v)	MAKE SURE (v)	MAKE SURE THAT THE FITTINGS ARE TIGHT.	Verify the tightness of fittings.
VERTICAL (adj)	At 90 degrees to the horizon	MEASURE THE VERTICAL DISTANCE BETWEEN THE TWO POINTS ON THE GRAPH.	
VERTICALLY (adv)	At 90 degrees to the horizon	THE POINTER MOVES VERTICALLY ALONG THE SCALE.	
VERY (adv)	To a high degree	ADD THE OIL VERY SLOWLY.	
via (prep)	THROUGH (prep)	GET ACCESS THROUGH THE No. 6 BREAK-IN PANEL.	Get access via No. 6 break-in panel.

Word (part of speech)	Approved meaning / ALTERNATIVES	APPROVED EXAMPLE	Not approved example
vibrate (v)	VIBRATION (n)	IF THERE IS VIBRATION IN THE UNIT, DISCONNECT THE POWER SUPPLY.	If the unit vibrates, cut the power.
VIBRATION (n)	Regular movement from a center position	PRESSURE SURGES AND VIBRATION CAN CAUSE WEAR ON THE HOSES.	
vicinity (n)	NEAR (prep)	MAKE SURE THAT SOLVENTS ARE NOT NEAR THE ENGINE EXHAUST.	Make sure that solvents are not in the vicinity of the engine exhaust.
	ADJACENT (adj)	DO AN INSPECTION OF THE DAMAGE AND OF THE ADJACENT AREA.	Do an inspection of the damage and of the immediate vicinity.
VIEW (n)	The ability to see something	MAKE SURE THAT YOU HAVE A SATISFACTORY VIEW OF ALL COMPONENTS.	
view (v)	SEE (v)	THE BOLT WILL BE AT THE 2 O'CLOCK POSITION WHEN SEEN FROM THE REAR.	The bolt will be at 2 o'clock when viewed from the rear.
	LOOK (v)	THE BOLT WILL BE AT THE 2 O'CLOCK POSITION WHEN YOU LOOK AT THE PUMP FROM THE REAR.	The bolt will be at 2 o'clock when viewed from the rear.
vigorous (adj)	FORCE (TN)	WHEN YOU CLEAN THE CARPET, DO NOT USE TOO MUCH FORCE ON THE BRUSH. TOO MUCH FORCE CAN CAUSE DAMAGE TO THE CARPET.	Vigorous cleaning with a brush can cause damage to the carpet.
vigorously (adv)	FORCE (TN)	WHEN YOU MOVE THE CONTROL WHEEL, DO NOT APPLY TOO MUCH FORCE.	Do not move the control wheel too vigorously.

ASD STE 100

Word (part of speech)	Approved meaning / ALTERNATIVES	APPROVED EXAMPLE	Not approved example
visible (adj)	SEE (v)	MAKE SURE THAT YOU CAN SEE THE OIL LEVEL THROUGH THE SIGHT GAUGE.	Make certain that the oil level is visible through the sight gauge.
	VIEW (n)	WHEN THE INDICATOR COMES INTO VIEW, STOP THE PUMP.	When the indicator is visible, stop the pump.
VISUAL (adj)	With the eyes	REMOVE THE VISUAL INDICATOR FROM THE VALVE.	
VISUALLY (adv)	With the eyes	VISUALLY EXAMINE THE DUCT.	
vital (adj)	IMPORTANT (adj)	AFTER THE TEST, IT IS IMPORTANT TO SET THE INDICATOR BACK TO ZERO.	It is vital to set the indicator back to zero after the test.
	MANDATORY (adj)	AFTER THE TEST, IT IS MANDATORY TO SET THE INDICATOR BACK TO ZERO.	It is vital to set the indicator back to zero after the test.
	NECESSARY (adj)	AFTER THE TEST, IT IS NECESSARY TO SET THE INDICATOR BACK TO ZERO.	It is vital to set the indicator back to zero after the test.
VOICE (n)	The sound you make when you speak	SPEAK INTO THE MICROPHONE IN YOUR USUAL VOICE.	
volatile (adj)	💡 Use a different construction. Tell the reader what the risk or effect is.	BE CAREFUL WITH THE SOLVENT NEAR FLAMES OR SPARKS. THIS SOLVENT CAN RELEASE FLAMMABLE FUMES.	Be careful with the solvent (this solvent is volatile and can be dangerous).
VOLUME (n)	1. The space that an object fills	MEASURE THE VOLUME OF THE OIL CAREFULLY.	
	2. How loud a sound is	TO ADJUST THE VOLUME, USE THE BUTTONS ON THE SIDE OF THE PHONE.	

Word (part of speech)	Approved meaning / ALTERNATIVES	APPROVED EXAMPLE	Not approved example
WAIT (v), WAITS, WAITED, WAITED	To stop doing something while another thing occurs.	(1) IF THE STATUS OF THE FAULT IS "NOT CONFIRMED": (a) OPEN THE APPLICABLE CIRCUIT BREAKER. (b) WAIT FOR 4 MINUTES. (c) DO THE BITE TEST.	
WALK (v), WALKS, WALKED, WALKED	To move on foot from one location to a different location	DO NOT WALK ON THIS AREA.	
WANT (v), WANTS, WANTED, WANTED	To intend, to desire	RECORD THE NAME OF THE FILE THAT YOU WANT TO DOWNLOAD.	
		IF YOU WANT TO STOP THE PROCEDURE, RECORD THE NUMBER OF THE LAST COMPLETED STEP.	
WARM (adj)	Moderately hot	KEEP THE GASKETS IN A WARM DRY AREA.	
warm (v)	WARM (adj)	MAKE THE MIXTURE WARM BEFORE YOU USE IT.	Warm the mixture before use.
warn (v)	TELL (v)	TELL PERSONNEL TO STAY AWAY FROM THE CONVEYOR SYSTEM.	Warn personnel to stay away from the conveyor system.
	WARNING (TN)	IF THE INSTRUCTIONS GIVE A WARNING ABOUT DANGEROUS PRESSURE, DO NOT OPEN THE CONTAINER.	If the instructions warn of a dangerous pressure, do not open the container.
wash (v)	CLEAN (v)	CLEAN YOUR HANDS WITH SOAP.	Wash your hands using soap.

Word (part of speech)	Approved meaning / ALTERNATIVES	APPROVED EXAMPLE	Not approved example
watch (v)	MONITOR (v)	MONITOR THE SPEED INDICATION CONTINUOUSLY UNTIL THE END OF THE TEST.	Watch the speed indication for the duration of the test.
	LOOK (v)	LOOK FOR AIR BUBBLES.	Watch for air bubbles.
watertight (adj)	SEAL (v)	MAKE SURE THAT THE TANK IS SEALED.	Check that the tank is watertight.
way (n)	PROCEDURE (n)	DO NOT USE OTHER PROCEDURES TO REPLACE THE UNIT.	Do not use other ways to replace the unit.
WE (pron)	The manufacturer or the company which releases the documentation Do not use this pronoun for other meanings.	WE DO NOT RECOMMEND OTHER ALTERNATIVES.	
WEAK (adj) (WEAKER, WEAKEST)	With small strength, power, or concentration	USE A WEAK CLEANING SOLUTION.	
weakness (n)	WEAK (adj)	THERE IS A WEAK POINT IN THE STRUT.	There is a point of weakness in the strut.
WEAR (v), WEARS, WORE, WORN	To become damaged by friction	THE CABLE CAN WEAR QUICKLY IN THIS POSITION.	
	For other meanings, use: USE (v)	DURING THE SOLDERING PROCEDURE, USE A PROTECTIVE SHIELD.	During the soldering procedure, wear a protective shield.
	PUT ON (v)	PUT ON PROTECTIVE CLOTHING WHEN YOU USE THE SOLVENT.	Wear protective clothing when you use the solvent.
WEATHER (n)	Conditions of the atmosphere : temperature, moisture, winds, and clouds	STEP 2 IS APPLICABLE ONLY IF THE WEATHER IS WET.	
weep (n)	LEAKAGE (n)	IF THERE IS FUEL LEAKAGE FROM THE COUPLINGS, REPAIR THEM.	If there are fuel weeps from the couplings, repair them.

Word (part of speech)	Approved meaning / ALTERNATIVES	APPROVED EXAMPLE	Not approved example
WEIGH (v), WEIGHS, WEIGHED, WEIGHED	1. To measure the weight of something	WEIGH THE TWO PARTS OF THE COMPOUND.	
	2. To have a specified weight	THE UNIT WEIGHS 20 KG.	
WEIGHT (n)	The force caused when gravity acts on the mass of an object	THE BASIC WEIGHT OF THE UNIT DOES NOT INCLUDE ALL ITEMS.	
well (adv)	CORRECTLY (adv)	MAKE SURE THAT THE BEARING IS CORRECTLY INSTALLED.	Make sure that the bearing is well seated.
	GOOD (adj)	THERE MUST BE A GOOD AIRFLOW IN THE WORK AREA.	The work area must be well ventilated.
	FULLY (adv)	ALL LABORATORY EQUIPMENT MUST BE FULLY CLEANED.	All laboratory equipment must be well cleaned.
WET (adj) (WETTER, WETTEST)	That has liquid on it, in it, or absorbed into it	DRY THE WET SURFACES.	
WHEN (conj)	At the time that or during	WHEN THE PISTON MOVEMENT STOPS, MEASURE THE TRAVEL.	
whenever (conj)	WHEN (conj)	STOP THE TEST WHEN THE PRESSURE IS MORE THAN 7000 kPa.	Stop the test whenever the pressure is more than 7000 kPa.
WHERE (conj)	At, to, or in which location	CLEAN THE AREA WHERE YOU APPLIED THE SEALANT.	
whether (conj)	IF (conj)	THIS LIMIT IS APPLICABLE IF THE AIRCRAFT IS ON THE LANDING GEAR OR ON JACKS.	This limit applies whether the aircraft is on the landing gear or on jacks.
WHICH (pron)	The thing or things that	EXAMINE THE EMERGENCY FUEL PUMP, WHICH IS ON THE LEFT SIDE.	

ASD STE 100

Word (part of speech)	Approved meaning / ALTERNATIVES	APPROVED EXAMPLE	Not approved example
whichever (pron)	THAT (pron)	USE THE ADHESIVE THAT IS AVAILABLE	Use whichever adhesive is available.
WHILE (conj)	At the same time	MAKE SURE THAT A PERSON HOLDS THE ITEM, WHILE YOU DISCONNECT IT.	
whilst (conj)	WHILE (conj)	DO NOT OPEN THE HOUSING WHILE THE ELECTRICAL POWER IS CONNECTED.	Do not open the housing whilst the electrical power is connected.
WHO (pron)	The person or personnel that	PERSON B, WHO OPERATES THE REAR WINCH, MUST LOCK THE FIXTURE	
whoever (pron)	WHO (pron)	ALL PERSONS WHO ARE IN THIS AREA MUST USE A RESPIRATOR.	Whoever is in this area must use a respirator.
whole (adj)	FULL (adj)	DO THE FULL PROCEDURE.	The whole procedure must be done.
	ALL (adj)	EXAMINE ALL OF THE SYSTEM TO FIND THE CAUSE OF INTERFERENCE	Examine the whole system to find the cause of interference.
wholly (adv)	FULLY (adv)	THE SYSTEM IS FULLY AUTOMATIC.	The system is wholly automatic.
whose (pron)	Use a different construction.	THE GENERATORS SUPPLY A THREE-PHASE VOLTAGE. THE FREQUENCY OF THIS VOLTAGE INCREASES WHEN THE GENERATOR ROTOR SPEED INCREASES.	The generators produce a three-phase voltage whose frequency is proportional to the generator rotor speed.
WIDE (adj) (WIDER, WIDEST)	That has large width	REPAIR ALL CRACKS THAT ARE WIDER THAN 0.05 mm.	
WIDTH (n)	The smaller of two dimensions, the second-largest of three dimensions	MEASURE THE WIDTH OF THE CRACK AT THE WIDEST POINT.	

Word (part of speech)	Approved meaning / ALTERNATIVES	APPROVED EXAMPLE	Not approved example
WILL (v) 💡 No other forms of this verb.	Helping verb that shows simple future tense	WARNINGS AND CAUTIONS IN THIS MANUAL WILL HELP YOU TO DO THE WORK SAFELY AND CORRECTLY.	
WIND (v), WINDS, WOUND, WOUND	To move around and around an object	WIND THE TAPE ON THE REEL.	
windy (adj)	WIND (TN)	WHEN THERE ARE STRONG WINDS, OBEY THESE SPECIAL PRECAUTIONS.	Take special precautions in very windy conditions.
wipe (v)	CLEAN (v)	BEFORE EACH CYCLE, CLEAN THE INDICATOR.	Wipe the indicator surfaces before each cycle.
wire (v)	ATTACH (v) (WITH WIRE [TN])	ATTACH THE HOSE TO THE FIXTURE WITH WIRE.	Wire the hose to the fixture.
wire-lock (v)	LOCK (v) (WITH LOCKWIRE [TN])	LOCK THE FOUR BOLTS TO EACH OTHER WITH LOCKWIRE.	Wire-lock the four bolts to each other.
	SAFETY (v) (WITH SAFETY WIRE [TN])	SAFETY THE FOUR BOLTS TO EACH OTHER WITH SAFETY WIRE.	Wire-lock the four bolts to each other.
WITH (prep)	Function word that shows association or relationship, help or sharing, a means or instrument	ALIGN THE MARK WITH THE LONGITUDINAL AXIS.	
		ATTACH THE FLANGE (10) WITH THE FOUR BOLTS (15).	
		REMOVE THE VALVE (2) WITH THE EXTRACTOR.	
withdraw (v)	REMOVE (v)	REMOVE THE INDICATOR FROM THE INSTRUMENT PANEL.	Withdraw the indicator from the instrument panel.

ASD STE 100

Word (part of speech)	Approved meaning / ALTERNATIVES	APPROVED EXAMPLE	Not approved example
within (prep)	IN (prep)	A FILTER PREVENTS CONTAMINATION OF THE COMPONENTS IN THE SYSTEM.	A filter prevents contamination of the components within the system.
	IN...OR LESS	LIGHT L4 COMES ON IN 5 SECONDS OR LESS.	Light L4 illuminates within 5 seconds.
	IN LESS THAN	MAKE SURE THAT THE WARNING LIGHT COMES ON IN LESS THAN 3 SECONDS.	Make sure that the warning light illuminates within 3 seconds.
WITHOUT (prep)	Not with	SOME DAMAGE IS PERMITTED WITHOUT REPAIR. REFER TO TABLE 1 FOR THE APPLICABLE LIMITS.	
withstand (v)	RESISTANT (adj)	THIS MATERIAL IS RESISTANT TO FIRE.	This material can withstand fire.
WORK (n)	That which you do when you use physical strength, or mental power	DO THE WORK IN A CLEAN AREA.	
work (v)	WORK (n)	BE CAREFUL WHEN YOU DO WORK NEAR FUEL TANKS.	Be careful when you work near fuel tanks.
would (v)	CAN (v)	SOLVENTS THAT STAY ON THE PART CAN CAUSE CORROSION.	Solvents left on the part would corrode the part.
wrap (v)	PUT (v)	PUT THE PART IN OILPAPER.	Wrap the part in oilpaper.
	WIND (v)	WIND MASKING TAPE AROUND THE PART.	Wrap masking tape around the part.
WRITE (v), WRITES, WROTE, WRITTEN	To record data or information as words, letters, or symbols	WRITE THE TEST DATE ON THE CERTIFICATE.	

Word (part of speech)	Approved meaning / ALTERNATIVES	APPROVED EXAMPLE	Not approved example
wrong (adj)	INCORRECT (adj)	IDENTIFY THE BELLCRANK AND SHAFT WITH MARKS. THIS WILL PREVENT AN INCORRECT INSTALLATION.	Mark the bellcrank and shaft to prevent wrong installation.
wrongly (adv)	INCORRECTLY (adv)	IF THE HOSES ARE INCORRECTLY INSTALLED, DAMAGE CAN OCCUR.	Damage can occur if hoses are wrongly installed.

ASD STE 100

Word (part of speech)	Approved meaning / ALTERNATIVES	APPROVED EXAMPLE	Not approved example
YES (adv)	Function word that shows the positive answer to a question	DOES THE LIGHT COME ON? YES OR NO?	
yet (conj)	BUT (conj)	TIGHTEN THE NUTS, BUT KEEP THEM SUFFICIENTLY LOOSE TO REMOVE THEM WITH YOUR HAND.	The nuts should be tightened, yet loose enough to remove by hand.
	AT THIS TIME	DO NOT REMOVE THE FIXTURE COVER AT THIS TIME.	Do not remove the fixture cover yet.
YOU (pron)	The reader or the user	YOU CAN CONTINUE THE TEST.	
YOUR (adj)	Related to the reader or the user	IF YOU GET SOLVENT IN YOUR EYES, FLUSH THEM IMMEDIATELY WITH WATER.	
yourself (pron)	YOU (pron)	DO NOT USE YOUR HANDS TO PREVENT MOVEMENT OF THE LP COMPRESSOR. IF YOU DO, THE LP COMPRESSOR CAN CAUSE YOU INJURY AND CAN CAUSE DAMAGE TO THE EQUIPMENT.	Do not use your hands to prevent movement of the LP compressor. If you do, you can cause injury to yourself and damage to the equipment.
zero (v)	ZERO (TN)	ADJUST THE METER TO ZERO.	Zero the meter.